G000123587

THE PSYCHOLOGY
OF HEALING

Murry Hope is one of the foremost authors on esoteric wisdom, ancient magical religions and related subjects. She was the co-founder of *The Atlanteans* society in 1957 and served as its president, principal teacher and healer for twenty of the forty years she has been engaged in metaphysical studies. In the early 1950s, Murry trained and worked for five years as a professional counsellor and case worker in the Officer's Association of the British Legion in London. Since then, she has worked as a journalist, teacher, lecturer and professional classical singer. In 1988 she established the *Institute for the Study and Development of Transpersonal Sensitivity* in the USA. Murry has published many books, run lectures and seminars, and appeared on radio and television worldwide in her capacity as an expert in this field.

THE PSYCHOLOGY
OF HEALING

Murry Hope

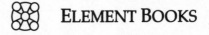 ELEMENT BOOKS

First published in 1989 by
Element Books Limited
Longmead, Shaftesbury, Dorset

Designed by Jenny Liddle
Cover design by Max Fairbrother
Cover illustration from a painting by Robin Harris

Typeset by Selectmove Ltd., London.
Printed and bound in Great Britain by
Billings, Hylton Road, Worcester.

British Library Cataloguing in Publication Data
Hope, Murry
The psychology of healing.
1. Man. Therapy. Alternative methods
I. Title
615.5

ISBN 1–85230–107–4

To all who serve the healing cause,
whichever banner they may fly.

CONTENTS

The impact of sociological, religious and philosophical influences on diseases that have dominated certain periods of history. The Death Syndrome: primitive views contrasted with the modern approach. The side-effects of abortion.

Genetic and congenital conditions. Childhood hazards. Immunisation. Teenage suicide. Occupational diseases and disabilities. Infectious and viral diseases. ME post-viral syndrome. Degenerative disorders. Psychosomatics. Disabilities caused by accidents or the antisocial behaviour of others. Mental handicap and mental illness – the difference.

The mind–body conflict. The Growth Factor. Punitive karma. Genetic connotations. The group-soul experience. The 'respectable exit door' theory. The PK element in disillusion and despair. The Wheel of Karma. Medical astrology. The genetic death-program. Free will?

Damage effected by the philosophy of Descartes. Birth of psychoneuroimmunology. Effect of mind on the immune system. The relaxation response. Brain/Mind/Psyche – the distinctions. Freudian and Jungian views. Correspondences between physiological and psychological types. The work of Kretschmer and Wolff. Personality types as defined in modern psychiatry. Psionic medicine. Somatic allusions. The 'dreambody' theory.

Illness and death resulting from suppressed emotion. Possession used as an attention-gaining ploy. The 'occult attack' syndrome. Hypnosis as an exposer of our wants as against our needs – cases analysed.

PSI/PK phenomena – the parapsychologist's view. Subtle bodies or frequency variations? The Psi Mediated Instrumental Response (PMIR) factor. The energy exchange principle. Genetic, somatic and mental evolutionary development. The Chaos Theory as applied to psychology. Atmospheric conditions: nuclear, electromagnetic and other forms of radiation – their effect on health.

The adverse effects of nineteenth-century materialism on the medical profession. The 'drug for everything' practice. Thalidomide and the side-effects dilemma. Treatment of symptoms rather than causes. Technology – the ally of medicine. Enter holism. Slow changes in attitudes. The virtues and shortcomings of the medical profession. Vivisection – the ethic. Placebos. Prince Charles on hospital environments. The bedside manner revived.

Our social conscience. Standards of living and their effect on disease: the social dilemma. The self-destruction syndrome. The power of social collectives to influence physical and mental health. Socially related diseases. The damaging effect of role models advertised by the media. The dehumanising influence of the 'group-entity'. Peer pressure in modern social and sexual taboos. The socially sick, is there an answer? Individuation and soul-age. Religion and sex – a strong connection. The ethic of caring awareness.

New information on our simian ancestry. DNA fingerprinting. The healing power of trees. Animal healing. Dr David Greene's work with cats: two specific cases. Cats as psychic healers: true stories. The healing potential in dolphins and other creatures. Earth healing energies. Feng-shui. Geopathic stress. Gaia's chakras and ley lines.

Instinct – is it cerebral? Genetic patterns in the animal and insect world. Animal instincts. The ethics of genetic engineering. Caring for our bodies, or over-caring? The dangers inherent in current diet and exercise fads – the medical view. A healthy life-style – does it affect longevity? The dangers of complacency.

The various branches of psychology and psychiatry defined. Health dangers involved for practitioners. The British attitude. A brief history of psychiatry and the various treatments it has effected to date. Freudian or Jungian? Social dangers in over-emphasis of psychological factors. Mental illness, or break-down? The 'stability' myth. The 'Experimenter Effect'.

Healing in ancient Egypt as recorded by Clement of Alexandria. Egyptian healing skills comparable to modern medical practices. Oriental medicine. Similarities between the healing shrine of Kuan-Yin and Lourdes. Ayurvedic medicine. Medicine in classical and pre-classical Greece. The physicians of Cos (Kos). Hippocrates, father of medicine – the *Corpus Hippocratium*. The divinities of healing in the ancient world. The Essenic Therapeuts: their knowledge preceded the Flood. Healing in Celtic Druidism. The Kahuna healers. The ignorance and superstition of the Dark Ages. Enter Paracelsus.

Part 2. Alternative Therapies, Complementary Medicine and the Healing Vocation

(The following chapters contain a short history of each therapy, it's Modus Operandi and a Psychological Suitability Assessment.)

Osteopathy. Cranial osteopathy. Chiropractic. The Alexander Technique. Reflexology. Applied Kinesiology/Touch for Health.

Auric therapy. Chakric healing. Radiance techique (reiki). Shamanic ecstatic healing. Exorcism.

Psychic diagnosis. Kirlian photography. Palmistry. Iridology. Biorhythms. Astrology.

Visualisation and imaging. Medical attitudes and approaches. Silence vs. sound. Fear: the part it plays in our lives and health. Chaos science and the Fear Syndrome. Individual responsibility. Huna self-healing. Foundation and work of the Bristol Cancer Help Centre. Guided imagery techniques. The Chaos element in cancer. Jung on the Mercurius. Cheating the Grim Reaper?

The over-worked GP or the need for a change? Case examples. The importance of patient/therapist cooperation. The incompatibility factor – the wider choice in alternative therapies. A few cautionary words.

Are healers born or made? The PK element as viewed by parapsychologists. The qualities of a good healer. Many doctors work intuitively, while some healers are not psychic. The need for a silent or tranquil atmosphere in the healing area. The miracles of Jesus. Is accurate diagnosis essential to the cure? Counselling as distinct from healing – the pros and cons. Dr Arthur Guirdham on the healing temperament.

The need for a balance and co-operation between orthodox

medicine and alternative therapies. Looking inwards or outwards? Attitudes towards instinct and intuition. The transpersonal quest and our *raison d'être*. Looking to the future.

ACKNOWLEDGEMENTS

I am deeply indebted to Brian Inglis and Ruth West for their informative and comprehensive work, *The Alternative Health Guide*, which has proven an inestimable source of reference to me during the writing of this book.

My sincere thanks also go to Dr John A. Cosh, MA, MD, Cantab., FRCP; Elaine Sturgess, DO, MRO; Nerys Dee and Chloris Morgan for additional material and valuable assistance and advice.

THE MANY BRANCHES OF THE HEALING TREE

INTRODUCTION

THE HIPPOCRATIC OATH

I swear by Apollo the physician and Asclepius and Hygieia and Panacea, invoking all the gods and goddesses to be my witness, that I will fulfil this Oath and this written covenant to the best of my power and of my judgement.

I will look upon him who shall have taught me this art even as on mine own parents; I will share with him my substance and supply his necessities if he be in need; I will regard his offspring even as my own brethren, and will teach them this art, if they desire to learn it, without fee or covenant. I will impart it by precept, by lecture and by all other manner of teaching, not only to my own sons, but also to the sons of him who has taught me, and to disciples bound by covènant and oath according to the law of the physicians, but to none other.

The regimen I adopt shall be for the benefit of the patients to the best of my power and judgement, not for their injury or for any wrongful purpose. I will not give a deadly drug to anyone, though it be asked of me, nor will I lead the way in such counsel; and likewise I will not give a woman a pessary to procure abortion. But I will keep my life and my art in purity and holiness. Whatsoever house I enter, I will enter for the benefit of the sick, refraining from all voluntary wrong-doing and corruption, especially seduction of male or female, bond or free. Whatsoever things I see or hear concerning the life of men, in my attendance on the sick or even apart from my attendance, which ought not to be blabbed abroad, I will keep silence on them, counting such things to be as religious secrets.

If I fulfil this oath and confound it not, be it mine to enjoy life and art alike, with good repute among all men for all time to come; but may the contrary befall me if I transgress and violate my oath.[1]

Noble promises indeed, but who out of the many that have repeated these words over the centuries have lived strictly by them? And have those who have strayed from the path really reaped the questionable harvest of their misdeeds in accordance with the final sentence?

We may choose to make use of the names of the gods and goddesses of ancient Greece to witness our sincerity as we embark on our healing journey through life. If, however, we believe them to be simply the figments of the imaginations of past cultures, does that exempt us from either the positive or negative implications of our promise? These are all matters for the individual conscience but (as the metaphysician would see it and some psychologists might well agree), in the final analysis, it will not be a resplendent Olympic deity who judges us. Rather, it will be the Apollo or Asclepius within our own psyches (the divine gift of healing and our personal propensity for discharging it with love and care) who will judge whether we have dispensed our skills wisely and generously – or otherwise!

A reasonable state of balance is essential to the successful functioning of any organism – from the life-force of the earth itself, to the tiniest particle – with degrees of imbalance naturally varying according to the proximity of the angle to order or chaos. Healing is all about the correcting of imbalances within the human body, mind and spirit so the healer does, in fact, operate at one or all of these levels in accordance with his or her expertise.

Irregularities can, of course, manifest in any and all avenues of existence and it is a fact of life that we must learn to live and deal with them to the best of our ability, using whatever methods we may deem fit to correct any imbalances. The rationalist approach usually consists of 'logicising' the problem within the framework of genetics, dialectical materialism and acceptable behavioural patterns. The psychologist or metaphysician, on the other hand, may consider the irregularities in terms of essential growth experience or the natural evolutionary process of spiritual development.

Problems of ecological imbalance in today's world have been highlighted by the media as never before. For many people this has resulted in new cognisance of the intrinsic web of existence of which we are an essential part, while at the same time emphasising our dependence on all those other life-forms with which we share this planet. Side by side with this growing global awareness, a finer state of consciousness of the human condition – at all its levels of experience – has developed. This may vary from the ever-expanding and continually adjusting field of quantum and particle physics, with its almost esoteric concepts of space-time, superstrings and parallel universes, to the personal need felt by many to explore the inner universes of their own bodies and minds, and come up with at least some of the answers to their imbalances.

Since this is a book about healing, it is to the latter consideration that our observations and research will be directed. There is more and more call for systems which enable the individual to help him or herself, so while allopathic medicine gratefully utilises the discoveries of science and technology on the one hand, the purveyors of alternative therapies and personal DIY therapy kits flourish and multiply on the other. Both have their advantages and their failings, for we are all individuals and that which is helpful to one person may not suit the temperament or physiology of another.

As the ensuing study covers such a wide field, to do anything resembling full justice to the subject matter would be impossible within the scope of one book. I have, therefore, attempted to render a brief outline of the background behind the cause, diagnosis and cure of some of the many kinds of illnesses and disorders that afflict our present world, and the numerous efforts made at different levels to combat them.

Due to the ever-increasing number of alternative therapies, my policy has been to concentrate more on those systems which have been tried and tested, interspersed with a few new and perhaps revolutionary ideas. How and why any of these work (if in fact they do) is taken into account, plus the patient's own contribution towards the 'cure'. The omission of a particular favourite should not, therefore, be taken as a judgement or dismissal of the therapy in question. There are also a number of other techniques which I have omitted on the grounds that they are self-discovery packages rather than therapies, for example, Elemental Formula, Inner Track

Learning, and Neuro-Linguistic Programming, (NLP), which are doubtless of benefit to many who use them.

My aim has been to give an honest assessment of the overall picture from which the reader may draw his or her own conclusions. Two factors should be borne in mind, however. Firstly, that our mental attitudes and our somatic responses are inexorably interwoven. In other words, we are capable of accepting personal responsibility for ourselves if we care to make the effort. Secondly, we will not master those imbalances which give rise to sickness and disease until we have learned to live in harmony with and understand the nature and needs of both our own planet and the cosmos, of which we are each an essential particle.

Endnote:

1. *The Legacy of Greece – Medicine*, C Singer, pp. 213–214.

Part 1

MALADIES, CAUSES AND CURES

Chapter 1

INFLUENCES PAST AND PRESENT

Since the dawn of civilisation, and earlier no doubt, mankind has fought a continual battle against physical and mental afflictions. When viewed in the light of modern knowledge, our past endeavours may appear unscientific, illogical, and even bizarre. Yet there has always been a glimmer of truth, albeit dim at times, that has prevailed against the darkness of ignorance, superstition and fear. Tenuous though this thread may be, it has survived and the gap between the lost knowledge of the past and the technological achievements of our modern world is slowly and mercifully closing.

The causes of disease appear to be legion: but are they? And to what extent have the environmental milieu, religious dictates and philosophical trends of the past contributed to their birth, growth and perpetuation? While many of the illnesses which predominated in earlier times were obviously encouraged or exacerbated by prevailing social conditions, there have always been those perennials that are as much in evidence in modern society as they were in ancient Egypt. For example, it has ever been the lot of women to suffer from conditions peculiar to their age and sex; while nervous breakdowns afflicted the civil servants and business executives in earlier empires in much the same way that they do their twentieth-century equivalents. There are, however, many diseases that man has brought on himself either through pure ignorance, blind faith, or deliberate misuse of mind and body. One trusts that the improvements in educational facilities, plus the recent accent on self-knowledge and self-help, will assist in eradicating some of these.

Recent medical studies of mummies and skeletons from early Egyptian times have shown that while the people of those erstwhile days were apparently not exposed to many of the diseases prevalent today, they did, for example, suffer from severe infestations of intestinal worms. And because they were mostly unshod, they were also vulnerable to attack from those parasites that enter the body via the feet. Their eating habits may have been considerably healthier than ours, but the type of hard labour required to eke out an existence, especially among the poorer sections of society, was hardly conducive to longevity. However, those privileged people who could afford to pay others to relieve them of some of the stresses of day-to-day living – and who often kept a private physician in their household – did manage to make old age by our standards, as history bears witness. The early Egyptian physicians (Priests of Thoth or Imhotep) were highly knowledgeable, and archaeology has evidenced their employment of anaesthetics and surgical skills comparable to those in use in the twentieth century (see Chapter 12).

Logic might demand the assumption that it has ever been the lot of the poor to sustain the greater burden of physical and mental suffering, but this was not necessarily always the case. There are many instances of emperors, kings, rulers and rich men who died in their prime from some virulent disease, or whose offspring were born with gross abnormalities. Of course, the hardships so frequently imposed upon their subjects by the ruling classes did nothing to increase their life expectancy or cure their ills. But since so many past rulers engaged in the game of political musical chairs, rich and poor alike could fall victims to the deprivations and tortures that resulted from the prevailing affrays.

In ancient Greece, a few physicians – in true dedication to their calling – would treat rich and poor alike, but we are told that such men were sadly in the minority. For some years female babies, viewed as additional burdens on the family economy, were left outside at birth to die. This custom was fairly widespread, and by no means limited to pre-classical Greece. Celtic legends abound with instance of unwanted infants (of both sexes) who shared the 'Moses Syndrome', and no doubt those children who did survive and were taken in by some kindly foster parent paid for their experience in later life.

I attended a lecture some years ago in which the speaker, a physician of some note, remarked on how the middle and upper classes in the days of Imperial Rome frequently had more to worry about than the masses. This resulted in a very high incidence of nervous complaints among the educated which, in turn, gave rise to the growth of Temples of Healing appropriate to the relief of those conditions. In any society where government service and commerce are in either dictatorial or democratic hands (yes, it is just as worrying to think that one might be voted out as thrown out!) there are bound to be those insecurities which so easily give rise to the stress factor. Add to this the whims of a mentally unbalanced Emperor and it is little wonder that mental illness ran a close rival to its physical counterpart.

Following the collapse of Rome much of the civilised world fell into chaos and the dark forces of ignorance spread their reign of terror. The Middle Ages witnessed plagues and epidemic diseases which rapidly spread their evil tentacles from country to country, leaving thousands of dead in their wake. Many of these can be blamed on the rats which infested the towns and cities of the times, but a truer reason would surely be the filthy conditions in which people lived. At least the Greeks and Romans, for all their faults, understood the necessity for cleanliness!

The lack of personal hygiene persisted in many sections of society right up to the nineteenth century, when cleanliness suddenly became fashionable. However, I was born in 1929 and I can clearly recall being told in my childhood and youth by certain persons not in my immediate circle that too much washing and bathing weakened one!

Tuberculosis flourished in Victorian and Edwardian times. My nanny used to refer to it as 'consumption', often of the 'galloping' variety! The grime and smoke of the industrial towns poured ceaselessly into the congested living quarters. Pollution had arrived. Many of the poorer people were ill-fed and ill-clothed, and consequently suffered from severe malnutrition. As a result, children were born with disabling deformities such as rickets, and the genetic irregularities caused by breeding under such conditions are still being dealt with by the National Health Service to this day.

Malnutrition can sometimes, however, result from ignorance rather than unavailability of good food and the money with which to buy it. Research undertaken by nutritionists has shown that eating the wrong kinds of foods can be just as damaging to health as going without. In fact, according to a recent report in the *Guardian* (20 July 1988), eating less may even prolong life. An article in the health supplement of the *Washington Post* mentioned evidence to the effect that sensible calorie restriction increased the life-span in animals. The scientists concerned, however, were unsure as to whether longer life actually arises from a decrease in food-related ailments, such as heart disease, or whether low calorie diets retard ageing by inhibiting the development of cancer.

Disease and death have always marched hand in hand, one always hinting at, if not actually resulting in, the other. The death syndrome has been a taboo subject in polite society for many years. One simply does not talk about it, in much the same way that one did not mention sex (especially in the presence of the opposite sex) until the liberated sixties. And yet the 'inevitable' is something that we must all face sooner of later. New approaches to the psychology of the death syndrome are being tried among the terminally ill, both in hospices and among those who have chosen to spend their numbered days with their families or loved ones. Counsellors working in this field have discovered that patients are able to come to terms with the situation once the initial fear has been eliminated.

Many people do not actually fear death itself, but rather the way in which they might effect the transition. One often hears the statement,'I hope that when I go it will either be in my sleep, or very quickly.' The prospect of months of pain and medical experimentation in a dreary hospital ward is enough to daunt even the strongest heart. Many may feel that when their time has come they should be able to exit at *will*, so that no blame for their decision is placed on others. Shamans and wise men from certain tribes whom we might disrespectfully refer to as 'primitive' (implying that they do not live by our accepted Western standards) are able to do just this. The gift is not altogether lost in modern society, however. In 1985, my husband and I met with Dr Hugh Schonfeld the celebrated author, Hebrew scholar and mystic, who told us that he had only three years in which to complete the tasks he had still to achieve. Last year we were saddened but not surprised to read that Dr Schonfeld died precisely as he had foreseen, in 1988!

The loss of a loved one is known to be one of the most stressful or trauma-inducing events in life. Primitive society readily acknowledged this fact, and created elaborate rites to help the bereaved assuage their grief.[1] The subject has obviously come under recent review by the medical profession, which is now suggesting that bereaved people are helped to grieve if they see the body after death. The *British Medical Journal* recently reviewed the significance of parents holding a stillborn baby, and intimated that avoiding viewing a mutilated body may well contribute to the psychological after-effects of a loss. Among relatives of people killed in a train disaster, twenty-seven of the thirty-six who did not see the body regretted their decision after eighteen months, compared with only one of the eight who did. Seeing the body, doctors feel, gives people a chance to say goodbye (reported in *Health Guardian*, 26 October 1988).

A final word on the subject of death – this time, however, brought about legally and voluntarily – abortion. The ethics of such an act are a matter for the conscience of the woman concerned, and her alone. While many may feel strongly about the subject, an equal number see it as no more a crime against humanity than many other prevailing social misdemeanours which pass unnoticed. Those who are of Christian inclination might be well-advised to heed the words of their Lord and consider their own faults before casting the proverbial 'first stone'. Whether the act be right or wrong by Cosmic Law (as against man-made statutes), intention alone will be the deciding factor when that individual comes to judge herself, as she inevitably will in some other time, if not the present. A woman who has had an abortion is not necessarily ill, although she may have been under stress at the time of making her decision. However, having effected it, she may well be faced with conflicting emotions which may make her feel that she is not entitled to sympathy. Subsequent reactions may also be unexpected and regrets may take time to surface. If left unexplored these could give rise to protracted misery. Psychologist Denise Winn's new book *Experiences of Abortion* will help women deprived of counselling to come to terms with a painful and often secret experience.

I drew attention to this very problem in *The Psychology of Ritual*,[2] following a suggestion I had read that there should be a special rite for both the aborted or miscarried child and the mother who has undergone the associated experience. The body registers a degree of discomfort at the abrupt cessation of the cycle which it had been programmed to set into motion. This alone is trauma-inducing, without taking into account the emotional factors involved. In primitive tribes, elaborate rites were carried out to ensure that the spirit of the miscarried or naturally aborted child was helped on its way with love and understanding, while the mother was also given appropriate therapy[3].

Endnotes:

1. *The Psychology of Ritual*, Chapter 24, 'Modern Healing Rites', M Hope, pp. 223–227.
2. *Ibid*. Chapter 9, 'Rites of Death and Departure', pp. 85–93.
3. *Ibid*. p. 227.

Chapter 2

DISORDERS AND MALADIES

The disorders that serve to inconvenience our daily lives are legion, while a reasonably comprehensive catalogue of the somatic and psychological malfunctions that qualify as illness or disease would doubtless span several volumes of medical erudition. However, as the aim of this book is to concentrate more on causes and cures, and on the psychology behind them, it will be those conditions appropriate to this study that will be selected for emphasis and comment.

Many people may feel that life has treated them unfairly because they are born with physical or mental disadvantages. After giving birth, the first question most mothers ask is: 'Is he/she all right?', meaning healthy and well-formed, of course. There are many that are not. Sometimes these mental or physical handicaps can be traced to a specific cause, for example rubella, or a traumatic event in the life of the mother during pregnancy. Or they can result from some chromosome abnormality as in the case of Down's syndrome, which received its name from John Langdon Down – the physician who classified it – who died in 1896.

Then again, there are those deformities which result from drug abuse on the part of the user (mother), or the side-effects of medication administered by a qualified medical practitioner under perfectly legal circumstances. Anyone can make a mistake and incorrect diagnoses are not uncommon, as we all know. The side-effects of certain chemicals are well publicised, however, and those women who insist upon ignoring advice are risking not only their own health, but also that of any child which might be born if their condition is allowed to run to its full term.

Yet not all congenital conditions can be blamed on persons or circumstances. There is such a wide variance in the nature, type and intensity of this category of disability, that to render anything resembling full justice to its definitions would require a course in medicine. In whichever form these may manifest, however, there is little doubt that the distress waves they inevitably cause are by no means limited to the aura of the sufferer. The strain is frequently shared by other members of the family, medical staff and social workers, and breakdowns resulting from the associated stress are by no means uncommon. The burning question as to why some of us are born whole and others are not will always be hotly debated by metaphysicians, religious leaders, doctors and sociologists alike – to which ardent flames of enquiry the ensuing pages will doubtless add even further fuel.

Assuming that we do survive the birth experience and proceed to maturity, our childhood paths are anything but strewn with roses. Some children fare better than others in the health stakes, and as the young are not known for their tact and understanding, a sickly child can often suffer a double dose of punishment in the form of abuse from his or her siblings or peers. Childhood ailments may not seem much as we look back on them and for many of us they did, no doubt, serve as immunising factors against later manifestations of the disease which are not so easy to cope with in adulthood – mumps, for example. Due to modern medicine, which has done much to eliminate many ailments, such as diphtheria and whooping cough, which were killers in earlier times, childhood is thankfully a less perilous time for many.

There are always those individual cases which do not appear to fit into the general picture however: the new MMR (combined measles, mumps and rubella) vaccine for example, and the case of the mother who had received an anti-rubella vaccine prior to planning her first pregnancy, which she understood guaranteed her lifelong protection against the disease. As her first child was born without problems, she embarked on a second pregnancy, only to discover that her immunity had lapsed prior to conception, with disastrous results for her second son. Although such instances are rare, they are nevertheless possible and research is beginning to throw some light on why one person's immunity breaks down and another's does not (see Chapter 4).

So we progress to puberty, with its required physical, mental and social adjustments. Suicides among young people in their teens are becoming more frequent, and not for the sort of reasons we tended to think of in the past. Common causes for teenage suicide a few decades ago were being jilted by a lover, abandoned in pregnancy, or turned out of home and threatened with the dreaded 'workhouse'. Nowadays it is anything from drug abuse to the greenhouse effect, including the usual romantic disillusionments, possibility of nuclear wars, inability to integrate into society, problems with studies, being unable to make up one's mind about what to do with one's life, religious or idealistic fanaticism, AIDS . . . As someone once remarked to me, 'the choice in today's society is so wide it is confusing, and many youngsters are simply unable to handle it'.

Many of the occupational diseases that take their toll in our working lives could be avoided and precautions are now being taken against the damaging effects of materials such as asbestos. Dealing with dangerous chemicals of any kind always constitutes an occupational hazard, although a physician recently pointed out to me that there are probably more severe disabilities and deaths resulting from drunk driving, or road accidents generally, than from handling unstable chemical elements. Nevertheless, there are many areas of employment that do carry risks, and even comparatively harmless jobs can bring about problems.

Repetitive Strain Injury (RSI), a blanket term for a range of injuries to the hands, wrists, arms, shoulders, neck and back, is believed to be brought on by repetitious movement. Before the microchip, RSI was largely confined to the production line, but now it has spread to other areas of employment. Many computer operators have found themselves suffering from arm and shoulder problems that have rendered them unemployable again in that capacity – a fact that has not gone unnoticed by the insurance companies, which have promptly covered their tracks as a result of numerous claims against employers.

The natural process of ageing is the 'Grim Reaper's' closest ally, however. As the years roll by, like Dorian Gray, we are faced with the portrait of our former life and behaviour. While there are many maladies that are precipitated by adverse social conditions, there are just as many that we bring on ourselves which result from how we feed, clothe and use our physical vehicles – and our minds, for that matter. Have we over-indulged at the expense of our health? Put alcohol and cigarettes before a warm home environment? Refused to accept advice regarding diet or exercise? If so, then we have only ourselves to blame for at least some of the ills of senior citizenship.

A surgeon once complained to me about people with kidney problems who insisted on keeping their toilets arctic in mid-winter and then complaining to him when they developed an infection: 'They get up out of a warm bed and expose their buttocks to an icy seat in front of an open window in freezing temperatures. Now, is that the action of a sane person?' From the psychologist's point of view such behaviour is the result of earlier programming, the logic of which they have not seen fit to question.

There are people in the United Kingdom who still labour under the misapprehension that it is a form of weakness to heat a bedroom. Many an elderly soul, crippled with arthritis, will suffer a night of severe pain through the cold rather than break with his or her past conditioning. I have also witnessed young children, shivering, coughing and fighting for breath under an open window in freezing weather. In fact, a 17-year-old youth known to me personally actually died from pneumonia as a result of being sent to a freezing room as a punishment after returning home soaking wet and a little late. The father, now deceased, confided to me the feeling of guilt that he carried to his grave: 'I was only trying to toughen him up; it seemed the right thing to do at the time. A boy of that age should be able to take a little hardship.'

It is bad enough when we are assailed by the natural phenomena of advanced maturity, but when our imbalances are attributable to either illogical stupidity on the one hand, or hedonistic excesses, such as the abuse of food, alchohol, drugs and other harmful dependencies, on the other, the time has surely come when we need some form of help to make us more aware of our responsibilities towards ourselves.

Sometimes, however, it is none of these things that has made us ill. The imposition of physical or mental stresses which the body is not constructed to accommodate, or the mind programmed to handle, can be as damaging as any chemical dependency. I used to counsel a lady who worked full-time on an office switchboard. She had a teenage son and a bully of a husband who required her to carry out physical tasks in and around the home that were just too much for her. She was obliged to leave the office ten minutes before anyone else because, if her son arrived home before she did and there was not a cup of tea on the table for him, he would strike her. Any efforts on her part to effect a defence, either verbal or physical, would meet with derision from her husband, his philosophy being that it was her duty to provide the son with what he needed and stop thinking about herself. Needless to say the poor soul died of cancer before she was 45, a happy release from an intolerable situation. Many readers may ask why she did not just walk out. I think one would have to be a certain type of woman to understand the answer to that one – someone who has been programmed into the 'responsibility at any cost' mode.

The diseases to which all and any of us are probably subjected at some point in our lives are those of infection and contagion. Viruses, in particular, are prevalent these days, or so we are told. Whether these have always been there or are a recent phenomenon is highly debatable. Some doctors swear that there are new strains constantly testing our immune systems; others believe they are nothing new; while a third school of thought, much favoured among alternative therapists, opines that many of these viral indispositions are the result of our tampering with the natural ecological balance of the planet and letting in bugs from outer space.

Myalgic Encephalomyelitis (ME), or post-viral syndrome, which affects the central nervous system and muscles, has been called the mystery disease of the eighties, and for which there is still no known cure. We are told that no one who has not experienced this first hand can have any idea what a person with ME really feels. A very good friend of mine sustained an attack last summer and was able to describe to me the sheer fatigue and total lack of life energy she experienced. The importance of the immune system in controlling viruses and allergies has now been realised, and how this can be affected by diet, stress and even atmospherical disturbances.

Nor is ME the only medical enigma of the age. When enquiring after the health of a friend or acquaintance who has been indisposed, one is frequently informed 'Oh, it's only a bug, the usual kind of thing. My doctor says there's a lot of it about.' After listening to the words of others over many years (and hearing them myself), I have decided that 'there's a lot of it about' is now old enough to qualify for one of those long, medical descriptions which translate clinically as 'We don't really know but try this for size!'

Diseases of degeneration can attack people of all ages, and the tragedy is often accentuated by the fact that the sufferer has no one to look after him or her and faces a future among the likewise afflicted in a State home. One story (to which the metaphysically inclined will probably hasten to attach the karmic label), which was brought to my attention, concerned a young man who had just received a multiple sclerosis diagnosis following a period of difficulty with muscular activity.

He was feeling utterly shattered as he collected his daily needs from the local supermarket, and wondered how many more times he would be able to carry out this necessary chore without mechanical aids. To add to his woes he was an orphan with no relatives, living in a bedsitter. In his efforts to remove the goods from the store trolley and place them in his plastic shopping bag, he dropped several items. A young man standing next in the queue hastened to help him pick them up. As he left the shop, the young man joined him and asked if he was feeling all right. Perhaps, he suggested, a rest and a cup of tea might be in order. Feeling the need to talk to someone, the afflicted man gladly accepted the offer and confided his problem to his new acquaintance in a nearby café.

It turned out that the other young man was also alone in the world, his parents and sister having been killed in a car accident. But he had inherited a nice house. How would it be if the sick man moved in with him and shared the expenses, in return for which he would look after him? A friendship was struck from that very moment, and they enjoyed many happy years together. After the inevitable passing of his friend, the compassionate man was able to settle down to a happy marriage, his karma fulfilled.

How many of us have found ourselves suddenly subjected to aches and pains, sometimes quite severe, that appear to have no logical explanation. In the first instance, rather than bother the doctor we rush to our medical dictionaries, ask a friend down the road who is in the nursing profession, or discuss it with our colleagues at work. And sure enough, there is always someone who knows someone who had exactly the same thing, who went through all hell before finding a cure, or who died from it! Previously undiscovered lumps suddenly assume ominous proportions, while a digestive upset resulting from some nervous tension causes us to fear the very worst. So we eventually pluck up courage and descend upon our overworked GP, who promptly reaches for his pen and arranges for us to see the Consultant. After a long wait (assuming that we are dealing with the National Health Service and live in an inner city area), we finally confront a surgeon who is already tired after a morning of consultations at his private clinic. He gives us a little note and up to X-ray we go.

Sometimes the tests are extensive and spread over several weeks, and when we are finally presented with the results it is a rather acid Registrar who tells us in polite, but plain, words that there is basically nothing wrong with us. As we return wearily home, nursing a mixture of guilt about wasting government money when there are people dying with cancer and similar major diseases, and at the same time wondering whatever can be causing our pain, we are forced to face the reality of the 'psychosomatic syndrome'. Is it all in our mind? But if that is the case, why does it hurt so much?

Psychosomatic conditions can be induced subconsciously by conflicts arising from unresolved problems, traumas, and situations we refuse to face up to. Being a workaholic, I some-times push my body to its extremes. Does it protest? Of course it does, but not always in the way one might expect. I have found that different parts of my anatomy play up at different times, according to the nature of the problem I am trying to cope with mentally. The son of a friend of mine developed a terrible rash and blotches on his face when he could not 'face up' to a situation. Once the problem was resolved, the affliction left him. Think about it!

Other people are sometimes directly responsible for our disabilities, as in the case of those unfortunate souls who are severely injured in car accidents caused by careless or drunk driving on the part of another. Sometimes rehabilitation does work, however. One case known to me concerns a teenager who was knocked from his motorcycle by a driver who went the wrong way up a one-way street. His back broken, the boy was faced with being confined to a wheelchair for the rest of his life, a promising musical career nipped in the bud. After the initial shock, pain and trauma he slowly adjusted to the inevitable and is now gainfully employed in a responsible position which requires his fine mental faculties, but asks nothing of his body.

Physical or mental impairment may also result from criminal acts or military duties. In the case of the former, women appear to come off worse although grievous bodily harm can cripple either sex. Rape, we are told, leaves a permanent scar, as does childhood abuse by parents or guardians. I have counselled more cases of the latter than I could keep count of. It makes one question the values and emphases of the society in which we live, which surely brings us back full circle to the imbalances of body, mind and spirit which are part and parcel of life on the planet we call Earth.

A mistake frequently made is to equate mental handicap with mental illness. There is a vast difference which should be borne in mind in all clinical or sociological observations. Physical or mental handicaps can be either inherited (cystic fibrosis and Huntington's disease), congenital, or the consequence of accidents, physical or mental abuse, or the side-effect of a disease. Mental illness, on the other hand, while its syndrome might also be inherent in the genes, more frequently results from life's stresses and our own inability to cope with them. There are many more causes, but this is not a medical textbook and there has to be a point at which we call a halt.

The modern approach to the mentally sick is to try to give them a sense of purpose within the community, if this is at all possible, rather than incarcerating them in institutions. To a degree this has worked, but more psychiatric social workers are needed to make the scheme really effective. A recent television programme featured the case of a lady suffering from schizophrenia who was allowed to return to her home, as she was reasonably lucid while under medication. But she was incapable of filling in the necessary forms to apply for money for food, and as a consequence she was almost starving when finally taken to hospital after collapsing in the street. I am sure that many of you who read this book will have suggestions as to how she and others like her could be helped, but whether the system could afford to carry them out, assuming they met with its approval, is another matter.

Known cases of criminal insanity are kept in protective custody, but what about those that are undetected – the Jack the Rippers of our society who can appear as sane as the next person during the normal course of life? Incidences of child abuse, rape, mugging and similar social evils are all symptomatic of mental imbalance on someone's part. And yet many of those who perpetrate these dastardly acts probably walk freely amongst us – our acquaintances, perhaps, those we sup or drink with, or even members of our own family!

On the surface it would appear that each of these afflictions falls into a different category, some being self-induced and others resulting from circumstances beyond the control of the sufferer. Closer scrutiny at the psychological or transpersonal levels will reveal far more, as we shall shortly see.

Chapter 3

CAUSES AND CONTRIBUTORY FACTORS

Is the suffering caused by sickness and disease really necessary?

This is a question that has been posed by the afflicted and the whole alike. Theories as to why we have to fall victim to physical and mental imbalances have been debated by physicians, philosophers and religious adherents down the ages. These range from the practical considerations of dialectical materialism to the abstract speculations of metaphysics.

One thing is certain, however: the winds of change are blowing across all horizons, gently at first, but with increasing velocity as the new 'awareness factor' begins to take a stronghold in the collective psyche of Homo sapiens. Emphasis is slowly shifting away from the pathogenic concept, as the increasing inflow of new evidence continues to highlight the role played by the mind in the arena of human suffering. Coming to terms with the effects of mind over matter could revolutionise the whole face of medicine, or at least its attitude towards disease. But surely, if much of what we suffer is caused by our own minds, attitudes and lack of adjustment, should we not seek the cause at that particular level and, if possible, use that very tool that has wrought the imbalance to correct it?

Of course – and it is upon this premise that many alternative therapies are based. But unfortunately it is not that simple. As a youngster I was taught that to know one's enemy is half the battle. Few of those who do suffer as a result of their own mental processes are willing to acknowledge the existence of such contingencies, let alone accept advice on how to set the downward spiral into reverse. And this kind of attitude is by no means limited to those of little education.

Returning to the mind–body conflict, it would appear that at times our minds do punish our bodies for their own subconscious frustrations, a process which is clinically described as somatisation. Sometimes life imposes upon us a set of circumstances which run contrary to what we feel we would really like to do. Perhaps we are forced into an academic life in order to please our families when we would much rather be carving wood or tilling the land, or the reverse. But we feel it is our duty to our loved ones to comply with their needs – after all, the world might think of us as irresponsible hedonists if we did not! So we undertake our studies and spend the next fifteen or more years sitting behind a desk dreaming of being an airline pilot, cattle farmer, ballet dancer or TV personality, always taking good care (albeit unconsciously) to criticise anyone we might meet from those professions.

During the course of my studies and consultations I have met many people who fall into this category. They usually announce themselves quite lucidly with the identical phrase, 'Of course, I'm just an ordinary (working) person (housewife).' When anyone greets me with this statement I immediately detect a resentment or hidden frustration. Nobody is 'just ordinary'. We each have something unique to offer. I have rubbed shoulders with people from all walks or life, classes and professions, the 'see me, I am ordinary' syndrome crops up everywhere and anywhere, and is frequently indicative of envy, self-deprecation or personal frustration. As the counselling progresses the barriers descend. There is the woman who has spent the first three sessions assuring her therapist that she is the devoted mother and wife, only to blurt out at some later date how she cannot stand her husband, actually dislikes her children, and regrets giving up her earlier studies for marriage. 'My professor told me I was a natural for law (medicine, music, art, or whatever),' while her male counterpart relates his dreams of world travel, his own business, or that great novel he knows he could produce if it were not for screaming children, fences in need of mending, mortgage repayments and a million other such excuses.

So where does all this fit in with mental frustrations and the diseases resulting therefrom? Obviously, many of the people in the cases I have just mentioned are reasonably well-adjusted, and simply using the therapist as a medium for catharsis. Given the chance to abandon their domesticity in favour of flying a jumbo jet, pirouetting across the stage at Covent Garden, removing someone's gall bladder, or writing a sordid pot-boiler, they would probably opt for the cosiness of a warm, family atmosphere, regular meals and the camaraderie of the chaps at work or the local Women's Institute – although this does not apply in all cases.

Assuming the mind to be the bogey, or at least one of them, in the disease machine, what is to be done about eradicating its influence, or at least turning its obvious power to advantage? There are numerous appropriate therapies – orthodox, fringe and alternative – which will be dealt with in Part 2 of this book. What we are trying to achieve at this stage is a broad understanding of what the healer is up against and why. Here are a few of the ideas I have encountered during the course of my own studies and research.

1. The Growth Factor

Popular in the United States, this concept suggests that we unconsciously place ourselves in situations in life that will afford us the opportunity to suffer, so that we may add to what is popularly termed the 'growth experience'. Illness, disappoint-ment, disillusionment, emotional upsets, financial disasters, family problems, and so forth, can all be categorised as encoun-ters essential to our psychological and transpersonal growth; how we handle them (or do not, as the case may be) being indicative of our level of maturity. People who have suffered a major illness often comment that the experience has helped them to reappraise life. A recent publication explores the way in which people understand those sicknesses which interrupt normal patterns of work and relationships. Anything from flu to muscular dystrophy can inflict pain, distress and dependence on others. Pat Kitto, a counsellor with cancer patients writes: 'When we become ill there is often the overwhelming realization that we can show emotion.'[1]

2. Punitive Karma

This is a popular metaphysical variation of the 'sins of the fathers' theme, the idea being that we will be required to return to atone for those misdeeds we have perpetrated in former lives (assuming an acceptance of the *linear* reincarnation theory – which your author does not). This expiatory process may be undertaken in any one of several ways:

1. Transmutation of karma through service to a principle in whichever guise one may see fit to acknowledge it (i.e. a favoured ideal, religious calling, sociological humanitarianism, art, and so forth);
2. Realisation of the suffering one has previously imposed on others by taking on a similar condition oneself;
3. Effecting family connections with the mentally or physically disabled which require great personal sacrifice;
4. Entering life with congenital or genetic defects which throw one onto the mercies of others for care and protection; or,
5. Working in a field in which one subconsciously feels one has wronged others.

Here are a few illustrative examples based on cases I encountered during my many years working with a healing group in central London and later in private counselling:

(1) A very down-to-earth couple were referred to me by a local Presbyterian minister with whom they had exchanged harsh words regarding their son's choice of career. The father was a chartered surveyor and his wife a prim Scottish lady whose life energies had been devoted entirely to her husband and their only son. Both were dedicated socialists and atheists. Their son, however, had, upon reaching school-leaving age, decided to make the Methodist Church his career, much to his parent's chagrin. Endless theological arguments had ensured, as a result of which the family had become estranged. Oddly enough, the father was more open to metaphysical considerations than he was to orthodox religion, believing the latter to be nothing short of smug hypocrisy. After a long talk, during which the couple furnished me with a fairly concise (and accurate) assessment of their son's character, I suggested to them that he might

possibly feel drawn to the cloth as a statement of a 'principle' rather than on purely religious grounds. Those who are strongly propelled towards a particular idealistic principle, for no apparently logical reason, are usually utilising that avenue of expression as a convenient outlet for a subliminal prompting.

The son naturally refused to see me or anyone from my group, dismissing us as 'servants of the devil', which served to anger the parents even more, pushing them ever nearer to the 'karmic' camp. Eventually he took his Orders and sailed happily away to some far–off missionary post in the fervent belief that he was required to serve God in that particular way. As for the parents, the mother subsequently died 'of a broken heart' (which statement calls for analysis in a later chapter), and the father remarried a young lady and became converted to paganism! To my knowledge he never reconciled with his son, but that was some fifteen years ago so anything could have happened since then.

(2) My next example concerns the case of a lady who was convinced that the sight in her left eye was rapidly decreasing. She was referred to her doctor, who sent her to a specialist who could find nothing wrong with the eye and told her so. But she was sure that he had missed something in his diagnosis and insisted that she was slowly losing the sight in that eye. A period of time passed and her doctor again referred her to a specialist. This time he was able to find a slight fault which, he assured her, could easily be corrected by minor surgery. She agreed to the operation and, against odds of a thousand to one, it misfired, permanently impairing the sight in that eye.

A few months later she complained of difficulty with her right eye. Once again she was seen by the specialist who assured her that it was nothing more than strain caused by over-compensation for the loss of vision in her other eye. But she would have none of it, and in time exactly the same thing happened as with the left eye. A fault developed and another surgeon undertook to effect the correction. Once again the surgery misfired, leaving her almost totally blind. Coincidence? I have personally never believed that there is such a thing. However, from that time on she became much more at peace with herself. She learned braille and took up a new life. Sometime later I saw her again briefly and she joyfully announced to me that she felt so much better now that she was blind. I asked her if she could explain why.

She answered, 'Well, I know this may sound strange, but I used to have a recurring dream that I was a man in a torture chamber during the Spanish Inquisition, and it was my job to put out people's eyes. The dream left me with a terrible feeling of guilt, and I knew that I had to experience blindness for myself so that I could understand what those poor people went through. Since I've been blind the dream has never recurred.' I am inclined to think that this was a typical case of self-inflicted punitive karma.

(3) I am reminded of the case of the late Douglas Hunt and his wife. Hunt was a brilliant man with a Cambridge Masters Degree which earned him the headship of a public school. His wife was also a teacher, and their only son, Nigel, was born to them fairly late in life with Downs Syndrome. Firmly believing that a Downs child had the potential to participate in a much wider social arena, the couple gave up their careers to raise Nigel. So successful were their efforts, that by the time he reached his teens, the boy was able to wwrite a book explaining how his condition had affected him and his view of a world from which he was, to a degree, mentally isolated. Shortly after the publication of the book, Mrs Hunt died, and it was not long after that Douglas himself passed away, a victim of cancer. I visited him in hospital just prior to his death and he told me that he sincerely believed Nigel had been born to him and his wife so that together they could contribute to the understanding of Downs Syndrome children. His work having been completed, Douglas felt he could now leave his body and depart in peace. He was the author of several scholarly books on metaphysics and was, in my opinion, the stuff of which real saints are made.

(4) The above case also serves to illustrate the next category in one way, although there can be variations on the genetic or congenital theme. I have encountered numerous cases of children who have been born with physical or mental disadvantages into families ideally suited to coping with them. The cases of two lady doctors, who lived in the locality where I was residing were brought to my notice, also four school-teachers (three males and one female) and two social workers, all of whom had children who were either Downs, spastic or mentally retarded

or who suffered from spina bifida. Logic prompts one to suppose that the arrangement was a mutual one prior to incarnation, the sufferer somehow agreeing to endure the affliction, either to aid the parent's growth process, or to assist in the development of new technology that allows the brilliant mind trapped in a severely physically handicapped body access to the expression of its creativity. It is also interesting to observe that the children themselves are frequently happy in spite of their disabilities. Having responsibility for life's decisions assumed for them by their families or guardians leaves them with more time and space simply to *be*.

Sadly, not all such cases are so blessed. Sometimes the parents are unable to cope and the poor children are condemned to life in an institution or special school. Perhaps they are fortunate in that the staff are appropriately qualified and are therefore able to help them to develop what potential they do possess, but one shudders to think of what must have happened in the unenlightened ages of the past.

It should be borne in mind, however, that the expiation of karma is commensurate with the suffering endured, and sometimes a finely tuned body, and a brain in possession of its full faculties, can suffer the sort of excruciating physical and mental pain that would not be experienced by someone who was less mentally or physically aware. Besides, the whole idea of the incarnation may have been to afford others: parents, guardians or tutors for example, the chance to expiate *their* karma.

The biblical reference to sins of the father's being visited on the sons could also have more genetic connotations. After all, the brutal mother or father from the past who has caused great suffering to their children could well be born again into that very same family generations later to face the parenthood of those very children they formerly abused! It would seem that the members of a group soul do continually come together, albeit in different guises. One's father might be a brother in one life and granddaughter in another, while one might wed one's twin soul in one period of history and be born its identical twin sister in another. As no one can actually prove or disprove any of these hypotheses, much of this is conjecture, but even speculation can be based on logic and years of observation and study, which is surely what true scientific research is all about.

Karma also works the other way, of course, handicaps and illness being by no means the only things we are likely to

inherit. Mathematical, musical and artistic skills can also run
in families, and geneticists working on the Genome Project,
which aims to categorise the complete genetic structure of
Homo sapiens, hope to use the information gleaned to eradicate
many of today's inherited afflictions.

The Polynesians, like the Chinese, are great ancestor wor-
shippers. I can recall an occasion in the past at the Festival
of Mind, Body and Spirit in London when an elderly Chinese
gentleman engaged me in conversation. We discussed Chinese
astrology and while we were talking I watched him carefully
scrutinising my aura.

'You have been having much trouble lately?' he enquired.
'Yes,' I answered.

'And you have much more still to come,' he replied, nodding
his head sadly.

'But you will overcome it, for I see you have very powerful
ancestors who will help you through.' I tried to find out how he
was able to detect this, but at that point he dismissed me with
a smile, a kindly wave of the hand and the parting words: 'One
day they will show you,' before disappearing into the milling
crowds.

(5) This category is a fairly simple one to work out if you
think about it. It frequently encompasses those people who
have miraculously recovered from some severe accident or
crippling disease and thenceforth devoted their lives to helping
others in that field. One case in particular springs to mind
of a lady who underwent an NDE (Near Death Experience)
some twenty-five years ago from which she made a surprising
recovery, claiming afterwards to have been reborn as a different
persona. I realise that there are several psychological explanations for this, ranging from shock to the nervous system to
schizoprenia, but she has shown no subsequent signs of mental
illness and is more at peace with herself than many others I can
think of who consider themselves a cut above the intellectual
average.

And now I would like to examine another hypothesis that is
fast gaining popularity among those of metaphysical inclination: the 'respectable exit door'. Teachings regarding this theory
have come through several channels in many esoteric disciplines and are to be found in detail in my own work *The Lion
People*. We are informed that it is not the natural lot of mankind to

die in agony of some insidious disease, but rather the individual should be able to reach a stage where he or she simply says: 'I have fulfilled my karma for this life and would now like to leave in peace.' After which friends and family can gather round to say their fond farewells and allow the exiting spirit to slip quietly into a painless and peaceful sleep.

Now wouldn't that be nice! But would we be allowed to do it? Of course not! Mother, father, Aunt Jane or brother Bill would upbraid us for our selfishness! How could we just leave them like that after all the love they have given us? Who would look after the children, pay the mortgage, feed the cat? So the spirit decides upon what it feels to be a respectable exit that will upset no one and bring nothing but kind wishes and sympathy, and programmes the brain accordingly. Of course, there are those who will vehemently protest that no one in their right mind actually chooses to die of a painful and disabling disease, and why should a young life be cut off in the prime of its youth?

Enter the free will factor, and the many levels at which this might operate. We may express our free will in the choice of a partner (in most societies), house, job, personal habits, and so forth. But when it comes to leaving – oh dear, free will has to stop at that point, or does it? People of all ages die in spite of the protests.

Recently, I was quite shocked to hear of the death of a young woman with whom I had enjoyed a brief, but stimulating, acquaintance. She was one of the most self-assertive people I have ever met – totally confident and frightened of nothing and no one. She was also blessed with above-average good looks and a fine figure that many might envy. She enjoyed sport and was an excellent horsewoman. Probably because she found that life slipped easily along for her, she had little time for those who were sick, slow on the uptake, or unable to match her creativity and quick wit. She died of cancer at the age of 32.

For days I sat and puzzled as to why such a strong character could have succumbed to the disease when there are known cases of people who have overcome cancer by sheer will-power and lived to write books about the experience. I discussed it with my husband, as he also knew her, and we came to the conclusion that outer strength is not synonymous with inner strength. Although, of course, one could play devil's advocate and suggest that being strong-minded she had chosen her exit door as a growth experience at exactly the time of life *her* choice dictated, and not what convention demanded. Interestingly enough, she was a lady with little respect for convention, and was totally individuated from the collective. So there we are!

I do not think for one moment that our psyches rationalise their choice of exit and then feed the information to our subconscious minds. What seems more likely is the PK (psychokinesis) theory favoured by parapsychologists and some philosophers – that when we experience feelings of despair or disillusionment with what life has to offer us, we exude a certain PK frequency, the quality of which attracts energies of a similar nature. And if one's mind has designated these to be negative, destructive or terminal, then what we draw unto ourselves will also be negative, destructive, or terminal in nature.

Some evidence for this is to be found in psychological evaluations based on recent clinical studies which suggest that cancer is frequently an alternative to despair. Observing those personally known to me who have been claimed by the disease over the past few years, I think I would be inclined to agree. One is impelled to ask what has made them so desperate, which question brings us right back to the case I mentioned earlier of the woman who was terrified of her husband and teenage son.

Some of us do appear to become locked in ever-rotating grooves from which we feel unable to escape in this life. Try as we may there is no 'comfortable' way of changing our circumstances, so we succumb to them and subconsciously hope for a better deal next time round. In the East they speak of the Wheel of Karma, from which one can only effect an escape by a process of spiritual enlightenment and progression. Part of that transpersonal quest entails breaking one's bonds and facing the painful consequences. Many have yet to find that courage, so they rotate from life to life, being faced each time with a variation of the same theme. In ancient Egypt this was seen as a net through which the initiate was required to cut his or her way with the help of the gods. But the tools necessary to effect the cutting had to be earned, as Hercules, Perseus and other heroes of old were well aware; they were not just there for the taking. All signs point to our need to extend our conscious awareness to acknowledge the existence of our potential to control our lives and circumstances, the mastery and understanding of which could alleviate the necessity for utilising the exit door of the painful demise.

Of course, all this assumes an acceptance of the separate

identities of psyche and brain (spirit and body), and that we are, at conception, attracted to the genetic structure most likely to offer us the experience we need for our transpersonal development or evolutionary progress. Medical astrology would have much to say about this, no doubt, but it is a complex subject to which it would be impossible to do justice in a few pages. Suffice it to say, however, that there are indications in our natal charts as to both our time of demise and the way in which we might choose to exit.

Nor is the moment of birth the only counter of our days. Our future would also appear to be influenced somatically, our genes carrying the cynotype of our potential strengths and weakness. The thymus gland, one of the endocrine or ductless glands situated just behind the top of the breast-bone does not act by secreting hormones, unlike the other endocrines. Its main role is performed in the latter part of foetal life and in early infancy when it processes lymphocytes, which it endows with the power to distinguish between 'self' and 'non-self' cells and proteins. Processed lymphocytes (*T* lymphocytes) circulate in the lymphatic system and settle in lymphoid tissue (mainly in the lymph modes). Their successors subsequently alert the body's immune defences against foreign proteins, tissues and micro-organisms, and activate *B* lymphocytes which generate antibodies against foreign protein and toxins (antigens). Some lymphocytes are killer cells, a fact I find interesting as it would seem to indicate that the thymus plays a part in programming our future health from a very early stage in our development. In metaphysical terms it could be said to effect a blueprint or karmic pattern of our life ahead, and having done its duty it then withdraws. Question: Where does free will start and end – before or after birth?

Endnotes:

1. *The Meaning of Illness*, ed. Mark Kidel, and *Illness*, ed. Mark Kidel and Susan Rowe-Leete.

Chapter 4

MIND AND MATTER

As the foregoing chapter assumes an acknowledgement of the mind as a separate and distinct entity from the brain, my more sceptical readers may see fit at this point to question this premise.

For four hundred years the philosophy of René Descartes has dominated Western thought. His separation of the mind and the body had the effect of erecting a formidable barrier between medicine and mysticism, materialism and metaphysics. Prior to Descartes, men of all religions believed in the power of the mind and the efficacy of meditation and prayer. Nowadays, for many the only acceptable remedies are those dispensed in bottles. Western thinkers demand scientific and logical explanations for everything without which any idea, however old and well-tested, has nothing to offer high-tech living. A new breed of men and women are emerging from this left-brain hemisphere chaos, however, to show us that mind and body are indeed one. And incredibly they are not philosophers, priests or quacks, but scientists whose methods and results would defy even the most modern sceptic.

Systematic investigation, mainly in America, has led to the growing realisation that the mind can heal the body. Research, never before possible, is convincing scientists that there are chemical communicators which link mind and body. The enormous potential of this discovery has so fired the Americans that they are posed to spend hundreds of thousands of US tax dollars investigating it at their nation's top research institution. Sadly, the British response has been one of no money, no interest. In the United States, however, members of a new branch of the medical profession, the psychoneuroimmunologists, are realising that to fail to embark on a thorough investigation of the findings that have so far emerged would be to miss one of the greatest opportunities of all times.

The Mail On Sunday (3 April 1988) reported the publication of a controversial new book on the subject, *The Healing Brain*, by Professor of Neurobiology at Stanford University, Robert Ornstein and physician David Sobel. In their book they argue that it is pointless for Western governments to throw more and more money into health care. For too long, they say, modern medicine has separated mind and body. The key to future health is the recognition of the fact that 'the brain minds the body' and to start asking why some people become ill when others do not.

Already the US National Institute of Mental Health (NIMH) has turned an entire team to exploring this new field of psychoneuroimmunology, scientists working on it having virtual *carte blanche* to study and spend what they want. Behind their excitement are some astonishing discoveries! Research is showing that the brain and state of mind can directly affect the body's immune system which is our defence against disease.

The very chemicals in our brain which influence emotion and our ability to feel pain may directly interact with cells in the immune system. Researchers have discovered receptors for these chemicals, the endorphins, both in that part of the brain which gives rise to emotions and on the very white blood cells that attack invading foreign bodies. There is also evidence that one of the most exciting families of natural anti-cancer chemicals yet discovered – the interleukins – may directly link with centres in our brain.

On another level, it is now known that people prone to chronic anxiety, tension, pessimism and sadness are more likely to develop disease. People *can* die of a 'broken heart'. During the six months following the death of a wife, a widower over the age of 55 is 40 per cent more likely to die than other men of his own age. Dr David Barron, Deputy Clinical Director of the NIMH stated: 'There is really exciting research going on. We are on that critical edge of putting together information from basic science – the people trying to find out what the mechanism might be – and the clinical application.'

We now know that a poor state of mind can damage health, and that the brain and the immune system work together. Can we show that a better state of mind will help produce a healthier body? There is already evidence that this is so. A massive study of health statistics held by one of the largest health insurers in the United States has recently shown that people who practise some form of meditation seek less health care, or become ill less than half as often as other people. And this is true of a variety of illness from heart disease to cancer.

Even on this side of the Atlantic some doctors are convinced this research is on the right track. At Charing Cross Hospital in London, Dr Peter Nixon and his colleagues are using relaxation – this time through sleep – as one of their main weapons against a threatened heart attack. At the Marylebone Healing and Counselling Centre in the crypt of St Marylebone Church in north London, doctors offer yoga classes and other forms of relaxation to patients under stress. Nor are they ashamed to be associated with a Church which offers the laying on of hands.

Dr Herbert Benson, Associate Professor of Medicine at Harvard Medical School, believes that we each have within us a 'relaxation response' which could be used to benefit us both mentally and physically. He also draws disquieting parallels between the ancient arts of meditation and prayer which many of us have forgotten, telling us that: 'There is nothing mysterious about it. You simply close your eyes, keep repeating a word or phrase, shut out everyday thoughts and your body relaxes. The same things happens of course, during prayer or hypnosis.'

The NIMH scientists now want to embark on systematic, scientifically watertight trials to see just what power the mind does have over the body, and to demonstrate any links in a way that the Western world and its scientific adherents can never doubt.

Journalist Lorraine Fraser, to whom we are grateful for her illuminating article, signed off with the following statement:

> Across the centuries, our priests, philosophers, poets and writers have talked ecstatically on that altered state of mind deep contemplation can bring. Modern science, and the very scientific philosophy which turned the majority of us into sceptics may yet explain why meditation, prayer and peace of mind can bring health and happiness.

Meditation, contemplation and prayer, however, are only truly beneficial if the individual is free to choose his or her own personal path to the transpersonal, and if rules are not laid down by any state, convention or collective regarding the way in which this is done and the representation of the deity to which it must be addressed. Any such rules, albeit unwritten, might well cause just as much stress and anxiety to some nonconformists, and therefore as much illness or mental strain, as they would suffer without their transpersonal efforts. Here I speak from firsthand experience, both my own and that of others who are my close friends or whom I have counselled in the past.

I was careful to observe that in the aforegoing report the terms 'brain' and 'mind' were spoken of in a single context. Whether this was purely the semantics of Ms Fraser's reporting or whether, in fact, the scientists concerned saw it that way was not clearly defined. As a definition of terms is obviously called for, what actually is the mind as distinct from the brain? And are mind and psyche necessarily synonymous?

The dictionary defines the word *psyche* as: 'the human mind or spirit,' with synonyms anima, essential nature, individuality, inner man, innermost self, personality, pneuma (philosophy), self, soul, subconscious and true being.

Next we enter the worlds of psychology/psychiatry and philosophy, with each specialist school proffering its own set of descriptive terms. There are three main schools of belief concerning the nature and function of the mind:

> 1. Monoism. That is purely the expression of the physical brain, the size nature and internal working of that organ being the deciding factor as to what sort of mentality the individual may possess.
>
> 2. Dualism. That it is concerned with some external and to date immeasurable energy field that exerts a programming influence over the physical brain, the latter being, in effect, a highly complex computer.
>
> 3. The metaphysical concept that it is directly concerned with the psyche, soul or spirit.

The fact that the brain can be altered surgically and the mind still remain strong leaves (1) open to question, while (2) could simply be a more scientific way of describing (3). Although the term would appear to mean different things to different people according to which school of psychology, humanism, metaphysics or religion they adhere to, there is little doubt that the 'mind' as such, no matter what its true nature or function might be, is a force in itself that does motivate the growth and behaviour of matter. This influence may apply negatively (as with psychosomatic illnesses) or positively (through self-healing and self-programming), according to the inclination and strength of character of the individual.

Freud defined the personality as having three vital strands: the id, the ego and the super-ego, the former being totally unconscious and the latter two a mixture of conscious and unconscious. The id, sometimes referred to as the animal energy, is concerned with instinctive impulses and demands for immediate gratification of primitive needs and desires. As the boiling cauldron of the personality, it represents a strong force which often finds expression in fantasies. Being amoral, it has no sense of right and wrong; hence its association with man's darker nature. Desire, aggression and need are said to emanate from the id and its power to affect our physical responses may be evidenced in the sexual effects of fantasising. On the other hand, religious fantasising has been known to produce stigmata, so I do not feel that we can necessarily allocate all somatic responses to mental stimulus to the chthonic regions.

The ego was viewed by Freud as the conscious driving force that controls the id and prevents it from having its own way, the ego only allowing the id to fulfil those desires which are not to its detriment. Following Freud's death a group of psychologists, led by his daughter Anna, broke away from his original concept, believing that the ego had its own store of energy which enabled it to satisfy its personal, social, and creative needs independent of, and without constant conflict with, the id. Today, however, the term ego is more generally used to denote the 'I', or unique expression of the individuality rather than the mind or psyche. While Freudian psychology views the ego as a personal value system, the upper layer of the personality, or super-ego, is seen as an amalgam of belief systems based on external standards set by society, its main role being to suppress the unseemly desires of the id by forcing the ego to ignore all the id's basic urges. Its reward, should it succeed in this mission, is societal approval.

The popular use of the term 'psyche' can probably be attributed to the work of the late Carl Gustav Jung, who deviated from Freudian thinking in his belief in the collective unconscious. He called the whole personality the psyche and maintained that it has three levels: the ego, which is the conscious mind; the personal unconscious, in which is stored all our repressed fantasies, dreams and desires; and the collective unconscious, which is part of the primordial past and which each of us inherits. It is from the latter that we derive our image of archetypes, which prove so important in subconscious communication and therefore exert a profound effect on our state of balance or otherwise. Jung also conceived of the 'shadow' or darker side of the self, which needed to be faced up to and overcome.

Many other threefold references have appeared since the time of Freud and Jung, although there are an equal number which were acknowledged in metaphysical circles long before the advent of modern psychiatry, the natural/instinctive, rational/intellectual and creative/intuitive for example, and the threefold nature of the Triple Goddess – maiden/mother/crone – each of which represent different aspects (or spiritual growth stages) of the whole psyche or self. The term 'psyche' is also used among certain groups to describe either the superconscious, higher or transpersonal (all-knowing) self, or the soul or spirit which is believed by many to be the spark or intelligence that gives life to the body and programmes the brain.

As to the brain itself, new knowledge regarding its neutral processes and functioning are being discovered with such rapidity that yesterday's reference books are out of date almost before they leave the printers. I covered the subject with illustrated detail in *The Psychology of Ritual*, but no doubt by the time I have completed this book there will be considerably more to add.

Having established both our mind/brain distinctions and our different terms or reference, let us return once more to the question of how the physical body mirrors its mind or psyche. Ernst Kretschmer, a Professor of Neurology and Psychiatry, made a special study of the correspondences between a person's physiology and their mental make-up. Dr Charlotte Wolff, who studied with Kretschmer, wrote several books on the human hand, based on Kretschmer's findings. I discovered these some years back and was immediately impressed with the resemblance they bore to the age-old practice of palmistry. I was extremely fortunate in that Dr Wolff granted me a personal interview in which she discussed both her somatically related psychological studies and her later interest in the Jungian study of dreams, especially in relation to forthcoming events which were already known to the collective unconscious. Dr Wolff was able to look at a face or hand and tell its owner his or her genetic history, psychological type and to which diseases or disorders he or she would most likely be prone. Without my feeding her even the slightest information she described my ethnic background, psychological type and physical disposition as related to illness, etc., all of which was – to say the least – spot on! She then went on to explain how this was done.

Kretschmer and Wolff observed that there were correspondences between physique and temperament which appeared to go hand in hand with certain illnesses. Recognition of the somatic statement therefore helped them to erect a psychobiogram which served as an aid both to psychoanalysis and the diagnosis of future potential physical problem areas.

PSYCHOLOGICAL TYPES

Psychiatrists and psychologists to this day acknowledge that we can all be classified according to given psychological types, or combinations thereof, the main personality types being defined as follows.

1. The Hysterical Personality

Contrary to popular belief this occurs in both males and females. Such people have an immature quality about them and a low tolerance threshold, which inclines them to sudden swings of mood and irrational outbursts. Much to the consternation and perplexity of those around them, they soon recover from these tantrums and proceed to act as though nothing untoward has occurred. In spite of being difficult and child-like they are never dull and often give a great deal of themselves to their friends and those they love.

2. The Obsessional Personality

Obsessive types are conscientious, tidy, critical, punctual, pedantic and repetitive. They do not like change of any kind or alterations in their routines and they are reluctant to show their emotions. As they have difficulty in adapting to new ideas or concepts, they are best-suited to avenues of expression which are of a regular nature.

3. The Schizoid Personality

This personality type lacks emotional warmth and friendliness, preferring his or her own company. Such people are not interested in others and are therefore unsociable, preferring to be left alone to do their own thing. They can make good careers for themselves, however, and frequently do well in research science and computer studies.

4. The Paranoid Personality

Paranoics are touchy, oversensitive, and incapable of accepting criticism. Included in this group are those who feel that the whole world is out of step with them. Such people are difficult and almost impossible to work with, but under suitable social conditions they are capable of rising in the world through their own efforts, and may often be seen leading new groups or sects – Adolf Hitler being an example.

5. The Depressive Personality

I think we have all met those pessimists who turn every statement into a negative. If one tells them, for example, that one has a bad knee, they will inform one that *both* of *their* knees are bad – also their shoulder, stomach, and a few other parts of their anatomy. Likewise, if one makes the mistake of mentioning to them that one is broke, or having emotional problems, one's woes are inevitably 'topped'. A sense of inadequacy is, of course, the problem here.

6. The Cyclothymic Personality

These people react to life's situations with emotional excess, fluctuating between joy and despair, depression and elation, pessimism and euphoria. They are seldom, however, on a regular even keel. Like the depressive personality, they are plunged into deepest gloom by loss or failure, although their reaction to success is one of wild joy and abandonment. It is interesting to note that recent research into cases of manic depression as related to genius (the two frequently go together and are generally included under the cyclothymic heading) can be traced to a certain gene. In other words, the gift of genius and the personality discomforts that would appear to accompany it in many cases are inherited!

7. The Anxious Personality

People of this personality type are inevitably apprehensive, believing that disaster is lurking around every corner. If all *is* going well, they will search for something to worry about, and if there is nothing on the immediate horizon, then they will create it, or see its possibility in the future. Strangely enough, when faced with real difficulties, the anxious personality is often competent and decisive, but it is when he or she feels him or herself to be stagnating that the problems start.

8. The Narcissistic Personality

Here we have a person who is unable to separate his own feelings and needs from the people he encounters. All must reflect himself and his own needs and wants. Narcissistic people are prone to Mirror Complexes, in that they see their faults or idiosyncrasies in others rather than in themselves. Such people love the limelight, and are able to achieve much in worldly status as long as their preoccupation with the self is well catered for. Hence they are to be found among the celebrities of the entertainment and political worlds, or any sphere of life which caters for the ego-conscious.

Very few people represent any one of these groups *in toto*: most of us are somewhat of a mixture. None the less, these groupings may help us to recognise more obvious personality traits that could aid the assessment of our strengths and weaknesses.[1]

INTROVERT/EXTROVERT

The introvert – extrovert complex as drawn up in the following chart [2] by consultant psychiatrist Peter Dally might also be of interest to the reader:

INTROVERTED

Passive	Quiet
Careful	Unsociable
Thoughtful	Reserved
Peaceful	Pessimistic
Controlled	Sober
Reliable	Rigid
Even-tempered	Anxious
Calm	Moody

STABLE   UNSTABLE

Leadership	Touchy
Carefree	Restless
Lively	Aggressive
Easygoing	Excitable
Responsive	Changeable
Talkative	Impulsive
Outgoing	Optimistic
Sociable	Active

EXTROVERTED

PHYSICAL TYPES

Another system of classification is based on the popular concept of three physical types: the Ectomorph – lean, long,
narrow-jointed, with low body fat and muscle; the Mesomorph
– compact, broad-shouldered, well-developed arm and calf
muscles, and the Endomorph – wide hips, larger joints, high
proportion of fat to muscles. A detailed breakdown is to be found
in the book *The Varieties of Temperament*, by W H Sheldon and
S S Stevens under the headings: Viscerotonia, Somatotonia and
Cerebrotonia. The definitions given accord with Kretschmer's
delineations of leptosomes (a less common variety being termed
asthenics), athletics and pyknics.

As with the psychological types, however, we would all
appear to be a mixture of several, so if and when one does
choose to use Kretschmer's method of assessing the temperament and its associated strengths and weaknesses, one should
be sure to bear this in mind. For example, a broad-hipped but
very thin person would represent a combination of the former
and latter, as would also a small-boned overweight person!

PERSONALITY AND DISEASE

Cranial osteopath Elaine Sturgess, who specialises in psychosomatic illness writes:

> Although it is difficult to demonstrate a clear link between
> personality factors and disease, many practitioners have ob-
> served that when a prolonged stress response affects a particular
> personality configuration a specific order will result. Personality
> clearly influences the way a person handles stress. Evidence is
> accumulating that specific personality types may be associated
> with heart disease, cancer and arthritis as well as migraine,
> asthma, ulcerated colitis, and other disorders generally classi-
> fied as psychosomatic or stress-induced. I refer the reader to
> the works of Friedman and Rosenman regarding the type A
> individual who is aggressive, egotistical, controlling and ruth-
> less, and a primary candidate for heart disease. Cancer victims
> are frequently described as exceptionally fine, thoughtful, gentle,
> uncomplaining people – almost too good to be true. Underneath
> there are feelings of unworthiness, self-dislike, and feelings of

hostility are bottled up and suppressed. It has been speculated that 'the too good to be true' martyr-like quality masks a low-key depression (Green and Miller 1958, Klopfer 1957, LeShan 1961). Migraine patients can be rigid, somewhat self-righteous and at time almost fanatical. They try too hard at everything they do and defeat themselves in the process.

Rheumatoid arthritis, osteoarthritis and ulcerated colitis are classified as auto-immune diseases. Some researchers (Moos, Soloman and Engels) have wondered whether a particular form of self-destructive personality might not translate into an auto-immune neurophysiological self-destructiveness. The rheumatoid arthritis patient tends to be self-sacrificing, masochistic, conforming, self-conscious, shy, inhibited, perfectionistic. (Moos and Soloman 1965). A classic study by Engels (1955) of the ulcerative colitis patients revealed obsessive compulsive behaviour involving excessive neatness, indecision, conformity, over-intellectualism, rigid morality and anxiety. Like the patients suffering from rheumatoid arthritis disorders, they could not express hostility or anger directly and seemed immature and dependent.[3]

New theories regarding the origins of illness are now being accepted in certain branches of the medical profession. Psionic medicine, for example, combines orthodox treatment with aspects of radiesthesia and homoeopathy, and is based on the assumption that disease results from the disruption of vital forces within the body. Diagnosis relies heavily on the use of dowsing, in which a pendulum is held over the body, or over hair or blood samples. Exponents assert that certain ailments, measles for example, create what are called *miasms*, or predispositions towards other diseases. According to the psionic theory, a sufferer from tuberculosis – a hereditary miasm – can impart to his or her descendants a tendency towards asthma, hay fever, diabetes and leukemia.[4]

In view of the aforegoing and similar studies in psychology and psychiatry it would appear that different parts of the body register different aspects of the mind or psyche. Could this possibly be the origin of a series of popular anatomical references or somatic allusions that are used glibly in everyday life without forethought as to their origin or real meaning? Here are a few better-known examples: To vent one's *spleen*. To *bellyache* (complain). To have that *gut* feeling. To *shoulder* a burden or responsibility. Having too much *gall*. To take it on the *chin*. To be *spineless*. Not to have the *heart*, or to lack the *guts*. To die of a broken *heart*. Cannot *face* or *stomach* it. It makes you *sick*. On your *head* be it! Not in one's right *mind*. All *choked* up. He gets up my *nose* – has no *balls*, and many others.

The use of the word 'bloody' in anger could also fall into this category, being symptomatic of the sanguine state which, according to Hippocrates, denoted a fiery temperament, while expletives such as 'pissed off' have body connotations connected with the eliminatory processes which are, I feel, self-explanatory.

There are doubtless many, many other everyday sayings that would qualify for inclusion in this list. My nanny used to say: 'I knew something was wrong there – I could feel it in my water.' And right she inevitably was! Somatic language or Freudian slips? Either way it would appear that our bodies and minds are inextricably linked so that even if we do not consciously acknowledge this as a fact our subconscious believes there to be no two ways about it!

American psychiatrist Arnold Mindell, who resides in Switzerland, had devoted much of his time and observation to this study. In his Dreambody series, he postulates a relationship between the chakras (see Chapter 17), their related endocrines and corresponding points in the physical anatomy, and the mental and physical disorders to which many of us are prone. The body would certainly appear to mirror the mind or psyche, so perhaps the problem of diagnosis may not be the bogey we suspect – providing, of course, we have the learning, clarity and openness of mind to read the signs.

In his book *Mind as Healer, Mind as Slayer*, K Pelletier offers the following quote from E Prendergrass:

> He [the practitioner] must understand man's basic need and his means of adaption in a physical, organic, and social environment. He must study the phrases of adjustment and define more clearly their determinants and what constitutes meaningful stress. He must study and devise new and effective means of aiding the adaptive efforts of the patient. He must be aware that many of the signs and symptoms manifested by the sick person are attempts of adaption and expression rather than disease itself. Such thoughts must be kept in mind; otherwise the attempts at therapy will deprive the patient of defences without making more suitable ones available.[5]

Endnotes:

1. *Psychology of Ritual*, M Hope, Chapter 23.
2. *Psychology and Psychiatry*, P Dally and M J Watkins, p. 132.
3. 'Stress, Psychosomatic Illness and Osteopathy', E Sturgess, Dissertation for the European School of Osteopathy, pp. 77–78.
4. *Readers Digest Family Medical Adviser*, p. 438.
5. *Mind as Healer, Mind as Slayer*, K Pelletier, p. 154.

Chapter 5

CONSCIOUS VS. SUBCONSCIOUS

Science having finally come up with some answers regarding the connecting link between mind and body, how does all this translate into the language of the psychologist, the mystic, and that mythical person: the man in the street? Inner conflicts inevitably produce outer tensions, but the sad thing is that many who are suffering this way refuse to acknowledge the fact. They blame it on all and anything – the people they work with, their finances (or lack of them as the case might be), their physical appearance, the process of ageing, the Government, politics, social services, religion – you name it.

I once recall saying to a psychiatrist friend, 'I feel under such strain at the moment that I think I'm going nuts!'

'Never,' he replied, wisely. 'The ones who do go over the top seldom admit that there is anything wrong with them. There is a vast difference between feeling tired, overwrought and near the edge, and a state of real mental illness.'

Years of observation have borne out this statement. Tensive energies can be either contained or externalised, thus creating introversial or extroversial behaviour patterns.

I used to know a man who was kindness itself. He was generous to an abnormal degree, in fact, and would part with his monthly pay packet to anyone who expressed an urgent need. For the remainder of the month he would be broke, however, and therefore reliant upon his friends. When I first met him he was in his late thirties and something of an alcoholic, but he became converted to a metaphysical way of thinking, gave up alcohol, and proved himself to be an excellent trance medium. But he had one personal problem which he confided in me one day – he had never been able to cry since early childhood. His background was Cambridge and the Royal Navy, where men were 'thought of as sissies if they carried on like that'. At the age of 43 he developed cancer of the liver. It all happened very suddenly. First came the pains which his GP casually diagnosed as a digestive disorder, but these worsened before he had time to report again to the surgery. A friend of mine discovered him collapsed in his flat and helped carry him to St Mary Abbot's Hospital in Kensington where his condition was diagnosed immediately. Surgery was effected, but it was all too late and within a week he was dead.

He has haunted my subconscious for many years, not that I was personally involved with him, but because of certain things he had disclosed to me over the period I had known him. It all added up to the anatomy of despair, deeply concealed beneath a cheery exterior. Knowing what I later came to know about this man, I can understand perfectly why he had had enough, but being conditioned never to show emotion he contained his feelings. In the light of more recent knowledge the results were to be expected.

Imbalances manifesting via extroversial behaviour are performed in somewhat different scenarios, however, and often accommodate delusory symptoms which are self-induced in order to gain attention. These frequently involve the 'child' syndrome of Transactional Analysis (see Chapter 19) – 'I will go down to the bottom of the garden, eat worms and make myself sick, then someone will come and love me and do what I want.' It is interesting to note how the word 'love' is frequently accompanied by a command: 'If you love me you will perform as I say, or I will not love you!' Emotional blackmail, pure and simple. Real love is totally unconditional.

Two classic cases of the use of extroversial behaviour to gain attention or alert others to a need for help spring to mind. The first involved a case I was called to some years ago. The lady in question, whom I judged to be about 35 years of age, was, or so I was told, possessed of an evil spirit which needed to be exorcised. The said entity would supposedly take over its victim and then proceed to hurl abuse at those around, loved ones and close relatives being the recipients of the worst attacks. Upon my arrival at the scene the sufferer assured me that it was indeed an evil spirit that assaulted her consciousness and begged me to remove it. When I searched her aura, however, I could see absolutely nothing. Nor were any of the usual signs of psychic fragmentation present. I soon realised what I was up against and confronted her with the situation.

'There is absolutely no one and nothing there, you know. So tell me, why are you contriving to make the lives of your loved ones such a misery?'

'Oh you are quite wrong,' she assured me.

But I shook my head and quietly insisted, 'No, I don't think so, so why not be honest with me?'

After I had finally gained her confidence she underwent a violent abreaction and the real truth came tumbling out. She had always been treated as the baby of the family. As they were well off, she was never allowed to go out to work or make a career for herself, and any male friends she chanced to meet were inevitably put off or discouraged by her older sister and elderly parents on the grounds that she 'isn't very strong, you know, and needs a lot of looking after', which naturally worked like a dream. Try as she could she was unable to find the courage to combat her overpowering family, so she subconsciously created a demon which would do it for her!

I was eventually able to confront her sister and other members of her family with the true situation. Needless to say, they were shocked and horrified, believing her to have been inadequate all along and not really capable of standing on her own feet. Soon afterwards she embarked on a training scheme and ended up in a good job in industry, to the utter amazement of all concerned.

Case number two was a very recent one, which I would classify as a typical example of the 'occult attack' syndrome. People who either feel inadequate or are mentally disturbed frequently look for some peg upon which to hang their problem, preferably of the attention-attracting variety. The recent resurgence of Wicca, magic, cults ancient and modern, and all forms of psychism have presented them with the perfect tool for their act – the *Occult Attack*!

It goes something like this. 'Jim Bloggs', who is suffering from a form of paranoia, is anxious to be someone and to gain as much attention as possible. He wants to live out his fantasies in real life. Now the normal material channels afford little chance of approbation to those outside of the genuinely talented or financially stable, which rather leaves 'Jim' out of things.

Then one day he happens upon a paperback which is all about magic and how people can make money, have themselves recognised and gain power over their fellow men with the aid of a few suspect exercises, and even more suspect rites! Utter trash, of course, but being of a simple mind, Jim overlooks the obvious and sees in this very practice the chance he has been waiting for. So, he makes it his business to bombard the author and several other writers on the subject (some genuine, some not so) with letters. The recipients (or their secretaries in most cases) do him the honour of referring him to some local group, healing or otherwise, where he might find an outlet for the many talents he has doubtless enumerated to them in his copious missives. This occurs in all walks of life and is usually referred to as 'passing the buck'.

Now it so happens that the local magical group nearest to where Jim lives entertains a variety of different personalities, most of whom are young and inexperienced, although fairly well versed in 'fireside occultism' (they have read a few books and think they know it all). There is much debate as to which system is the best for the group's working, some members favouring the Qabalistic approach, others Wicca, and others Christian hermeticism. In other words, there is no real harmony among them; so, in accordance with The Law of Equalities, the strongest personality inevitably assumes charge – that *not* being our Jim! This state of affairs naturally fails to suit the newcomer, however, who has deluded himself into believing that he is the potential magician *par excellence*, and so the trouble begins. The others quickly tumble to the fact that he is a misfit and it does not take them many sessions to realise that he is, to coin a common phrase, 'not firing on all cylinders'. So, they conspire to effect his departure, not in some magical way, but purely by suggesting that he does not quite fit in, or that he needs to study some more before he is ready to join them.

Of course, Jim will leave. This situation suits him nicely, as he realises only too well that these people have not been taken in by him. But from then on he will claim to be under occult attack from them, and the roundabout of attention will commence to turn. He will pass from healer to healer, and group to group, always telling his tale of woe, rejection and the machinations of evil forces that are intent upon his destruction. I knew one such case that went on like that for years, while the man in question carried on an otherwise normal life working in a canning factory. His wife was totally unaware of the problem, believing him to be taking evenings out to do social work among the poor!

Jim had approached several well-known and respected healers, therapists and occultists, none of whom were prepared to authenticate his fantasies, and each of whom rendered exactly the same verdict. Needless to say, our subject complained bitterly to everyone he met that not one of these was any good, nor were they in the same exalted class as himself!

One of the problems of working outside the orthodox medical field is that one has no come-back in such a situation. A doctor accused of incompetence or malpractice has the weight of the law to protect him and his reputation. Also, his qualifications and position in society entitle him to render a clinical or psychiatric diagnosis and submit his patients for the appropriate treatment. Several of the people I spoke to, whom Jim had dismissed with disdain, were perfectly aware of the kind of treatment he really required, but it would involve direct confrontation which needed to be carried out under the kind of controlled conditions only afforded by a hospital. However, as our example believed himself to be not only fully sane but also a magician of superior powers, any suggestion that a psychiatrist might help was naturally met with utter contempt!

Sad though the truth may be, over my many years in the field I have met more 'Jims' than I could count. I do not see them as occult casualties, but rather as victims of a system where the qualified and the unqualified fail to pull together, neither side being prepared to discuss each other's shortcomings or share each other's skills.

It has long been observed by therapists from all camps that the psyche, or subconscious mind as the case may be, would appear to have little regard for such material considerations as financial needs. Remember the case of the lady with the brutal husband and son I mentioned in an earlier chapter? Her subconscious mind frequently prompted her to 'up and out'.

'But where would I go,' she used to say to me, 'and what would I live on?'

'You have a good job on the telephone exchange,' I would reply.

'But I'd have to move somewhere else, or they would come after me. And I might not earn enough to pay for a rented place,' she protested.

Strangely enough, if one does take a chance against what appear to be overwhelming odds, things inevitably seem to work out. There is a PK answer to this one, of course, because by our very will to extricate ourselves from a difficult situation we set into force a quality of energy that will attract the right answers to our problems. Let us take a hypothetical case – the bullied lady, for example. Had she found the courage to walk out on her brutal menfolk and seek a job in another town she might well have fared much better financially, and also met up with someone of gentler character who would have helped her through the trauma of divorce. Once again, I can bring to mind several cases of ladies known to me personally to whom this actually happened, so our hypothesis is much nearer to life's truth than might be imagined.

So, while our subconscious promptings might *appear* to contradict our material needs, sometimes 'mother psyche' does know best. Illnesses and minor accidents are frequently visited upon us to allow for a much-needed period of physical rest. Speaking as a workaholic, I am fully aware that if my subconscious, higher self or what have you, did not occasionally bring down its heavy hand of physical restraint, I might not be here to write this book!

Hypnosis is ever an exposer of our needs as against our wants. A lady I know who had experienced a successful career for several years was, upon reaching her early forties, anxious to have a child of her own. Although she could not see this herself, it was quite obvious to the trained observer that this need had been promoted by her friends and peers who tended to make her feel inadequate by the way they talked about their progeny, the implication being that they had managed to succeed at something which she had not. The hypnotherapist, herself the mother of three, was perfectly sympathetic, however, and set out to ascertain whether the desire was genuine or imposed by the dictates of society. Under light hypnosis the subject continued to proclaim her need for a child, but upon entering a deeper state the tune changed and the interest became centred on a different, but equally creative line of enquiry. The lady eventually lost all interest in progeny and proceeded to embark on an entirely new and rewarding career which eventually took her into a different and more compatible environment.

A similar case was related to me by another hypnotherapist. It concerned a man whose life ambition was to travel for a large company and really succeed in business (or so he said). So great were his frustrations that his wife and daughters became seriously concerned for his health. Under deep hypnosis the therapist asked him why he wanted so much to travel, to which he replied, 'Travel! I'd hate it. All that chopping and changing, waiting about at airports, no regular meals, out in all weathers. No thank you.'

'Why then', the hypnotist questioned, 'do you tell your family that is what you want?'

The man appeared to hesitate for a while before falteringly replying 'Well, you see it's like this. There were these two chaps at work who were leaving the firm to take up glamorous, impressive overseas jobs and the girls in the office all treated them as heroes. So when I first mentioned it, it was only as a joke, as it were. But it somehow got out of hand and I found I couldn't turn it off.'

'Then why don't we both do just that right now,' said the therapist, and so they did. Although the man in question did not change his tune the very next day, nor the day after that for that matter, a few months later after receiving promotion within his firm he was heard to state that he had quite gone off the travel idea, and would have certainly got bored with it all after a while anyway.

Chapter 6

ENERGY FIELDS

Human beings, in keeping with all other life forms, emit energies which vary in frequency, amplitude, length and phase. Many different methods have been employed to observe and measure these emissions, ranging from Kirlian photography to recent studies in psychokinesis carried out by parapsychologists under controlled scientific conditions. One of the interesting facts which have emerged from this research is that those who are able to control their own personal energy fields can just as easily extend their influence to encompass the auras of others who are either unaware of the potential or less adept at its use. Mentally controlled energy emissions can manipulate the force-fields of other living things. In other words, we are faced with the old magical concept of the power of one mind to influence the actions and thoughts of another.

I am grateful to science for this kind of evidence, for one of the metaphysical enigmas that puzzled me for some time was the growing popularity of the idea that the 'higher self' was responsible for all the nice, clever things one does in life, to the exclusion of the influence of other minds or 'Essences'. Someone I know, who supposedly channels a wise and benign Teacher from another plane of consciousness, admits privately that it is really his 'higher self'. But surely, thought I, all these higher personas cannot exist as islands unto themselves without communication one with another. In which case there obviously must be a point at which our own transpersonal selves mingle with a higher group consciousness which possesses considerably more information about the running of the universe than we do in the here and now, and which is happy to filter through to our conscious minds such morsels as we might be ready to receive at any given time.

To return to the question of one mind being capable of influencing another, and taking into account the perverse side of human nature, it is logical to assume that such energies may be used positively or constructively, as in certain methods of healing, or negatively/destructively, as in the case of the primitive 'hex' where one person seeks domination over the body or mind of another. Nor is this principle limited to interflows between individuals, the Hitler regime being a prime example of how it works on a mass scale.

Let us take a quick glance at the parapsychologists' definition of the PSI/PK phenomena. In *Explaining the Unexplained*,[1] Professor Hans J Eysenck and Dr Carl Sargent proffer the following definitions:

PSI Phenomena: Four Variants on a Theme?

PSI
  ESP

Telepathy: Acquisition of information about another person, at a distant place, by means not involving the known senses or logical inference.

Clairvoyance: As above – but now the acquisition of information about an object or event.

Precognition: Similar information acquisition – but of information which will only exist in the future.

  PK

The influence of the human mind, by a direct action of will, on another person, object or event, not mediated by any physical force yet known!

Scientists have observed that the quality of PK and PSI varies from person to person, some people being more gifted 'receivers' and others better 'senders'. Gender, it would appear, plays no part in these abilities outside of the normal social conditioning imposed by society. When this is stripped away (the receivers and senders are not told which gender they are dealing with during the course of the experiment) good and bad receivers and senders are to be encountered among both males and females in equal proportion.

But this is surely to be expected, and as we are all individuals, each at our own particular stage of somatic and spiritual development, it stands to reason that there will be some with stronger PK or PSI energies than others. Whether we elect to make positive use of these gifts, employ them for selfish ends or ignore them completely, will no doubt be decided by what the dialectical materialist would see as compassionate humanitarianism, the psychologist would define as an individuated or well-integrated personality, and the metaphysician would judge as the soul-age.

An interesting corollary: parapsychologists investigating paranormal gifts across a wide range of subjects came to the unanimous conclusion that the psychological/personality-type producing the best and most accurate results was undoubtedly the stable extrovert! This discovery will, no doubt, throw cold water onto the beliefs of those who subscribe to the idea that all who are gifted with an above-average dose of PSI or PK undoubtedly rank among the mentally unbalanced. In fact, similar research carried out among the mentally disturbed showed their ESP/PK scoring to be well below the average. Unfortunately, many people who do suffer from some form of mental instability or psychoses are frequently attracted to the esoteric arts. But they are also to be found in equal numbers in orthodox churches, chapels, sports clubs, political groups – all arenas of life in fact. Placed therein they do not make good reading in the Sunday press, however, which, I trust, explains that one away.

Our personal energy fields are by no means limited to the immediate dimension of the material world. They may be manipulated by mind, and therefore extend their influence into those subtle realms to which the various arcane traditions and psychological disciplines have accorded a variety of nomenclatures. Thus we hear talk about levels of consciousness ascending in fineness of frequency from the Physical via the Etheric, Astral/Mental, Causal, Spiritual and thence to the Divine. Metaphysical literature abounds with such classifications and there are even a set of 'subtle bodies' appropriate to the negotiation of each of these realms. Oh, were it that simple!

These do, of course, give some points of reference to those who like their esoterica neatly pigeon-holed, and many people who indulge in practices of meditation and astral projection for therapeutic purposes are undoubtedly helped by following them. Nor are they limited to the transpersonal semantics of the present day. The ancient Egyptians had a similar list, and a series of suitable 'vehicles' appropriate to its negotiation – the physical body they called the *khat* (that which is perishable); the Astral body was the *ka* (double); the unconscious, which had a will of its own – the *khaibit* (shadow); the etheric body or spirit – the *khu* (that which is magical) and the Spiritual body which was the habitation of the Soul or Essence – the *sahu* (that which is abstract). So it has all been going on for a long time.

While it is appreciated that references of this kind are helpful to many, parapsychologists tend to dismiss them and view the whole scenario in terms of alterations in frequency or simple extensions of consciousness. My own experiences with absent healing, exorcism and astral projection tend to fall more into this category than the one mentioned earlier. If one is using mind to negotiate the barriers of time-space (the concept of linear time and limited space being relevant only to the frequency of frozen energy that we call matter), the necessity for assuming forms reminiscent of one's physical vehicle strikes me as rather limiting. In the world of the abstract surely all things are abstract: mind, intelligence, spirit, the essential Essence, or whatever name one chooses to apply to the continuing ego. Only when nearing or entering the denser frequencies is some form of physically recognisable manifestation called for.

But being human, and by nature insecure, most of us probably find it much easier to think in terms of the spirit of 'Aunt Flo' looking just like she did prior to her demise, or the influence of an overshadowing force-field from a finer dimension (popularly thought of in terms of Masters, Gods, Saints, Jesus, Buddha, etc.) in the flowing robes of Atlantis, ancient Egypt or Mesopotamia. In other words, we like to put handles on those force-fields with which (or with whom) we make contact during our esoteric work.

None of this makes the slightest difference to the outcome, however. Although a good healer may invoke Jesus, Kuan Yin, Apollo or Brahma, the results achieved will not necessarily be decided by the names employed in the process, but rather by his or her own ability to utilise the PK or PSI best suited to the patient's problem. No doubt the name invoked does serve to trigger a corresponding archetypal resonance within the self, or higher self as the case may be. But the intensity and therefore the efficacy of that frequency will again be regulated by the healer's own ability to translate or convert it to the quality appropriate to the need.

The American parapsychologist, Rex Stanford, suggests that *everyone* may have psi powers which operate below the threshold of normal consciousness. Even more startlingly, he has proposed that people may be unconsciously using these powers all the time in order to search the world for information which is to their advantage. For example, most people have experienced unexpected but useful coincidences. Might it be, Stanford asks, that these coincidences are due not to chance, but to the individual's psi abilities gleaning information and manipulating events so that all parties to the coincidence will be in the right place at the right time? He refers to this kind of process as *Psi-Mediated Instrumental Response (PMIR)*. And, since the heart of his argument is that these psi activities take place without the conscious intention of the individual concerned, he calls them *non-intentional psi*.

The stronger the need, the stronger the ESP, but there are limits, however. Experimental psychology has shown that if the need is very high, behaviour becomes disorganised and performance breaks down, which rule would also appear to apply in some self-healing or self-programming systems. Parapsychologists have established that the stable extrovert makes the best psychic, and probably the best healer; PMIR, PK and similarly related paranormal gifts being systematically distorted in neurosis. Another factor to take into consideration is the compatibility of energies, or lack thereof, between healer (be it a trained physician, psychologist or alternative therapist) and patient. But more of this in a later chapter.

There is little doubt about the fact that some people are able to negotiate energy frequencies that differ considerably from those normally encountered in the ordinary run of life. These people are the mystics, enlightened ones, saints and great healers who can make their appearance in any walk of life, colour or creed. They simply employ the available facilities to go about their tasks of caring, comforting and healing. I have met very few in my life, however, and strangely enough those with whom I have been privileged to rub shoulders were not all overtly dedicated to the so-called 'spiritual' path! One was a scientist and Nobel Prize winner whose expertise contributed considerably to our knowledge of the universe, another a quiet, unassuming GP.

An instinctive eco-consciousness appears to be slowly emerging from the collective unconscious in the form of a resurgence of old beliefs which accommodate the 'exchange of energy principle' – that one must always give in order to receive. The psychological consequences of living in a continual state of 'take' is abundantly clear, a fact which many psychiatrists and psychologists will, I am sure, be happy to endorse. People who are essentially takers, who give nothing in return, either spiritually, emotionally or practically, are more prone to neuroses and psychoses than those of a more generous inclination. The eventual disenchantment with each new acquisition, be it personal or inanimate, is inevitably followed by boredom as the psyche convolutes inwards in ever-decreasing spirals until the back-up of accumulated energies manifests as antisocial behaviour, psychosomatic illness or mental imbalance. It was for this reason that many tribal or early cultures instituted rites, both collective and personal, which involved the act of giving out before one could take in, thus lessening the tendency towards mental and psychosomatic problems and engendering a sense of responsibility to both the community and the environment.

While on the subject of ecology, it is as well to bear in mind that we are not the only life-forms on this planet endowed with the power to heal – but more about this is Chapters 9 and 15.

Many early cultures that may appear as primitive by our Western standards possessed a knowledge of energy fields far in advance of our own. The shaman, for example, was (and still is, in many cases) able to extend his or her aura of influence beyond the human sphere into the animal, plant, mineral and elemental kingdoms. Paraphernalia or no paraphernalia, shamans can still effect what we might see as miraculous cures (see Chapter 20). There are several theories as to how they learned these skills, the most credible from a logical standpoint probably being that they developed instinctively in the normal process of genetic evolution as part of the mental survival kit, the preservation of the species being a prime factor in genetic, somatic and mental development.

In his best-selling book *Cosmos*, Carl Sagan writes:

> Were the Earth to be started over again with all its physical features identical, it is extremely unlikely that anything closely resembling a human being would ever again emerge. There is a powerful random factor to the evolutionary process. A cosmic ray striking a different gene, producing a different mutation, can have small consequences early but profound consequences late. Happenstance may play a powerful role in biology, as it does in history. The farther back the critical events occur, the more powerfully they can influence the present.
>
> For example, consider our hands. We have five fingers, including an opposable thumb. They serve us quite well. But I think we would be served equally well with six fingers including a thumb, or four fingers including a thumb, or maybe five fingers and two thumbs. There is nothing intrinsically best about our particular configuration of fingers, which we ordinarily think of as so natural and inevitable. We have five fingers because we have descended from a Devonian fish that had five phalanges or bones in its fins. Had we descended from a fish with four or six phalanges, we would have four or six fingers on each hand and would think them perfectly natural. We use base ten arithmetic only because we have ten fingers on our hands. Had the arrangement been otherwise, we would use base eight or base twelve arithmetic and relegate base ten to the New Math. The same point applies, I believe, to many more essential aspects of our being – our hereditary material, our internal biochemistry, our form, stature, organ systems, loves and hates, passions and despairs, tenderness and aggression, even our analytical processes – all of these are, at least in part, the result of apparently minor accidents in our immensely long evolutionary history. Perhaps if one less dragonfly had drowned in the Carboniferous swamps, the intelligent organisms of our planet today would have feathers and teach their young in rookeries. The pattern of evolutionary causality is a web of astonishing complexity; the incompleteness of our understanding humbles us.[2]

In the distant past, the erratic behaviour of nature was believed to be subject to the whims of the Gods, who needed to be placated in order to prevent chaos effecting yet another destructive mark on our planet. Over a period of several thousand years, however, these irregularities became analysed, predicted and exploited to the extent that eighteenth- and nineteenth-century scientists were convinced they possessed all the answers. Immutable laws were ascribed to the action of every particle and for a while we were led to believe that we lived in some kind of mechanistic or clockwork-type universe.

Come the 1980s and enter the New Physics which promises to revolutionise science and alert us to the realities of 'Chaos'. The cycle has come full turn, but at a higher level. Systems obeying what we felt to be immutable and precise laws cannot be guaranteed to act in predictable and regular ways. Simple laws may not produce simple behaviour, while deterministic laws can produce behaviour patterns that appear random. In other words, order can breed its own kind of Chaos.

The implications of this discovery have yet to make their full impact on our scientific thinking; the repeatable experiment, for example, so beloved by the methodological schools of science and medicine can, when seen through the eyes of Chaos, take on new aspects and pose new questions especially where the paranormal is concerned! The new mathematics of Chaos will, it seems, render us a better understanding of the irregularities in nature in that systems which have hitherto appeared as structureless may be seen to obey definite laws, while more complicated systems could be simplified. Deterministic Chaos has its own laws and inspires new experimental techniques in that it can link well-understood rules with poorly under-stood behaviour. The motions of the Chaos/Order complex are determined by 'strange attractors' and 'fractals' which recreate the patterns with a new geometry. This could have dramatic repercussions in the fields of medicine and healing, which, in accordance with Jung's famous 'Law of Synchronicity' have already started to emerge via the intuitive faculties of many people throughout the world. 'Unpredictable oscillations can create islands of noise and confusion in the orderly operation of electronic circuits; or similar events can create the arhythmic pattern of heartbeats preceding an attack.'[3]

The Chaos Theory postulates that discernible patterns of order exist even in apparently turbulent systems, chaos itself containing the components of order, which renders the term something of an anomaly. A single movement, such as the flutter of the wings of a butterfly, can apparently alter a weather pattern. By the same token, a single act or circumstance can produce a future chain of events that could change the face of society, or even our planet. But while these random factors are all too apparent to the scientist, one is reminded that what may appear as chaotic at close range often assumes a pattern of great beauty and symmetry when viewed from a distance. An interesting psychological corollary to this may be observed in the fact that many of those who display chaotic or antisocial behavioural patterns in youth frequently mature into highly disciplined pillars of society, converts of any kind generally tending towards over-zealousness, if not actual fanaticism! However, many of us would like to believe that there is an intelligent force at work behind the pattern of development assumed by our own genus and other species on this planet.

The Chaos concept should be converted into a system of psychology based on an understanding of its principles which, I feel, would serve to explain enigmas that have perplexed both orthodox medicine and alternative practitioners. I have, in fact, already begun working along these lines.

There is also another theory, more immediate but less easily proven, as to where many of the earlier cultures obtained their knowledge of the close mind–body relationship which science is only now on the brink of reconsidering. There must have been, at some period in pre-history, an advanced culture well-versed in medicine, psychology and science, whose records were lost in some major global catastrophe (the Chaos Principle up to its old tricks!), but the remnants of whose knowledge lingered on, eventually degenerating into tribal myth and superstition. That the ancient Egyptians possessed this knowledge is highlighted in their myths; Osiris (form or order) being usurped by Set (chaos) who is in turn overthrown by Horus, son of Osiris (re-form and re-order). Behind all magic, primitive and otherwise, I see a glimmer of *real* knowledge, the essential essence of which has been long since forgotten.

Of course, human energy fields are not the only ones that influence us and affect our lives and health. Many people suffer from depressions resulting from adverse weather conditions, seasonal changes, sunspot activity and lack of sunlight. The pineal gland has proved to be the culprit in some of these cases. A small, reddish vascular body in the posterior part of the third ventricle of the brain, until recently its function in Homo sapiens was uncertain, although in other animals it is known to secrete a substance called melatonin. Recent research, has come to link it with the effect of light and seasonal variations on the bodily functions. Seasonal depressions are now believed to have pineal origins, while the pigment melatonin appears to be connected with skin colour. One cannot help thinking that the originators of the Seasonal Rite long, long ago might have been aware of all this, the rite being evocative of energies designed to effect the seasonal adjustment.

Exponents of the New Physics are beginning to acknowledge the interaction between all life-forms and their associated energy fields, and how even the minutest particles are able to communicate with each other regardless of time and space. To this phenomenon, scientist Dr Rupert Sheldrake has accorded the term 'morphic resonance'. The extent to which we do or do not choose to harmonise with this universal web of consciousness can undoubtedly affect our health.

There are, however, some alien energy fields that exist within the environment of our own planet, which pose a considerable threat to our well-being. The damaging effects of nuclear radiation are all too well known, while electromagnetic radiation, and too close a proximity to electrical force-fields, can also adversely effect the health of many people. Nor are all the external cosmic rays that bombard our planet of a beneficial nature. The threatened greenhouse effect hardly bodes well for the health of future generations, while many who accept the Gaia hypothesis (that the Earth herself is a living, evolving entity) believe that our planet's own tolerance of the destructive interference visited upon it by certain of the intelligent life-forms it hosts is fast wearing thin. Should those limits be surpassed, conditions conducive to life here as we know it might well vanish for ever – unless we, the guilty race, could repay some of her kindness and render some healing to Gaia. It bears thinking about.

Endnotes:

1. *Explaining the Unexplained*, H Eysenck and C Sargent, p. 11.
2. *Cosmos*, C Sagan, p. 282.
3. *Equinox*, A guide to the 1988 Channel 4 television series, p. 8.

Chapter 7

ALLOPATHIC MEDICINE

Allopathy is the usual method of treating disease by inducing a condition different from the cause of the disease, unlike homoeopathy which employs substances of the nature of the disease itself.

A century ago it was taken for granted that disease is an organic, physical process, caused by pathogens – germs, viruses, toxins and similar constituents. Each specific disease was believed to have its own specific cause, and if that cause could be identified and a cure found for it then so much the better. Medical students were taught that the mind and the emotions played no part in the disease process. A medical prescription was the panacea or all ills, anything which defied its efficacy being viewed as either incurable or a suitable case for the surgeon's skills. Even mental illness, it was assumed, would eventually be traced to some biochemical malfunctioning and those who were suffering from neurotic or hysterical disorders were seen as not *really* ill in the strict sense of the word, but rather as social misfits who should be pulling themselves together and not wasting the doctor's time.

All physical ailments had to be the result of somatic disturbances. Until psychiatry and psychology made inroads into the citadels of established medical thought there was no other factor to consider. Fringe practitioners such as osteopaths, chiropractors or homoeopaths were viewed as quacks, charlatans, or at best well-intentioned cranks.

In his introduction to Ernst Kretschmer's *Text-Book of Medical Psychology* (1952), E B Strauss, MA, DM (Oxon) FRCP, Physician for Psychological Medicine, St Bartholomew's Hospital and lecturer in psychological medicine at St Bartholomew's Medical College, University of London, wrote:

> One of the most deplorable effects of nineteenth-century philosophical materialism has been the lopsided turn it gave to medical education and training. St Thomas Aquinas and the other scholastic philosophers of the so-called Dark Ages who at least realized that man is a *body–soul* unit held more balanced views than modern highly scientifically trained representative of Lamattrie's outworn doctrine of *L'homme machine*. It is undoubtedly a fact that the average student of medicine leaves his medical school with scanty understanding of the mental side of his future patients. He has only too often been trained to treat 'diseases' and not men and women (as though diseases had any independent existence apart from the body-mind units in which they occur!) Mental reactions are apt to be regarded as 'belonging to' psychological medicine or psychiatry, a *special* branch of medicine.[1]

Regretfully there are still some areas in medicine and science where this attitude persists, in spite of the mountain of evidence which highlights its limitations. But with the growing acknowledgement of the role played by the mind, exploration into the causes and factors contributory to disease is now moving into different areas of research.

New drugs which were discovered in the 1940s and 1950s appeared to produce such miraculous results that the public at large became conditioned to their common usage without questioning such things as side-effects. The few doctors who stood out against this trend became the objects of derision by their colleagues, while the term *psychosomatic* and all it stood for was scorned by the public. That was until the thalidomide tragedy shocked the world.

It was in the early 1960s that the first elements of doubt were witnessed. Hundreds of babies were born deformed because their mothers had taken thalidomide during early pregnancy. As the drug had not been officially licensed by the Federal Food and Drug Administration in the United States, the Americans were mercifully spared its tragic results. However, the report published by the US Senate Committee under Senator Estes Kefauver showed that it was only the most serious of a number of instances of lethal side-effects which were leading to the hasty withdrawal of several new drugs from the market.

The Kefauver Report criticised the medical profession for overprescribing and misprescribing on the strength of the drug companies' promotions. This was something which could be avoided, however, with a little more attention to the Hippocratic Oath and a little less to the bank balance, while more rigorous testing of drugs prior to their release to the general public could help prevent further unpleasant side-effects.

Sad though the truth may be, the medical profession would appear to be incapable of imposing the necessary discipline upon its members, while testing procedures, especially upon animals, cannot always detect dangerous side-effects early enough to prevent serious casualties later.

Brian Inglis and Ruth West, in their book *The Alternative Health Guide*, state categorically that research over the past twenty years has revealed that many of the scientific theories upon which modern medicine has been built are quite simply fallacious. Disease is not an organic process, they insist; germs, viruses and toxins play a part, but it is a relatively minor one. Just how minor a part has been exposed by research into heart disease and cancer in particular, as it has now been made clear that these diseases have no single cause, although there are several contributory factors which are mainly concerned with our life-styles.

Heavy smoking and the consumption of large amounts of animal fats increase our risks of falling victim to these two potential killers, while it has now been discovered that some personality types are more susceptible than others. People are at most risk when subjected to certain kinds of stress, retirement, redundancy, bereavement and similar traumas. So, our personalities dictate the type of disorders from which we are most likely to suffer, our life-styles decide the level of the risk, and our stress precipitates the outcome. As recently as ten years ago a pronouncement of this kind would have met with outright rejection by the medical authorities, but not so today.

Unfortunately, the medical profession as a whole, and the National Health Service in particular, is not really equipped to handle the situation. Apart from chronic hypochondriacs, people only visit their doctor when they feel they have something wrong with them, and GPs, being thoroughly overworked, give them short shrift if they cannot find any immediate physical cause and quickly pass them on to a specialist if they suspect they have. In other words, there is little if any communication of the kind that might reveal the real cause of the patient's discomfort or concern. Check-ups can be bought under private practice, but again the accent is on the physical. I underwent one of these myself and was assured that all my bits and pieces were where they should be and ticking merrily away. By that time I felt thoroughly guilty about about even mentioning a worry I had been nursing for some months, and crept from the expensively furnished surgery with my mental tail between my legs!

Like many British people I have always been reluctant to visit a psychiatrist for fear of being dubbed 'suspect' or 'unstable' on some secret records that might exist in the memory banks of a heartless computer. The Woody Allen syndrome – dashing off to an analyst whenever something goes wrong – somehow seems not quite the thing to do. One should stand on one's own feet, work out one's own problems. Therapy is all very fine for the mentally disturbed, who obviously benefit from it. Behind this myth, of course, lies the fear of exposing emotion and sharing vulnerability. But these days more and more people are facing up to lives of indifferent quality and trying, through therapy, to change their lot. However, therapists often cost money and GPs do not, so for the vast majority of us it is the local surgery or hours in the waiting room of a busy hospital.

Doctors continue to treat physical symptoms with physical remedies, with progressively less success. In his *Medical Nemesis*, Ivan Illich claimed that the medical establishment has in itself become a threat to health: 'The disabling impact of professional control over medicine has reached the proportions of an epidemic,' which statement was backed up by a mass of evidence the medical profession was unable to refute.

A recent television programme (8 November 1988) also tended to confirm this, highlighting the fact that many of the drugs administered to arthritics to relieve pain were, in fact, actually hastening the destruction of their joints!

According to Inglis and West:

The bleak fact is that the profession as it stands cannot change its ways, certainly not fast enough to meet the public's need. It is largely self-governing, and the ruling 'establishment' consists not, as is commonly thought, of the professional trade unions such as the British and American Medical Associations but – in Britain – of the Royal Colleges. These colleges are controlled by specialists, and the specialists control medical education.[2]

As long ago as 1937, Lord Horder, surveying the future of medicine, pointed out that it would be necessary for the family doctor to concentrate on preventive medicine:

> 'If it is advanced that the doctor's training has not, up till now fitted him for work of this sort then the sooner it does so fit him the better,' Horder argued. 'Inevitably the doctor's work in future will be more and more educational and less curative. More and more will he deal with physiology and psychology, less and less with pathology. He will spend his time keeping the fit fit, rather than trying to make the unfit fit.'[3]

Sadly, however, little attention was paid to these words of wisdom and medical students' training became increasingly more hospital-bound. They have been programmed to think in terms of treating their patient's physical symptoms with the latest drugs, rather than admitting that many of these symptoms result from mental or emotional traumas, and it will take a long time for these views to change. Few potential GPs enter practice with knowledge of psychology and the humanities, although one must be fair and say that since the Inglis and West book was published in 1983 I have witnessed a small, but nevertheless perceptible, chink appearing in the armour of the medical establishment.

Expansions in the horizons of technology that inevitably follow in the wake of new scientific discoveries are affecting an emphatic, if gradual, change in perspective among the bastions of orthodoxy. The GPs at my local National Health Service practice, for example, have special interests in psychological medicine, acupuncture, homoeopathy, hypertension, behavioural therapy, emotional, psychological or psychiatric problems and encounter therapy. I have also been told of another, even more holistically inclined practice in a relatively small town in Sussex, which also offers the service of two psychic healers. And all this in addition to the normal medical service. Quite a turnaround from the not so distant past!

The term 'holistic' is much bandied about these days, both in the medical profession and among alternative therapists, but what exactly does it mean? Holism derives from the philosophical concept that the whole is greater than the sum of its parts. As applied to healing, it suggests that it is the whole patient who is being considered and not just his or her immediate or apparent symptoms. Alternative therapists tend not to treat symptoms as such, but rather to search for their initial cause. Doctors often point out that as medical students they were advised to think in holistic terms, although the specialised and highly compartmentalised structure of orthodox medicine has tended to make this rather difficult for the practising physician. GPs have little time for analysis anyway and on the odd occasion when some newcomer to the practice, fresh out of medical school, has dared to question a patient regarding the more personal aspects of his or her life, the short rejoinder evoked has usually been: 'Can't I just have the regular prescription, doctor, like the old doctor always gives me,' or, 'I only want a couple of days off work and I'll be right as rain.'

In 1978, a group of American doctors founded the American Holistic Medical Association, while an editorial in the *Journal of the American Medical Association* which appeared a few months later suggested that as its readers were unlikely to know the first thing about holism, it would pay them to make a point of studying it!

Although many practitioners of alternative therapies subscribe to the efficacy of holistic practice, not all of them observe it in their work. Some, for example, finding they are better equipped to handle one disorder than another, tend to fall into the 'specialist' category, in much the same way as it is only natural for a healer to serve where his or her talents are best placed for the good of the patient. The main thing is to keep the holistic principle in sight and not be too proud to refer a case to someone else if the specialised treatment is not achieving the desired results.

A one-day conference held on 19 November 1988 at Hammersmith Hospital marked a significant milestone in the progressive acceptance of the ideas of the Cancer Help Centre by the medically orthodox. Its subject, reports Dr John Cosh, MA, MD Cantab, FRCP, was 'Developing cancer care into the 90s: integrating holistic methods into the NHS'. Its organiser was Professor Karel Sikora of the Department of Clinical Oncology in the Royal Postgraduate Medical School at Hammersmith Hospital, in association with the Cancer Help Centre. Dr Cosh's full report is to appear in the *British Medical Journal* and *The Lancet*, but he has kindly supplied me with the gist of it in advance. The Conference was attended by over 400 people, mostly nurses, therapists, members of the public concerned with cancer and a number of doctors.

In addition to an updating on the latest advances in the field of oncology, Professor Sikora also illustrated some of the modern techniques of imaging the body and internal organs, which greatly assist diagnosis. Dr Michael Wetzler emphasised the importance of the patient's state of mind while also pointing out that there is substantial evidence to support the fact that some cancers are diet-related. Dr Tim Sheard stressed the importance of the Counsellor's help in combating the negative attitude to disease and the necessity for showing the patient how much he or she can do for him or herself, while spiritual, as well as psychological support was also advocated. The power of mind to influence matter was illustrated in cases described by experienced nurses who had been taught to lead patients in periods of meditation, relaxation and visual imagery. At one point, those present were asked to close their minds and accompany the speaker on an imaginary 'inner journey' which ultimately led to a spring of healing water. As Dr Cosh commented: 'It was certainly a new phenomenon in the Royal Postgraduate Medical School!' Professor Sikora has indicated his interest in introducing some of the Bristol Cancer Centre's practices into the new Oncology Department he is planning. May the Gods of Medicine be with him!

Here is a useful tip. When our GP hands us a prescription, it is usually for an analgesic, antibiotic, sedative, or some drug he or she has deemed appropriate to the relief of the symptoms for which we have sought help or advice. But how many of us know exactly what we have been given, and why? A helpful little publication entitled *Principle Drugs* by S J Hopkins is available from most bookshops. As it is now recommended that drugs should be prescribed by generic name, proprietary names appear in the appendix rather than the main text. Also included are additional short sections on Drug Administration and Responsibility, Controlled Drugs, Drug Compliance, Drugs and Breastfeeding, Oral Contraceptives, Intravenous Additives and several other pieces of interesting information.

In the previous chapter we discussed the existence of energy fields which were incompatible with the human body and mind.

We know, for example, that any form of radioactivity (natural – as with radon – or otherwise) has side-effects, which prompts one to question the wisdom of employing one alien energy field to drive out another. The side-effects of radiotherapy and chemotherapy are also well known, and yet many people opt for this type of suffering in preference to the prospect of death. Is life at any cost really the answer at this point in our evolutionary history? Well, I suppose it depends on the person concerned and the attitudes and beliefs of their families and loved ones, but for many it obviously is. And yet the members of that very family would probably not think twice about condoning an abortion.

Euthanasia is another emotive subject that is guaranteed to give rise to many ethical questions. Perhaps some future discovery or forthcoming event may help us change our perspective of these quandaries.

While it is all too easy to decry the shortcomings of the medical profession, in spite of their drugs, closed minds and disregard for the less obvious aspects of the human mental economy, where technology is concerned they have performed their own special brand of miracles. Early screening for cancer, for example, has helped prolong many lives, while enormous strides in surgery, including the use of lasers, have helped to alleviate much suffering, restore sight to many, and give children the chance of a life they might not otherwise have known. Perhaps I am among the fortunates ones, but I have received nothing but kindness, courtesy and much-valued help from the medical profession over the years – but then I always make a point of offering a short invocation to the Deities of Medicine before consulting with a surgeon or physician! In truth, there is surely an equal danger in placing too much faith in either scholarship and medical science on the one hand, or healers and alternative therapists on the other. Both have their successes and their casualties.

Many thinking, caring people believe that the methods employed by the medical profession in their search for cures contravene some natural law and are therefore bound to be thwart with dangers – which brings us to the thorny subject of vivisection. There are arguments for and against, most of the 'fors' being based on the concept that Homo sapiens is in some way superior to other life-forms on this planet. I am afraid I do not subscribe to this idea. As mentioned in the previous chapter, even scientists concede that it was only a random factor that decreed our species to be the one to advance into intelligence. As Carl Sagan writes:

> After we came down from the trees we evolved an upright posture: our hands were free; we possessed excellent binocular vision – we had acquired many of the preconditions for making tools. There was now a real advantage in possessing a large brain and in communicating complex thoughts. Other things being equal, it is better to be smart than to be stupid. Intelligent beings can solve problems better, live longer and leave more offspring; until the invention of nuclear weapons intelligence powerfully aided survival. In our history it was some horde of furry little mammals who hid from the dinosaurs, colonized the treetops, and later scampered down to domesticate fire, invent writing, construct observatories, and launch space vehicles. If things had been a little different, it might have been some other creature whose intelligence and manipulative ability would have led to comparable achievements. Perhaps the smart, bipedal dinosaurs, or the raccoons, or the otters, or the squid.[4]

As Sagan says, 'it might have been . . .'. It might well have been you and me, us furry little people from the past who remained in our trees to be experimented upon in the future by, perhaps, some educated raccoon in a white coat, or nimble-fingered chipmunk! Homo sapiens hardly shows a good track record in spite of his alleged 'super-intelligence'. Maybe some other species would have made a better, more kindly and caring job of it.

While on the subject of orthodox medicine one is constantly reminded of the psychology of the 'bedside manner'. Do patients really make better progress after an operation, or recover more rapidly from an illness if they are treated with kindness and courtesy by their attending physician? A recent television programme appears to offer evidence that they do. An experiment in the efficacy (or otherwise) of the placebo effect was carried out at the Dental Department of the University of California. Two male patients who had undergone surgery for the removal of obstinate wisdom teeth were separately treated. One was linked up to a machine which dispensed a powerful pain-killer and told that this would take approximately twenty minutes to take effect. The nurse who carried out the procedure was matter of fact and not particularly chatty. The other patient was visited personally by a doctor, complete with stethoscope, white coat and other impedimenta of his trade, who personally administered a hypodermic containing a fluid which, he assured the sufferer, would relieve his pain within twenty minutes. The doctor's manner was a good bedside one, displaying concern and a strong desire to help the patient to a speedy recovery, but his hypodermic had contained only a placebo.

Twenty minutes later the nurse attended each patient with a graph and asked them to fill in the point to which they felt their pain had decreased. The one who had received the drug complained that he was still suffering a deal of discomfort, although the pain had eased a little. The man who had received the placebo, however, said he felt much better and that the pain had practically gone. The doctors concerned agreed that the white coat and the bedside manner, coupled with the personal attention, did more to relieve the pain than the actual drug and commented how many people feel safe and secure when they are in what they feel to be the 'right hands'. The conclusion was that trust in treatment actually transformed into chemicals in the brain, which effected both the relief of pain and the cure.

This is exactly what happened in the Healing Temples of the earlier civilisations, when the Healer Priests would don the mask of Anubis (Egyptian God of Anaesthetics) before putting a patient 'under' for surgery, so that the sufferer sincerely believed that the god himself was with him and would see him through the operation. The same thing also took place in the Iseums of Greece and Rome, where those suffering from nervous breakdowns would be treated by incubation therapy or narcosis, the last thing they were shown as they drifted off to sleep being a Priestess garbed to represent the Goddess Isis.

A considerable amount of research is being undertaken at present to discover the origin of pain, especially of the sort for which there is no obvious physical reason. New methods of treatment are achieving excellent results in this area and the doctors concerned are taking into account the psychological factors – the mind punishing its body as a protest against its inner frustrations. It was refreshing to see physicians and psychologists working side by side, which is as it should be.

And now here is some good news for those who do subscribe to the idea that the bedside manner aids recuperation. Cambridge University have recently appointed the country's first lecturer in patient communication skills to teach medical students how to respond to patients. Dr William M Zinn is now advising doctors to keep in touch with their feelings when seeing patients. Instead of using cold logic, says Dr Zinn, doctors should rely far more on their emotions for a better diagnosis. (What *would* Sherlock Holmes have made of it all!)

The sick can also be aided in their recuperation by surroundings conducive to recovery. Certain colours, shapes and angles, for example, are known to induce more harmonious and therapeutic effects than others, a fact that did not go unobserved by the healer priests of old who consulted with their architects and builders to ensure that their healing temples were designed accordingly. Prince Charles emphasised this very point in a recent television interview, bringing the attention of the public to the appalling architecture and environment in many hospitals, which he described as 'faceless concrete edifices'. He felt that a hospital should display such healing features as fine columns, appropriate colours, greenery and water. He is perfectly correct, of course, but then we live in a society where greater values are placed upon other economic considerations, to the detriment, sadly, of the individual.

Surely, the most important factor in all forms of healing is the curing of the patient, not the pet theories of doctors, surgeons, acupuncturists, praying priests, manipulators or psychotherapists. Perhaps the day will come, dare we hope in the not-too distant future, when the prime concern – the health of the patient – will supersede all other reasons for dedicating oneself to the healing cause, and medical science will work side by side with its 'alternative' brothers to the ultimate benefit of all concerned.

Endnotes:

1. *A Text-Book of Medical Psychology*, E Kretschmer MD, p. v.
2. *The Alternative Health Guide*, B Inglis and R West, p. 9.
3. *Ibid*. p. 10.
4. *Cosmos*, C Sagan, pp. 283–285.

Chapter 8

COMMUNITY CARE AND THE SOCIAL SERVICES

We observe horrifying reports in the media of suffering on a mass scale in the world's poorer countries. The greater tragedy, however, is surely the misery endured by those people, albeit smaller in numbers, who eke out a wretched existence in the back streets of the truly wealthy nations. Their problems cannot be blamed on droughts, floods, the perversity of nature or the economic mismanagement of their governments, but rather on faults in the system on the one hand, or their own inability to handle life on the other.

To what extent are we, in fact, our brother's keeper? Should we feel responsible for his ills, and what good does it do to have a social conscience if we are not in a position to do anything about it? Are the socially and/or intellectually inadequate to be treated as 'sick'? If so, how can they be cured? Can violent offenders, child molesters and similar social misfits be helped to adjust to society, or is society itself the villain of the piece?

Sociological considerations tend to pose more questions than sociologists are able to provide answers for, and as this book is primarily concerned with the individual I will try to confine my remarks to this quarter and leave the broader issues to those more qualified to deal with them. However, a few comments are called for.

Many authorities feel that the answer to the social malaise

that afflicts our present-day society lies in education. But is this necessarily so? The erosion of human values appears to have escalated with the expanding educational availabilities and options. Crime and drug abuse have increased and morality has declined. Many of my generation and older can recall the days when one could leave one's door unlocked, the money out front for the milkman or the grocer, and walk the three miles home from school in perfect safety. Such a nice, cosy world for many, but then one is reminded of those who had no milk money to leave out, and no shoes in which to walk to school. And what about treatment for the sick?

I remember my nanny paying her sixpence a week into the Hospital Saturday Fund and waiting her turn at the 'panel' doctor's surgery when the necessity demanded. I can also recall the local District Nurse, then elderly, who kept a large box of false teeth, all shapes and sizes, which she had undoubtedly acquired in the course of her duties. The villagers used to drop in and 'try a set on' if they could not afford to buy their own. Nurse L frequently pulled an offending tooth or two herself, and supplied a very artificial looking replacement, to the delight of the recipient! If they did not fit to start with she would say in a delightful Geordie accent, 'Don't you fret now, pet, your mouth will adjust to it in good time.' There were probably many complaints and much discomfort. But I was too young at the time for anyone to confide them to me.

The exercise of looking back is always a fruitless one. One can only observe within the context of one's own, personal experiences which are sadly limited in youth. It is only when we mature that we become more aware of the needs and sufferings of others. Oh yes, we may well read sociology at university and step out into the world thinking we have the answers to all the problems we are likely to encounter. One hears it so often: 'It's all the fault of the politicians – get this lot out and our lot in, and all will soon be resolved!' or 'that opiate religion has brought on all this – see how badly the people fare in countries where the churches dominate politics.' And while the idealists spend their time airing their egos the suffering continues.

The increase in longevity, notably in Western society, is often credited to the medical profession. There are many more factors involved, however, and although our life expectancy may have increased, the burden and expense placed on the National Health Service by the growing number of elderly and infirm is beginning to pose problems at many levels. In fact, the overall care of the elderly leaves much to be desired, and in spite of our technological progress we could still learn a lot from anthropology when it comes to what constitutes the most caring and humane ways of dealing with the problem of ageing.

I had an interesting conversation with an inner city social worker who had decided to return to her native Africa. I asked her why. She was vehement in her reply: 'All one hears talk about here is politics, politics, politics. I get tired of it. Everything is made into a political issue, human degradation, illness, poverty. In my country all we want is to be left alone to live our lives in the traditional way. Education – yes, but as and when *we* choose. But whichever group assumes power they always want to push us around, uproot us, change our ways, impose their wills over ours. Politicians, missionaries, do-gooders – ego trippers! Heaven preserve my people from all of them!'

Is it really all that different anywhere in the world, and will conditions ever improve? For some they have already. Standards of living have risen in certain countries, and those consumer luxuries that were originally beyond their financial reach can now be obtained with comparative ease. Taking into consideration this aspect only, one then has to ask whether the new affluence has benefited health. Overall, the answer must be 'no'. While we may justly and proudly claim that these days people do not gallop to their demise in the saddle of consumption or depart through the dark gates of diphtheria before they have had a chance to reach maturity, they will happily stuff their poor bodies with more cholesterol, protein and artificial junk than they were designed for and then blame some questionable deity when the process catches up with them. There is a popular saying: 'All the fun things in life are either illegal, immoral or fattening.' It seems a great shame that pleasure and self-destruction should walk hand in hand. Would this not seem to indicate that there is something radically wrong with our social programming?

A few evenings prior to writing this chapter I watched a television interview. The programme presenter, a lady, referred to her young male subject as a 'goody-two-shoes' because he neither smoked, drank nor ate meat. There are an awful lot of people who neither smoke nor drink and are vegetarians. Would it not be more logical to think of these in self-disciplinary terms, or even as being selfless? They will doubtless prove less of a burden to the already overstretched National Health Service than their more indulgent comrades. As for the Mary Poppins image – Adolf Hitler was a non-drinking, non-smoking veggie, whose track record hardly qualified him for admission beyond the Pearly Gates!

Surely, what we are really talking about is fear and ignorance which encourage people to function in collectives or taboo-ridden group entities, wherein they are able to mask their fears and insecurities among the crowd – the 'everybody does it' syndrome, or safety in numbers. If you wish to abuse your body with drugs, assault your digestive system with unsuitable foods and chemicals, and rot your liver with alcohol, that's fine as long as everyone else you know does it. But when confronted with another human being who does not fit into this category, fear raises its ugly head and he or she becomes 'one of them', 'a crank', 'a nutcase', 'a weirdo'. In other words, they are not a member of your particular collective.

Social collectives can exert a damaging effect on the health of those who do not conform to their habits. I have counselled many people who were mentally disturbed as a result of being at loggerheads with their families or peers. Women who were ostracised because they were unmarried, or had no children; single men who were wrongly dubbed 'gay' because they appeared to have no partner. One sad case concerned a man in his forties whose wife and two children had lost their lives in a domestic fire. He had left the area where it happened and settled in another part of the country to help him forget. Being unaware of his tragic past, the local village gossips lost no time in referring to him as 'that old fag in the end house', a comment he unfortunately overheard and which precipitated his breakdown. Some people find it difficult to talk about their past tragedies, especially to people with whom they are only lightly acquainted. Perhaps in time the village would have accepted him and understood, but he *appeared* to break the local taboos, and that was unforgivable.

Another case concerns a young man who was obliged to leave his home and move to an another area because his interests differed from those of the other males in the family. Instead of football and the pub on Saturdays, he liked to spend his day in the local reference library, or visiting a museum. Life at home became intolerable, his own father being the worst culprit. In different circumstances he could have ended up a suicide case, but fortunately those days are now long past and he has found his niche in the academic world. However, to this day his family still refuse to accept him as he is.

Many socially related diseases are the result of pressure brought to bear on the individual by society, anorexia nervosa and bulimia nervosa being prime examples. The anorexia sufferer refuses food because of an unnatural fear of putting on weight, while with bulimia there are bouts of compulsive eating which are followed by self-induced and ultimately involuntary vomiting. Both are regarded by the medical profession as psychological disorders which can, if left untreated, result in death.

Many theories have been put forward regarding the cause of these illnesses, the two most popular probably being a need for attention, and in the case of teenage girls a subconscious fear of growing up. There is also another and, in my opinion, a more insidious agent: the pressure imposed upon young people, and women in particular, to conform to a certain size and shape. We are constantly bombarded with examples of what we should look like in order to meet society's approval, the insinuation being that anything less can only result in lack of acceptance, or at the worst total rejection. Actresses, models, today's 'beautiful' women (or so we are programmed to believe), all wear size eight clothes, do not need to wear bras and do not carry an ounce of spare flesh on them.

Their male counterparts are broad-shouldered, slim-hipped, Porsche-driving machos. Anyone falling short of these ideals is destined to lose out in the love stakes, or become the object or derision among their peers. Those fortunate ones whom nature has blessed with the currently popular physical requisites are either totally unaware of the sufferings of the 'have-nots', (or the 'overly endowed') or delight in lording their advantages over them. It is amazing how much mental cruelty is carried out under such comparatively simple guises. The rich may effect surgical adjustments to help them to conform to the popular image, but those whose incomes preclude them from the dubious blessings of plastic surgery or liposuction often develop complexes which can seriously affect their health. One cannot help asking who are those mysterious 'they' who decide how we should or should not look, and is it not time that someone told them a few facts about the essential dignity of the individual, which is surely contributory to our well-being.

During my counselling days I encountered young men and women who were being pressured by their peers to indulge in sexual and social practices which they personally found to be unacceptable for one reason or another; the resulting mental conflict often affecting their health. Students who refuse to involve themselves in excessive drinking orgies are frequently subjected to spiteful indignities while fears and phobias are cruelly exploited for amusement. One young man I knew personally lost his life in his twenties as a result of being constantly teased because he could not swim. Following a particularly harsh ragging from his peers he finally took the plunge – to his death!

One of the dangers of living in a free society is that many people do not feel sufficiently supported morally and ethically. Old established ways of behaviour are now considered *passé*, and the tendency, especially among the young, is *not* to be seen to be different. It takes a strong mind to stand out against the group entity, but it can be done and many who have tried it have survived intact and are stronger for the experience.

While collectives can afford great comfort and security to some they can also pose a threat to both the mental and physical health of others. The id, lower nature, or shadow, that aspect of the psyche that is kept submerged under the control of conscious discipline, is only too happy to raise its ugly head if given half a chance. Base instincts tend to surface in revolutionary or mob situations when emotion overpowers reason and the process of mass dehumanisation gives birth to the 'group entity'. Families, close friends, and people who have been known and respected for years suddenly assume the role of 'the enemy' because they appear to be on the opposing side. Politics and religion are noted dehumanisers and depersonalisers as they can exert the kind of mental influence that is encouraging of the rejection of long-standing relationships, friendships and loyalties to the extent that those who formerly occupied these roles are thenceforth seen as 'scabs', 'traitors', and so forth. The folly of irrational fanaticism was aptly summed up by the late Edmund P Bernard who was heard to say, 'The devil stuffs empty heads with straw and idealism,' a statement evocative of both amusement and concern, especially as the gentleman concerned did not subscribe to the existence of a personalised evil force outside of the mind of man!

Dehumanisation is the name given to the psychological process that takes place when a crowd or gathering of people assumes a group identity. This may be witnessed in witch-hunts, lynch mobs, unruly sports gatherings and incidences of emotionally or fear-induced mass hysteria. In his essay 'The Nature of Crowds' the distinguished author and scientist, Dr Lyall Watson, commenting on the views of the neglected writer Elias Canetti, states:

> Canetti regards the crowd as an organism in its own right. At one moment the street is empty save for a random scattering of individuals, and in the next, in response to a mysterious signal, there is a concerted action. People push together to form the nucleus of a crowd. Those involved in the action seldom know what has happened. If stopped and questioned they are unable to provide any reasonable reply.

As one reviewer remarked, 'This sinister dehumanisation is obvious at any political rally, football match or picket line.'

I can vouch for the accuracy of this statement. Two young people I knew some years ago used to demonstrate frequently for animal welfare and liberation long before these became popular banners behind which to march. During some particularly violent protests in the 1970s that took place outside the US Embassy in London, these two young people were among the protesters who stuck pins in police horses and placed painful obstacles under the animals' feet. Several days later I met them and asked them what they thought they were doing, attacking those same dumb animals they had demonstrated for the previous week. They both gave the same answer: 'We don't really know. We don't remember what we did. It all sort of happened. Now we feel dreadful about it and we're going to give some money to a donkey sanctuary to try to make up for it.'

It is worth remembering that just as we each have our personal shadow, groups or collectives also acquire a shadow identity which assumes the colour or emphases predominant in the shadows of its members!

When I mention these incidents at lectures I am usually bombarded with protestations: 'It could never happen to *us*! *We* wouldn't be caught out like that. *We* think for ourselves.' But so did a lot of people in Germany before Hitler conned them into the power of the collective. Maybe we should repeat the

question, 'Am I my brother's keeper?' How responsible are *we* for
the world in which we live, for the sickness of mind and body
in humans, animals, trees, plants, the Earth herself? Perhaps as
individuals we are mindful of these things, but when faced with
the intimidating attitudes of the collective our courage fails, and
we carry on contributing to the suffering . . . and contributing
. . . and contributing.

As the mind-over-matter theme is now growing in popularity,
even among the medical profession, the market is becoming
flooded with self-help and self-healing package deals. Hypnotherapy tapes and videos, visualisation programmes which
guarantee mind-control, freedom from insomnia, rashes, sexual
hang-ups, learning problems – you name it. Individual responsibility and self-sufficiency is *in*! For many this sort of thing may
work, for others not. What is giving a degree of concern to social
workers and counsellers is that those who are unable to compete
in the self-help stakes are tending to become looked down upon
as lacking in initiative or discipline and therefore a drain upon
society. This gives rise to the question: 'Are we all capable of
helping ourselves or will there always be those who are socially
and intellectually too inadequate to do so?' Let us say that our
answer to the latter part of the question is in the affirmative; then
are such people 'socially sick', and if so what is the criteria for
social sickness, and can it be cured?

Viewed in this context, Big Brother is likely to loom large
upon our social screens any day now. The world is made
up of individuals, and while it might be advantageous for us
all to come to terms with our own minds to the extent that
we could eventually liberate ourselves from the afflictions of
illness and suffering, the rate at which this can be achieved
is naturally going to vary with each person. Meanwhile, those
who are not yet ready to accept responsibility for themselves
will need the help of the more capable among us. After all,
if a person has a broken leg, or is incarcerated in a wheelchair for congenital or accidental reasons, we see nothing
intrinsically wrong in rendering them all the aid we can *because
their disabilities are obvious*. It could be a long time before those
genetic or congenital defects that cause severe disability are
finally conquered, although accidents will doubtlessly be part
of our lives for centuries to come.

In the same way, it may take several generations of good
education to accustom people to the idea that they *can* control

their own bodies, and to a degree their personal destinies, if they simply take the time and trouble to apply themselves to the principles.

Ah yes, I can hear my critics remark, but what about the 'skivers' who are perfectly fit, but refuse to work or contribute to society? Why should we, who work so hard, carry them along? A valid point.

Some people would appear to have a more structured discipline than others, and will readily admit to the fact. A young man I knew told me he hated his parents because they did not insist on his studying law when he left school. 'I am nothing but a bloody clerk now, and it is all their fault,' I heard him say. As I knew the parents in question, I made a point of bringing up the subject with them. 'Oh we offered to help him through university, but he said he didn't want us telling him what to do, and we don't believe in interfering with a young person's free will.'

Back to the young man: 'They didn't even try to make me change my mind, so I thought they didn't care enough about me to want me to succeed.' How many times have I heard the same argument from both sides!

I have often been asked whether I believe that violent offenders, child molesters and similar social misfits are actually mentally ill. If one answers in the affirmative, then the same criteria must also be applied to those people who lose their identities in group/collective situations, wreak havoc and even murder innocent bystanders. In such a situation, where socio-political schemes and carefully thought-out studies have failed to provide a satisfactory answer, the unwrapped bundles of sociological and psychological enigmas usually land unceremoniously in the lap of the philosophers or metaphysicians. While the latter may take some pride in their own sagacity, their elucidations are seldom taken seriously by the more materialistic elements in society, and those who do see fit to observe their advice would have sorted themselves out one way or another anyway. The psychologist or mystic may write copious books and articles explaining how, in spite of his environmental programming and link with the collective unconscious, man is capable of breaking from these mentally restrictive bonds, a process Jung referred to as 'individuation': but how many people would bother to read them? The individuated person is able to stand back and view life's problems from a different perspective, as was Jung himself, but individuation, the metaphysicians tell us, only comes with spiritual maturity, and as our planet would appear to be peopled by a preponderance of young souls we will probably have to let the natural process of maturation take its own time.

We are all, to a degree, responsible for both the conditions prevalent in the world in which we live, and those states of affairs that may be the current cause of our dissatisfaction with that world which we see fit to place at governmental feet. After all, it was the ethics of Homo sapiens that fashioned it that way. Individual responsibility? Yes, indeed! We should be responsible for our own bodies and learn not to abuse them. But are we not – each one of us – also single cells in a much larger organism: *the planet upon which we live*? And, if we care to view this clinically, then our area of responsibility does extend beyond the immediate self. Should our arm become cancerous, there is every likelihood that unless the condition is checked by one means or another, the cancer will spread. It is no use our lungs saying, 'Oh well, it's down there in the bowel, which is not our territory and therefore no concern of ours.' From the sociological viewpoint healing must surely be viewed in *gestalt*.

Let us return for one moment to the Introduction, which dealt with the subject of imbalance. Those who are out of balance are bound to display the symptoms of that imbalance, whether these be physiological, psychological, sociological or psychic. Imbalances, of course, vary in degree and intensity. So, dear reader, beware the trap of viewing yourself as a perfectly integrated and balanced person. Remember the old saying: 'There, but for the grace of God, go I.'

A recent survey of cases of rape (now accepted as a crime of violence) and child abuse highlighted an interesting factor; many of the offenders were quite unaware that they had committed a wrong. Ethics are comparative – perhaps those people did not steal, vandalise or tear down trees – in fact, several of them were members of established churches and pillars of society. How can one go about correcting an imbalance if one does not accept its existence? Surely the acceptance of the imbalance is in itself essential to the cure.

Psychologists have ever noted the strong connection between sex and religion. The libido finds many different avenues of expression, some of which are relatively harmless, while others do pose a threat to society. The well-known saying, 'A harlot when young, a devotee when old', pithily and concisely expresses the dynamic relations between sexuality and religious activity (here, admittedly, at their lowest levels). Kretschmer wrote:

> That a certain kind of bigoted religiosity is in fact a direct form of sexual substitution is quite patent. There are many transitional stages leading from this primitive kind of substitution to true *sublimation*, i.e. the transformation of primitive impulses into dynamically correlated religious, ethical, and artistic values.
>
> The transitional stages between crude substitution and sublimation are represented in the religious beliefs of many strange little communities, sects, and conventicles which form round the strongly affective personalities of certain eccentrics, paranoid prophets, and founders of religions. In the relationship between the heaven-sent prophet and his for the most part female adherents, religious veneration and erotic ecstasy are psychologically indistinguishable, in fact they constitute a single feeling. In more educated circles also, the same remarks apply to the comet's tail of female worshippers in the wake of a celebrated revivalist preacher, mystic, or theosophist. One would be inclined to regard the combination of sexual acts and sacramental ritual which characterize the worship of historical sects (like the one founded by the well known 'Imposter of Königsberg') as a rare curiosity, were it not for the fact that even today we can observe the same combination of feeling with almost identically the same ceremonial in modern paranoid conventicles. In the religious rites and ethical ideology of such sects the sexual impulse frequently exhibits the most sharply atavistic ambivalence as a kind of taboo, appearing as something which is both sacred and unclean and possessed of great and mysterious magic power.[1]

All that was written in the 1950s, however. Today it would be considered overtly sexist and therefore socially unacceptable in certain circles. I do not concur with Professor Kretschmer regarding the preponderance of female adherents – well, certainly not in popular modern cults and their associated minority collectives, although the situation might well have been different in his day when there were far more 'kept' wives with time on their hands. In fact, some groups attract far more men than women, and I can think of at least two which are exclusively for male homosexuals. Interestingly enough, it has been brought to my notice that since the spread of AIDS one of these groups has adjusted its rituals!

Whatever one's views may be regarding the ethics of the society in which we live, it seems to me, and to many others who share my views, that were we to work towards a more loving and caring social order in which people are naturally aware of and in harmony with all that exists around them – there would be less stress, less disease, less destruction and certainly considerably fewer social problems. A utopian dream, perhaps, but had dreamers never dreamed their dreams of a better life we might still be troglodytes!

I recently read a scathing comment about *Care Bears*, a cartoon which encourages children to do good deeds and care about life around them. 'Too boringly goody-goody and totally unrealistic,' the critic wrote. A little naughtiness never did any of us any harm, it is part of our normal growth process. But when altars are erected to its worship, and its gospel preached with questionable sociological sincerity, then that is the time for me to turn heretic! Being naturally subject to the same imbalances as everyone else on this planet (well, perhaps a little more than some and a little less than others) I cannot help wishing that all those hedonists who, like our critic, rejoice in their ids and delight in things 'illegal, immoral and fattening' would take off in a space ship for some planet, light years hence, where they could destroy themselves to their heart's content and leave the rest of us in peace and harmony!

Author's Note: Since completing this book earlier in the year, a report subsequently published in *The Guardian* reported that studies in US prisons have linked levels of the male sex hormone in saliva – testosterone – with violent crime and anti-social behaviour. Dr James Dabb, of Georgia State University, told the American Association for the Advancement of Science that links between salivary testosterone and aggression were also confirmed by studies of Vietnam veterans, vicars, boxers, post-menopausal women, pit bull terriers and even chess players! The themes that subsequently emerged dealt with the libido, independence and dominance, and included wildness, aggression and violence – especially when there were challenges of dominance. Other violent traits were also found to be chemically related, with cortisol – a natural steroid hormone – playing a significant role. One cannot help thinking that these chemical imbalances might originate from the mental make-up of the people concerned, rather than the other way round.

Endnotes:

1. *A Textbook of Medical Psychology*, E Kretschmer, pp. 192–193.

Chapter 9

TREE, ANIMAL AND EARTH HEALING

We discussed in an earlier chapter how the combined efforts of nineteenth-century philosophy and certain of the major religions conspired to separate man from the rest of creation. By designating him the only possessor of a soul, and therefore the only creature entitled to redemption, he and his kind alone could merit admittance to that ephemeral figment of sacerdotal imagination we call 'Heaven'.

Charles Darwin may have impressed the scientific profession with the results of his years of research, but until comparatively recently many followers of the religions popular in Western culture, notably the Fundamentalist Christians, still adhered rigidly to the Adam and Eve story. But the sad truth is that we hominids are simply another form of animal life on this Earth, and not the exalted genus many religious teachers and idealists would have us believe. Exciting new information from the field of genetics is adding a new dimension to the Darwin theory and carrying it even further along 'human animal' lines.

An article in the *Guardian*, entitled 'A Chimp off the Old Block', opened with the statement: 'If genetic fingerprinting is right we may all be more closely related to apes than we thought.' The reporter, John Gribbin, then goes on to explain how anthropologists are now getting excited about the possibility of the 'third chimp' – this one being ourselves! This somewhat startling claim results from the latest developments in the field of molecular anthropology. Since the 1960s, molecular biologists have been developing and refining techniques which compare the molecules of the blood or tissue of living individuals to see how closely related those individuals are to each other.

In the first instance, proteins from members of different species were compared, making use of the differences in the composition of the proteins to provide a measure of the degree of relatedness between the two species: a horse and a zebra, for example. This proved a useful tool in the drawing up of animal 'family' trees, but eyebrows were raised when it was applied to people.

The technique has now been developed to the point where a partial 'fingerprint' can be taken of the DNA itself, which is the molecule of life, in a small sample of blood or other material from an individual. This technique made headline news when it was employed to identify a rapist who had attacked several women in the Midlands. The idea of genetic fingerprinting has far-reaching implications in modern society. It can also be used to establish paternity in disputed cases, for example, while immigration authorities could doubtless put it to good use. The anthropological implications, however, are no less dramatic. Gribbin tells us:

> Because the variations in the genetic material – mutations – build up at a more or less steady rate, the closeness of these similarities established that human, chimp and gorilla all share a common ancestor as recently as five million years ago. The shock waves from that 25-year-old claim are still rippling through the anthropological community. But now it has been hit by another bombshell.
>
> It seems 'obvious' that the anatomy of a human being is different from that of the chimp or the gorilla, and that we stand at some distance, in evolutionary terms, from our hairy cousins. But researches at Wayne State University in Detroit, have now used the genetic fingerprinting technique to show that humans are more closely akin to the chimpanzees than either humans or chimps are to the gorilla. Only one per cent of our DNA differs from that of the chimps.
>
> Morris Goodman, of Wayne State [University], takes what must now be regarded as a cautious line in assessing the implications. He proposes that humans, chimps and gorillas, should

now be placed in the same new sub-family, Homininae, instead of leaving humans in proud isolation in their own classification. But other researchers, including Jared Diamond, of the University of California, Los Angeles, take things a step further.

There are two recognised members of the chimpanzee family, they point out, the common chimp and the pygmy chimp. These two chimps are more closely related to humans than either type of chimp, or humans, is to anything else, including the gorilla. So, logic dictates, the correct classification would put the three types of chimpanzee (common, pygmy and human) together in one group, contrasted with the gorillas.

On this picture, the gorilla line split off from the chimpanzee line between eight and eleven million years ago, while the split between ourselves and the other chimps occurred a little over five million years ago. It isn't cousins, but brothers and sisters, members of a sibling species, that we keep in our zoos to entertain us.[1]

So, Sagan was not far wrong in his earlier-mentioned speculation regarding the randomness of evolution and how intelligence could have developed in any one of several species. I have made a point of quoting this article in full, as a degree of comprehension of the principles of evolution and our real relationship with the other animals with which we share this planet is essential to understanding the healing power possessed by denizens of this planet other than man.

Herbalists have always been aware of the healing qualities of trees, that is, those properties contained in their leaves, bark, etc. But contrary to what Descartes and similarly opined authorities would have us believe, the tree, like every other living thing, has a soul or Essence, which is as eternally enduring as our own. The ancient Greeks called the the tree spirits Dryads and designated one branch of their kind, the Hamadryads, as being responsible for the growth of forests. This knowledge did not die with the ancients, however. There are still those around who have preserved the old ways – Dusty Miller, for example, who is something of a modern-day Tree Shaman.

How, then, can a tree heal? Mike Spring, paralysed from the waist down and in constant pain, sailed to the Azores and back. On his return, he confounded his TV interviewer with the statement that the only way he was able to obtain relief from the pain that continually racked his body was to press his back to an oak tree. This simple and cost-free action would then afford him several hours of complete relief and helped him to carry on in life. When asked for a scientific explanation, Mr Spring replied that he had none – it simply worked! He had heard of the treatment from an American Indian source and had been using it successfully for years.

So, one man achieved success, both in the eyes of the world and in his own battle for the control of his body, with a tree as his main ally. A new idea? Far from it. Trees have been recognised as healers by those in tune with nature for centuries. In fact, the healing talents of trees cover a far wider field than one might imagine at first glance. For example, there are some trees whose energies are best suited to psychological and spiritual needs, and others, like Mike Spring's oaks, whose therapeutic emissions meet the needs of the ills and accidents of the physical body.

The study of the healing powers of the tree and plant kingdoms is a subject that merits more time, space and research than this book will allow. Animal healing is, however, an area in which I have had a degree of personal experience. Nor am I alone in my belief that certain animals possess remarkable powers of healing. The medical profession itself has seen fit to employ them, especially in institutions for the mentally disturbed. The effect certain animals are able to exert over both the mentally and physically ill has been clinically observed for many years. Even the Victorians acknowledged this fact and used to encourage pets in those nursing homes and institutions that were able to afford to keep them.

In his book *Incredible Cats*, psychologist David Greene devotes a whole chapter to the healing power of cats, citing numerous authenticated incidents of where a cat or cats have been instrumental in effecting cures. One particularly moving case concerned Billy, a mentally sick child who had spent most of his young life in hospital. The only sounds he had ever emitted were high-pitched shrieks of annoyance if the nurse accidentally moved his bed away from a position from which he could observe a certain crack in the ceiling which appeared to mean something to him. All treatments failed to help him. And then one day the psychiatrist in charge decided to try something new. He brought to Billy's bed a fifteen-month-old marmalade cat named Rocky. At first there was no response from the child, but Rocky seemed eager to persist with the treatment and made a point of gently licking Billy's fingers before settling down and resting his head on the young boy's arm. The nurse showed Billy how to respond and before long a bond of friendship developed between the cat and the child. Rocky's obvious enjoyment at being stroked engaged Billy's interest and he started to caress him without further encouragement. In time, he learned to feed, look after and finally play games with his marmalade friend.

The breakthrough the doctors had been hoping for came one day when the formerly speechless child suddenly turned to the nurse and said quietly but distinctly: 'Rocky's hungry, he wants some more food.' Dr Greene tells us that today Billy is attending a special school and proving to be an intelligent young man, rapidly making up for the lost years. An animal – believed by many to have no soul – succeeded where medical science failed!

Some of the other cases cited are equally moving and accord with those shown in a recent television programme which concerned new ways of helping mental patients. A middle-aged lady (we will call her Dolly), who had sustained a severe shock in her earlier life, had withdrawn into a state of permanent silence and had not spoken a word in over twelve years. Although she would eat the food she was given by those who cared for her, there was never a hint of recognition or response and her condition appeared to be incurable.

One day, however, a newcomer arrived on the scene – a somewhat elderly tabby cat whom one of the nurses had found abandoned and rescued from being put down. From that day on our patient started to change. The cat appeared to single her out for attention, to which she responded with a degree of affection not witnessed by the doctors and nurses since she was admitted into their care. Dolly liked to share her meals with the cat and one day the matron chanced by and happened to notice this. Feeling that her patient might be jeopardising her health as a result, she gently suggested to Dolly that she eat the food herself as pussy was well fed in the kitchens. Registering the first sign of emotion in years, and addressing her answer to the cat, she replied indignantly, 'Tell the silly woman they don't give you enough to eat.' The breakthrough had come. After that she slowly started to talk again, at first through the cat, and then directly to the staff. She was eventually able to return to a reasonably normal and useful life.

David Green writes of the amazing powers of cats which enable them to:

Use extra-sensory perception to predict danger to themselves their companions and their owners.

Perform intellectually demanding tasks so difficult that many humans could not accomplish them.

Give early warning of natural disaster.

Cure apparently hopeless cases of mental and physical illness.

Save people from apparently inescapable injury or death.

Track down their owners across thousands of miles.

Survive accidents that would spell certain death to almost any other creatures.

Communicate eloquently with other animals and humans by means of a complex language of sounds, movements and odours.[2]

Some claims! But Dr Greene substantiates them well in his book and for those who might wish to learn more about their pets' gifts, and how these are likely to manifest, it is well worth perusing.

My own personal experiences with animals as healers also concern cats. While I was at college I shared a London flat with several other students. It was the custom for our friends from local bedsits to drop by evenings or weekends for a pot of tea and a chat about how we would put the world to rights! We shared our somewhat topsy-turvy dwelling with a black and white cat named Woodwee. He had originally been named Woody after a friend of mine, the 'wee' being added as he was rather small and dainty.

One particular evening we were visited by a young friend of ours whose name was Ron. He arrived with a very bad headache, however, and asked if he could just sit somewhere quietly. He refused a painkiller but accepted a cup of tea, and we found him a comfortable, high-backed chair to relax in and left him alone for awhile. It could not have been more than ten minutes later before he suddenly appeared at the door of our communal room, wearing a puzzled expression. We naturally enquired how he was feeling and he assured us that his headache had gone completely. What then was the problem, we asked? This is what he told us:

After settling back in the chair and making himself as comfortable as the pain in his head would allow, he suddenly became aware of a presence behind him. (No, he was not the nervous, hysterical type at all, quite the opposite, in fact.) He felt what he described as a soft, cooling breeze across his forehead and experienced a feeling of drowsiness. The drowsiness increased and he obviously slipped into alpha or theta brain patterns, as the 'presence' went about the business of removing his discomfort. Upon the resumption of full consciousness he determined to see who had effected the healing, believing it to have been one of us. He turned round and there, on the back of the chair looking straight into his eyes, was none other than Woodwee!

This was not the only healing incident that concerned this particular cat. Once we realised his powers, we would seek his help and always with good effect. We had no idea how old he was when he finally left us, as he had originally come to us as a stray. But in that life he gave more healing and comfort to others than many a hominid, for all our education and great technical achievements!

The second incident concerned me directly. A gentleman friend of mine who was one of the principal basses with the English National Opera telephoned me for help just before a performance in which he was to sing a major role. A believer in the powers of absent healing, he asked if I could help as he felt really ill and doubted whether he could get through the performance. In those days I worked with a healing group in Central London and the particular form of healing used required a partner or co-worker. On this occasion, however, I was alone. Realising my friend's problem, I had an idea. My Siamese cat, Athene, was sitting on my lap at the time so I asked her if she would join with me to send our friend some absent healing.

I decided to effect this on projection – to visualise myself in the dressing room at the Coliseum Theatre and administer the healing as though I were there in person. This I did, and as I positioned myself behind my friend, to my surprise, there was another 'person' standing in front of him, assuming the position that my fellow healer would normally adopt. As I raised my hands to work on the aura in the way I had been taught – so also did my co-worker, but to my amazement the outstretched limbs were dark brown, furry paws! The strange thing is that my helper appeared in human proportion, and not small like little Athene. 'She' used exactly the same form of healing as I did. Together we closed the patient's aura and I returned to my conscious self in my little flat. There was Athene, still curled up on my lap. A few minutes later the telephone rang. My friend was calling to tell me that he had made an amazing recovery.

'Your healing has worked like a miracle, I now feel I can make it through the opera.' (And he did.) Then he suddenly added: 'But why did you project over to me looking like a cat?'

'I didn't,' I answered.

'Then that is most peculiar,' he insisted. 'I saw, quite distinctly, a cat "person" standing in front of me with outstretched paws. I say "person" as it was about the same size as you, and in some sort of dress.'

I then explained to him how Athene had helped me. Later my thoughts strayed to Bast, the Egyptian Cat Goddess, who was one of the great healing deities of the ancient world, and I wondered if I had accidentally tapped into her healing ray!

Cats and trees are by no means the only living beings that are capable of transmitting healing energies or, as some parapsychologists might prefer to put it: 'Emitting a PK frequency that is conducive to correcting certain imbalances'. Recent experiments in France have shown that dolphins are also capable of feeling and caring for humans who are experiencing pain and suffering. These gentle creatures appear to understand the importance we place upon the preservation of life. A recent incident in Australia involved several dolphins successfully defending a young surfer against attack by a giant shark, and there are numerous instances of the lives of shipwrecked people being saved by their timely appearance, especially in the vicinity of coastal waters.

Stories relating to what people have believed to be healings effected by such creatures as dogs, goats and birds have also come my way. One lady who runs an absent healing group sincerely believes that their work is never so effective if her dog is not present during their sessions. As for horses, well, the ancient Celts swore by their powers, horse gods and goddesses usually being associated with the principles of death and rebirth, as may be evidenced in the many Hobby Horses that feature in those seasonal rites that have survived the centuries of repression and persecution.

In fact, the Earth herself has amazing healing properties which were understood by many of the ancient cultures, and are still used among those tribes that have preserved the old knowledge to this very day. But then this is hardly surprising, for according to arcane sources this planet has been designated the Planet of Healing, in that it offers the spiritually sick those experiences that can aid the correction of their imbalances. Many Red Indians, Australian Aboriginals, Eskimos, Siberians and other cultures that are still under shamanic influence work with and through the Earth.

The practice of Feng Shui (Wind-Water), the Chinese art of placement, is another example of a great civilisation that has retained the essence of many of its original beliefs and adapted them to modern life. Those who study geomancy will know that across the length and breadth of this planet there are right locations for certain things. For example, the Earth energies in one area may be suitable for the erection of a place of learning; in another – a place of recreation; another – religious devotion; and another – healing, depending on the quality of the emissions.

In counter-balance, there are also places where the earth energies are not right for, or out of harmony with the personal frequencies of certain individuals. Setting up a home or business on such a site could therefore have an adverse effect on health, to which phenomenon the term 'geopathic stress' has been assigned. So if you are obliged to make a move, and are unsure as to your compatibility with the location, a good geomancer or dowser can always help out. Three years ago my husband and I moved to what we saw as an idyllic spot, surrounded by the harmonies of nature – or so it seemed. Had we paid more attention to the earth energies and less to the physical panorama we could have saved ourselves a lot of money and stress. Gnomic lesson learned!

Being a living entity in her own right, Gaia, the Earth Mother or whichever name it may be convenient for us to call her by, can obviously utilise her own chakras for different purposes, just as our lower chakras process reproduction and elimination, while our higher ones are more concerned with our transcendental development. Coming to terms with the existence of the Earth Entity, therefore, constitutes a valid step towards the true balance that is essential to good mental and physical health.

Crystals, which are part of the mineral kingdoms, and one particular manifestation of the Elements of Earth, also contain healing properties. But as this is a currently popular form of therapy which merits more detailed analysis it will be covered in greater detail in Chapter 15.

I think we can safely conclude that the 'gift' of healing is not

the exclusive property of Homo sapiens, there being many other
sources of balancing energy from which we may freely draw if
we are brave enough to break with our years of conditioning and
view our own planet and the universe, of which we are a part, in
a different and more comprehensive light.

Endnotes:

1. 'A Chimp off the Old Block', by John Gribbin, *The Guardian*, (co-author, with Mary Gribbin, of *The One Per Cent Advantage*),14/6/88.
2. *Incredible Cats*, D Greene, p. 12.

Chapter 10

THE PHYSICAL BODY

Having established our furry ancestry, and the fact that we appear to have attained to a certain standard of intelligence (considered by some to be superior, which I tend to question!) that puts us a cut or so above our simian siblings and other members of the animal kingdoms, how do we compare with them in the care and preservation of our physical bodies? Given our accredited higher intellect, not very well it would seem. Animals are usually born with some idea as to what is beneficial for their survival and what is not. Information regarding diet, grooming, procreation and so on, is usually passed from generation to generation in a variety of ways. For example, a leopard cub raised alone by its mother in the wild will, upon reaching maturity, know exactly how to go about finding a mate and doing what is necessary for the perpetuation of its species. It does not need to observe these actions in others, it simply works on instinct.

But what is this faculty we glibly refer to as instinct? There are varying views regarding which area or areas of our brains control it. Most popularly favoured is the hindbrain, or rhombencephalon, the portion of the embryonic brain from which the metencephalon, myelencephalon, and subsequently the cerebellum, pons and medulla oblongata develop. The hindbrain's association with primeval development has prompted some researchers to link it with the collective unconscious on the one hand, and certain instinctive awareness patterns on the other.

Another contender for the title might well be the limbic system, which is located in a semicircle in the middle of the brain and governs basic activities such as self-preservation, reproduction and the expression of fear and rage. Scientists have also observed a connection between this system and the functions of memory and dreams, which have prompted some of them to consider the limbic system the location of the mind or psyche.

Finally, there is the thalamus (Greek for *inner chamber*), which is referred to by some scientists as the 'old' or 'reptile' brain. It consists of two egg-shaped masses which relay nerve impulses from all the senses, except smell, to the cerebral cortex. Experiments carried out at the Rockefeller Institute in New York established that people who claimed to have powers of clairvoyance, telepathy and extra-sensory perception were able to demonstrate their gifts with amazing accuracy when tested under rigorous scientific control. Psychoanalyst Dr Eric Berne, of Transactional Analysis fame, attributes this kind of highly developed 'sixth sense' to an exceptionally sensitive thalamus, while the late Dr Alexis Carrel, a leading scientist, wrote:

> Normally, the uncanny powers of the thalamus are smothered and overridden by the cortex of the brain. As science lifts the curtain on this mystery out of our primitive past we begin to understand why we are barely tapping our potentialities. And the certainty that the sixth sense exists makes the investigation of these long-dormant faculties of the mind an urgent and exciting task.[1]

There are many things that animals do learn purely by observation, of course. The domestic kitten born to a house-trained queen will follow its mother's actions and make correct use of the litter tray. At the other extreme it is now acknowledged by science that all living things are capable of communicating to each other over immense distances outside of the normal time frame. Signals of danger – either from natural sources or from man himself – supplies of food, good resting places, and so forth, can be conveyed to each other by insects, birds and mammals using what Dr Rupert Sheldrake has termed 'morphic resonance'. In all but a few human beings, however, this extra sense, or instinctive brain action, has either become atrophied or dulled by the overemphasis of reason.

Genetic patterns in the animal and insect world frequently display a more marked tendency to breed to order, whereas our own freedom from any such genetic restrictions is not always conducive to good health or the smooth and efficient running of our society.

For example, until recently colonies of social insects were conventionally compared to many-celled animals, different cells in different organs being highly specialised, but all containing exactly the same number of genes. The influence of the hormones and other chemicals playing on the cells differentiated them according to their required purposes within the community of the hive. In the same way it was believed that special diet, training and environment fitted worker bees, genetically very similar to each other, for different tasks. However, new information from two groups of American scientists have discovered that this is not so. It is, apparently, genetic differences that determine each worker's preference for a specific task. Drs Peter Frumhoff and Jayne Baker, of the University of California at Davis, have discovered that the extent to which bees groom each other to remove parasites and the degree of enthusiasm they have for that grooming are purely the products of heredity.

The value of this discovery could extend well beyond the scientific world. Parasites that weaken and kill bees prove a major economic problem to beekeepers, so bees bred to groom each other efficiently could prove a commercial boon! Grooming was only one task that turned out to be genetically determined, however. Drs Gene Robinson and Robert Page, of Ohio State University, have found that different genetic strains of bees also specialise in guarding the colony, disposing of dead bees, foraging for pollen, scouting for sites for swarming, nursing queen larvae and using their wings as fans to keep the colony cool.

These incidences of genetically induced talents or callings are probably not limited to the insect world. In humans it is known that mathematical ability, for example, can run in families, as can a talent for skilled technical work, music or writing (see Chapter 3 – the Genome Project). No doubt there are many scientists who would like to engineer these talents genetically, and more than likely a large number of people who would welcome the idea. The ethics involved would naturally present us with some volatile fuel for debate, but who are we to talk? After all, we have been tampering with the genetics of animals, vegetables, flowers and most growing things for centuries, and enjoying the fruits of our questionable labours. But then it all comes down to what one is experimenting with, and as there are still a lot of people about who appear to view a cat, dog, hen, flower or grain of corn as inferior to themselves, and therefore to be used as cruelly as they see fit for the comfort and preservation of their own kind, it is little wonder than the ethic is a conveniently movable one!

Let us gloss over our failings for a moment and consider what we have achieved in the healthy care of our bodies. A balanced life-style is the thing, the experts tell us: no smoking, no alcoholic excesses, and no heavy intakes of fat or sugar. Have regular exercise, plenty of fresh air, good posture; we have heard it all so many times from the healthy living pundits. But is it not possible to carry the physical side a little too far? Caring for the body or overcaring?

Take a popular example. Following the success of Jane Fonda's aerobic exercises in the United States, the idea quickly spread to the UK, with aerobic classes making their noisy presence felt in village hall, evening classroom, scout hut and sports centre the length and breadth of the land. Current fads of this kind seldom do much good in the long run. They may serve to remove the odd unwanted pound in the young and keep supple the limbs that are already sufficiently loose to accommodate their gyrations, but there have been casualties as many an orthopaedic surgeon and physiotherapist will be well aware. And not only among the older generations whose bones have become too set to cope! We come back to those social indispositions that inevitably result from 'keeping up with the Joneses', the Joneses in this case being the current collective.

There are a few health and diet myths which do call for questioning. For example, the belief that sportspersons and those who do spend more time than average attending to the development of their physical bodies are healthier and live longer lives than the rest of us. A healthy regimen can promote longevity in many cases, but it does not necessarily guarantee it. There are other, perhaps psychological, factors to be taken into consideration as we shall see.

Although many older people may adopt a healthy life-style in their later years, the damage could have already been effected during their youth as a result of too high an intake of cholesterol or other substances guaranteed to precipitate heart disease, strokes, gall bladder problems, and a host of similarly diet-related ailments. No doubt many of my older readers will hasten to point out that although they did enjoy large Sunday joints, they also ate fresh fruit and vegetables and not the overtreated convenience foods that are popular today. That is as may be, but nutritionists generally agree that in the past many people did partake of totally unbalanced diets (and still do, of course).

Doctors have now disclosed that cutting down on fat *does*, in fact, give you a longer life. The less cholesterol in your diet the better says an American study. Cutting out two eggs a day can add four years to your life and an overall reduction of cholesterol levels by a sixth adds six years. With low blood-pressure and no smoking the bonus is twelve years! These figures are derived from a study of 1,900 Western Electric employees in Chicago. In Britain, Professor Barry Lewis – a member of the government working group on artery-clogging fats and heart disease – stated: 'This really is a breakthrough in understanding what the right diet can achieve.'

While a balanced diet obviously contributes to good health, dieting, if taken to excess, can cause damage to the system. A woman I knew, who suffered from problems with her complexion, read in a book about a 'grape cure' which involved living on nothing but grapes – as many as one cared to eat – for several weeks. This, the booklet assured her, would cleanse the system of all impurities and her unwanted blemishes would disappear as though by magic. Being a very highly disciplined person, she kept rigidly to her grape intake and needless to say the flesh quickly dropped from her. After the requisite number of weeks she was like a skeleton, in fact, and when she tried to resume her normal eating pattern she found she was unable to. Medical help was immediately sought and a variety of tests were carried out. Finally, she was diagnosed as anorexic and obliged to negotiate the painful path to recovery, once again by her own will-power. Fortunately she succeeded, but the blemishes stubbornly remained.

It makes one wonder whether the originators of these punitive-type diets ever take into account the fact that, being individuals, our responses to certain foods or dietary disciplines are bound to differ, and sometimes with disastrous side-effects as in the case above.

It would seem that what we really need to do as far as the fuelling and maintaining of our bodies is concerned is to keep the whole matter in perspective. As many of us are busily engaged in earning enough to keep a warm roof over our heads, the popularity of the fast food business can easily be accounted for. An analysis of fast foods by the London Food Commission found that a half-pound burger may contain two ounces of pure fat, in addition to rusk, sugar, MSG (monosodium glutamate), coal-tar dye, and other preservatives. A double burger, chips and milkshake provide roughly half an average woman's daily calorie needs and 60 per cent of the fats required. At one end of the age-scale this kind of diet apparently promotes early puberty, while at the other, it can hasten our departure!

Insurance companies these days seem to believe they are onto a better thing with non-drinking, non-smoking vegetarians with low blood-pressure. As one such, I am frequently assured by the medics that I have little to worry about in the long run and, short of stepping in front of a bus, can expect an extended future. However, experience has shown me that it does not always work that way. When our time has come, as the scientists have already discovered, we may subconsciously alert our immune systems to ease off their tasks of protecting us, or effect some other steps conducive to an early demise. One can meet very old people who have been smoking, drinking, meat-eaters all their lives, and who have made 90 and more. I knew one such elderly gentleman whose name was George. He passed away three days before his century, much to his annoyance at the time. Yes, he had always smoked a pipe, had the occasional pint and enjoyed his Sunday roast, but as he never ceased to point out to me, 'Everything in moderation, my dear, and not too often. In that way you can look forward to it when you do have it.'

On the other hand, my late guardian, a very scholarly man who was most abstemious, lived to be 97 and died quietly in his sleep. During the year prior to his death his eyesight all but deserted him, but he was compensated with the sort of etheric sight for which many an aspiring mystic would have given their right arm. As a man of science, he had always believed in things metaphysical without need of ecstatic experience or scientific proof. Pure logic, he assured me, made them quite clear to him.

People who enjoy a generous quota of good health for long periods in their lives frequently display a marked intolerance for the less blessed. This can possibly be viewed psychologically as an extension of the childhood tendency to deride the disabled or disfigured, or in zoological terms the persecution of the weaker animals for the benefit of the strength and continuity of the tribe.

A woman with whom I was very closely associated appeared to sail through life with nothing worse than the common cold. Should any of us in her immediate vicinity dare to mention some indisposition, we would be greeted with the words, 'It's all in your mind, pull yourself together!' Or, 'What jobs are you trying to get out of this time?' She retired at 60 intent upon enjoying the same quality of health she had been blessed with up to that point. But then tragedy struck, first with one serious complaint and finally with intestinal cancer from which she eventually died. When she did finally succumb to disease, it hit her much harder, both physically and mentally, than it would have had she, like other members of her family, been the recipient of pain and discomfort in her earlier years. Perhaps there is, after all, something in the old saying 'Cracked crocks last the longest'!

Endnote:

1. *The Psychology of Ritual*, M Hope, p. 291.

Chapter 11

THE PSYCHOLOGIES

'Psychology' is one of those words which would appear to mean different things to different people. Those who have never encountered a working psychologist, either as a patient or through associated channels of employment, tend to view the world of the psychologist/psychiatrist with a degree of amusement, suspicion or fear. I once conducted my own survey, interviewing some 200 people or more over a period of months. My standard question was: 'What do you know about or feel about psychology and psychiatry?'

Well scripted, the answers would have made a first-class comedy show. They included such comments as:

'Trick-cyclists? Well, as they say, it takes one to know one, doesn't it!'

'You have to be nuts yourself to do that sort of thing, I would think.'

'Don't they sit you on a couch and talk about sex all the time?'

'I wouldn't want another man prying into my private life!'

'Why do they all have funny accents?'

'Are there any English psychiatrists? They all seem to be foreign.'

'My doctor suggested that my daughter go to see one, but I wouldn't let her. Once you've been to one of that lot, everyone thinks you're barmy.'

'Don't tell a soul, but I went to a psychiatrist several times – and was he *dreamy*!'

'I wouldn't mind going to one if it was a lady, but I wouldn't trust myself under hypnosis on a couch with one of those smarmy men!'

'You mean shrinks – everyone goes to them in the States, but then what do you expect over there!'

I could go on for pages. But that was all some eight to ten years ago, and mercifully we appear to be entering a more enlightened age where psychology, psychotherapy and allied skilled services are better known and understood among the majority of people. Although there will ever be instances where ignorance raises its ugly head, we live in the hope that these will slowly decrease as educators and media combine to make knowledge more readily available to the population at large.

For those who are unclear as to the distinctions between psychology, psychiatry, psychoanalysis, psychotherapy, and similarly related words, here are a few definitions which should help to clarify matters.

Psychology: From the Greek word 'psyche' (soul). In the strictest sense of the word, psychology therefore relates to the soul or spirit, but it is more commonly a study of the mind, or of human or animal behaviour.

However, none of these definitions are really broad enough to encompass the full range of studies that shelter under the psychological umbrella. For example, there is Social Psychology – the study of how people behave when in groups and communities; Educational Psychology – the way people learn; Industrial Psychology – social factors affecting efficiency and production; Cognitive and Experimental Psychology – which deals with memory and perception; Development Psychology – our emotional, intellectual and sexual development from childhood; Physiological Psychology – which deals with our bodies, their genes, hormones, nervous systems, and so forth.

Unlike psychiatry, psychology is not simply involved with

mental illness but with *all* behaviour, both normal and abnormal. A psychologist is therefore someone who is trained to function within the framework of these definitions. A clinical psychologist, as the name implies, works in a clinical setting such as a hospital, specialised addiction unit or regular clinic. A parapsychologist is one who studies mental phenomena, such as telepathy, extra-sensory perception and psychokinesis, which are beyond the scope of normal physical explanation.

Psychiatry: The branch of medicine that is specifically concerned with the diagnosis and treatment of mental disorders. The practice of psychiatry requires a full medical degree with further specialised training. A psychiatrist is therefore a fully trained doctor whose special subject is the mind.

Psychoanalysis: A practice based on the personality theories of Sigmund Freud but later refined, modified and altered by a succession of famous analysts. It involves a lengthy process designed to bring the patient's unconscious to his conscious awareness. Psychoanalysts undergo special training, but a medical degree is not a necessary prerequisite for analytical practice. No drugs or exercises are involved. Your psychoanalyst may not be a doctor, but probably has a much better knowledge of the mind than the average GP or surgeon specialising in more physical complaints.

Psychotherapy: The use of psychological (as opposed to physical) methods to treat mental disorders; also defined as a process 'whereby a patient is helped to understand and, ideally, to solve his or her problems through talking them over with a doctor'. As treatment of this kind can often involve both personality changes and transference, a considerable amount of pressure is placed on both patient and therapist. A degree in medicine or psychology is not, however, essential to the practice of psychotherapy, although specialised training is obviously an advantage to both patient and therapist.

Regarding psychotherapy, Inglis and West tell us: 'Nowadays it is often equated with psychoanalysis, but what really distinguishes psychoanalysis from less structured forms of psychological therapy is its contention that patients are unlikely to be aware of the basic nature of their problem, so that any "talking over" takes on a special character.'[1]

A whole series of new therapies which can be broadly labelled 'psychological' have mushroomed over the past few years, many of which are either extensions or revised versions of the above. I shall be dealing with these in Chapters 18 and 19.

On the occasion of the first lecture I attended on the subject of psychology, the speaker prefaced his lesson with the statement:

> Sooner or later someone along the line, probably one of my medical colleagues, is going to quote you the saying: 'The psychoneurotic builds castles in the air, the psychotic lives in them, and the psychologist collects the rent.' Ladies and gentlemen, I object! It is the psychiatrist who collects the rent, and a fat one at that. We psychologists can't afford rooms in Harley Street!

Years of observation, however, have tended to confirm that there is a fair living to be gained from all the psychotherapies – for those who can take the pressure. A career of handling other people's problem may not affect the less sensitive among us, but for many well-meaning people who genuinely wish to help their fellow men and women, but who are unable to detach themselves emotionally from the problems of their patients, it constitutes a mental disaster area. This no doubt explains the many jokes in circulation regarding the instability of the mental healing profession as a whole, and while such humour no doubt affords merriment to many people the truth behind it is really rather tragic.

There are a lot of books on the market which cover what is broadly termed 'popular' psychology. Many of these are purely statistical surveys which do not presume to touch on the human condition. If one does choose to read psychology at university, much of one's earlier studies will be concerned with statistics, however, their compilation and interpretation being essential to the study as a whole. Some psychologists tend to specialise more in animal behaviour, Dr David Greene, for example, to whose excellent study of felines I have already referred. Zoology and psychology can walk hand in hand in such surveys, so a broad understanding of many life-forms is to the advantage of the aspiring psychologist.

Psychological therapies are commonly divided into four categories: Psychotherapies, Behavioural Therapies, Humanistic

Psychologies and Transpersonal Psychologies. However, it is sometimes difficult to effect a separation when it comes to the question of treatment, as some practitioners may vary this according to the personality type with whom they are dealing. Transpersonal Psychology has been called the 'fourth force', which refers to its position as a more recent development in psychological schools of thought, Behaviourism, Psycho-analysis and Humanistic Psychology occupying the first three places.

Taken in the healing context, what is the success rating of the psychology/psychiatry complex? As few people in the UK care to admit to having received psychiatric or psychological treatment, this has been hard to assess from survey alone, but in the United States it is a different matter. Many well-known British subjects have recourse to American psychiatrists or psychologists as they feel that there is less stigma attached to the exercises than they would encounter over here. Actor Dudley Moore, for example, when interviewed for the *Sunday Times Magazine*, 13 December 1981, stated:

> I've been in therapy since 1964. I've had lots of shrinks. I've felt great greyness in my life, long bouts of depressions, and the feeling I wasn't driving my own train. I know it's viewed with a lot of scepticism, but therapy is very important. I've met some very helpful, insightful people through it. It's always a joke in England, or considered a rich man's pastime. But group therapy is cheap and most useful. I love the American attitude to psychology, its everydayness. In the past few years I've come out into realistic sanity. For me, therapy is the most important thing in life. It has made my professional life blossom. I can use what I have learnt.[2]

One wonders how many of us would benefit from the American touch? It occurs to me that the only drawback might lie in the initiation of dependencies. What we have to ask ourselves is: Are psychological services exclusively for the mentally ill, or do they have a role to play in the prevention of illness? Experience inclines me to the latter view. Problems encountered by many people I have counselled in the past, some involving mental disorders, others purely physical afflictions could, I believe, have been averted had the people concerned had someone to whom they could have initially unburdened themselves. Nor does this necessarily apply to mental disorders;

in several instances of physical abuse, for example, those concerned would have benefited considerably from both practical advice and someone to give them the necessary courage and confidence to carry it out.

Although many practitioners are of the opinion that the conventional forms of treating mental illness have proved disappointing, these need to be examined as there must surely be those among us who have received help from them in some way or other. Even the Royal College of Psychiatry admitted in a memorandum to the Department of Health in 1974: 'The average standard of psychiatric practice in Britain alone is abysmally low.'[3]

Scandals involving brutal and obscene practices at mental hospitals have served to awaken the public conscience to the suffering of the mentally ill, and there have doubtless been many other instances that have been conveniently hushed up.

In the early days of psychiatry, mental disorders were divided into diagnostic compartments: schizophrenics were differentiated from manic depressives, psychotics from neurotics and so forth. But as time progressed psychiatrists appeared to find little agreement when it came to diagnosis. A whole element of doubt arose regarding what did or did not constitute sanity, or indeed mental illness as a whole, many of the conditions formerly classified under this category proving to be nothing more than stress-related breakdowns, temporary emotional disturbances, or complaints symptomatic of the unconscious mind's rebellion when consciousness is unable to deal with the problem that confronts it.

Psychoactive drugs comprise much of the conventional treatment for the mentally ill. Sedatives, tranquillisers and antidepressants are now considered as only short-term harbours from the emotional storms that have brought on the condition in the first place, while long-term drug treatment, even of the milder type, has been proven to be addictive. Perfectly sane people who have undergone a period of intense stress or emotional upset following a divorce, family bereavement, rape or mugging, and having been prescribed valium, librium or similar drugs at the time, find themselves 'hooked'. The pattern of their lives becomes even more disturbed than it was during the initial period of their problem.

In mental hospitals, some of the stronger drugs that have been regularly administered as a matter of course have been found to cause 'persistent tardive dyskinesia' (one of the side-effects being endless ugly facial contortions) which apparently constitutes a life sentence for the sufferer!

Other treatments administered to the mentally sick under psychiatric direction include Electro-Convulsive Therapy (ECT); insulin coma therapy and brain surgery (lobotomy or leucotomy). Several of these have mercifully fallen by the wayside, but ECT has persisted, although it is fast losing popularity among the profession. A recent report in *The Guardian*, 26 October 1988, under the heading 'Punishing Cure', refers to the case of a former mental patient who describes what it is like to be on the receiving end of ECT in the magazine *Openmind*. ECT, it stated, has been condoned as helpful in cases of depression unresponsive to drugs. Jim Read, the man concerned, argued that patients feel despair at receiving something that feels like punishment when what they seek is comfort. In fact, they experience shame at requiring such extreme treatment. Weakness follows as they surface from the anaesthetic and deal with the inevitable disorientation and memory loss. Patients believe that their depression is diagnosed as endogenous (arising from within) 'because no one listens to us long enough to find out the real cause'.

Which brings us full circle to the analysts and psychotherapists. I am frequently asked if I know a good psychologist, and if the enquirer is a woman the preference is usually for a Jungian analyst. Freudian psychology, they believe, leans too heavily on sexual angles and not enough on the understanding of the emotions or liminality.

Here is a case in point: a lady I once worked with had sustained a nervous breakdown which manifested as an amnesic midnight trip to a local beauty spot clad only in a nightgown. Fortunately, a kindly constable spotted her and she was admitted to the local hospital for psychiatric treatment. She was a single parent who had been deserted by her husband while her son was in his infancy. She had made a first-class job of raising the boy, who had joined the Merchant Fleet and was doing extremely well. In fact, he had just announced his engagement to a Canadian girl, which probably precipitated her breakdown by unconsciously releasing the emotional build-up that she had so successfully suppressed over the years.

Although her amnesia quickly left her, the treatment afforded by the Freudian psychiatrist at the local hospital seemed to irritate rather than help her. Fortunately, he was professional enough to refer her to a Jungian analyst in Harley Street who was apparently adept in the treatment of the particular disorder. She described the contrast between the two psychiatrists, the former being the earnest, nervous, agitatory type and the latter of quiet, reserved mien. Her visit to Harley Street she was able to recall in absolute detail – with one exception, as we shall see.

The consulting room, she told me, was decorated in a Chinese motif with oriental rugs, vases and ornaments, also from the same culture and obviously very valuable; a slight aroma of incense pervaded and what struck her most forcibly was the utter silence and stillness. She felt immediately at ease and totally relaxed. The psychiatrist talked to her for a while in a quiet, cultured voice, showing full understanding of her life and its problems to date. Then he asked her to relax and said he would put her to sleep for a while (hypnosis?) From then on she remembered nothing until she was gently awakened over an hour later. What had happened, she enquired of her therapist?

'We have sorted it all out for you, and from now on you will be perfectly well,' he told her. And so she was. In fact, it was some five years later that she related the incident to me. There had been no recurrence, and her life had definitely altered for the better. She had a well-paid, responsible job. Her son had married his Canadian fiancée, but instead of making a life in Canada as they had originally proposed, the couple had settled nearby and a grandson had made a welcome appearance. She owed it all, she told me, to the kindly man in the Chinese room, who had somehow, as if by magic, transformed her life!

One of the aspects of psychology and psychiatry that does appear to annoy many people is the predisposition of its practitioners to make excuses for what would otherwise be considered criminal acts, lack of self-discipline, or normal growth experiences. Antisocial behaviour, the inability to contribute to society, hooliganism, vandalism – all are laid at the door of some supposed childhood trauma of the kind that most of us suffer at some time or other during our maturing years. 'Little Johnny beats up old ladies because he wasn't breast-fed!' There are millions of people who were not breast-fed and who do not proceed through life beating up the elderly!

It is all too easy to shelter from life's responsibilities under the cloak of a psychiatrist's certificate. Besides, there are quite a few 'skivers' about who make a point of reading up on their

psychology, and effecting the symptoms guaranteed to produce just the work-avoiding diagnosis that suits their chosen
life-style. It is currently fashionable to think of social misfits as
being mentally incapacitated, when this may not be at all the
case. The therapy they really need could probably be better
administered by sociologists or psychosocial workers who are
more familiar with the real conditions contributory to their
problem.

Depression has become the subject of considerable debate
and research of late, especially in the field of genetics. It is a
mistake, however, to lump all mood swings under the depressive umbrella as there is a vast difference, both genetically
and psychologically between, say, instances of melancholia
arising from personal loss or disillusionment, anxiety neuroses
and genuine manic depression. The latter is an inherited factor
which can manifest in any of several ways. With the less
afflicted, mood disturbances may be only bipolar or even
unipolar, while the more severe cases experience what is
termed 'rapid cycling'. During the 'high' manic phase of
predepression euphoria, some sufferers exhibit symptoms of
grandiose delusion while the more talented experience a highly
productive phase during which there may even be manifestations of genius. The genes of psychosis and creativity would
appear to go hand in hand.

Scientists observed that primates in whom the left brain
hemisphere is relatively undeveloped tend not to suffer from
mood swings, which has suggested some association between
excessive left hemisphere activity and mental illness. From a
transpersonal view this would certainly make sense, all the
exercises conductive to the relief of stress and mental equilibrium being predominantly right-hemisphere-orientated.

Initial research into the genetics of depression resulted in the
isolation of a single dominant gene located in chromosome
No. 11, which predisposes people to cyclothymic depressions.
Findings were submitted for laboratory scrutiny, and since
then, twenty other genetic markers have been located. When
this information can be defined in terms of cerebral functions,
it may help to throw some light on the nature of inherited
depression.

In the light of these findings, alternative therapists may well
find themselves wondering whether they can treat a disorder
that is basically biological. Psychiatrists are of the opinion

that self-help is possible up to a certain point, after which the biological processes become entrenched making it difficult to break the pattern. I came across this in my own work, the case in question being that of a middle-aged man who suffered a mild form of delusionary depression which was not obvious enough to interfere with his life and career. He had retired after serving a full term in the Royal Navy without anyone being aware of his problem, which took the form of delusions that he was being attacked at night by malevolent forces. In the cold light of day, however, he was able to rationalise the hallucinatory nature of the experience, but in spite of this it continued to haunt him for some time. It reminded me of a stylus that has become stuck in the groove of a record – the same phrase being repeated over and over again. One needed to lift the faulty mechanism somehow and replace it on the forward track. A cure was eventually effected, but it took several years before the pattern was finally broken.

Depression would appear to be part and parcel of the basic human emotional condition, which occultists have ever associated with the element of water. Some of us would appear to be blessed (or cursed as the case may be) with more than our quotient, and perhaps our karma for this life involves our coming to terms with this basic elemental imbalance. As Van Gogh said 'Emotions are the great captains of our lives,' but this need not necessarily be so. If mind can truly rule matter, which many of us believe to be the case, then we do possess the potential for helping ourselves or being helped to do so either medically or via the office of some alternative therapy.

Another factor which needs to be taken into consideration when dealing with certain emotional and psychological disturbances is the possibility that they might be diet-related. This would seem to apply particularly in the cases of hyperactive or disturbed children. One such case which was featured on television a few years back demonstrated the body's response to instant coffee, a relatively small intake of a popular brand being sufficient to induce an epileptic seizure. Food allergies have since been marked as potential areas for investigation in cases which defy normal categorisation.

In an earlier chapter we discussed the possible reasons for the current spate of hooliganism, mugging and allied manifestations of antisocial activity. Were the causes purely environmental, or do genetics and soul age also feature in the debate? The 'silk-purse/sow's-ear' argument will ever prove a thorn in the side of sociologists. However, a principle applied – the results of selected genetic breeding in animals, for example – cannot, from a purely logical standpoint, be conveniently discarded when it comes to man. Or can it? I fully realise that the heredity vs. environment issue is a highly emotive one which involves the tenets of several major religions, so rather than take sides I would prefer to go along with the soul age theory, which is, I feel, somewhat kinder in that it acknowledges the fact that we all start as infant psyches and proceed from there, our soul fragments, like the pieces of a shattered hologram, experiencing simultaneously in many other time-zones or parallel universes!

Our stage of spiritual evolution or soul age manifests in the 'awareness factor' – the more mature the Essence the more alert the individual to the many worlds and intelligences, seen and unseen, which are all around. The majority of us proceed through our lives as though asleep, totally unaware of the interpenetrative universe through which we are constantly moving. Old souls, however, are able to sense these frequencies and negotiate them without experiencing the fragmentation or disassociation that frequently accompanies the hallucinations of mental illness or drug abuse. This does not, of course, shield them from the normal contingencies of life on a disturbed planet, but they are at least able to rationalise their problems and keep them in sufficient perspective to enable them to stay on a reasonably even keel. Of course these theories are purely metaphysical and there is no empirical 'proof' to substantiate them. I am quite happy, however, to leave all that to the scientists, as they are making a rather splendid job of it already!

Different psychological types react differently to sickness, disability or handicap. Does our personality type in any way affect the diseases we are likely to contact or develop? Kretschmer obviously thought so, and so do many other authorities. The highly nervous person, for example, would be more prone to one kind of complaint than the overly emotional type, while the more stolid personality tends to attract a different kind of affliction.

Hippocrates classified what he described as 'the Four Humours', meaning temperaments. The sanguine, bilious or choleric, phlegmatic and melancholic. Since those times, astrologers have had a hey-day associating these with the elemental qualities of air, fire, water and earth respectively.

Earthy types, they tell us, dislike change and prefer not to have their cosy little mental worlds turned upside down by new ideas. According to Kretschmer, however, stable as such people may appear to the observer, like the biblical reed they are often unable to bend with the wind, and therefore when they are faced with situations which upset their ordered universe, they tend to react more strongly than, say, the more watery/emotional (cyclothymic) types, who make a great show about entering life's storms but are frequently to be found in some safe waterway at a later date, much to the surprise of those who had written them off as suitable cases for treatment. This quality is called 'resilience', and the more adaptable among us, therefore, stand the better chance of survival in an increasingly changing world. Outward stability can frequently be deceptive, and should be treated with the same suspicion as overt hystericism. Somewhere in the middle lies the balance. The same applies in those mystical pursuits that are believed by some to be so very therapeutic. There is an old, but true psychiatric saying – ecstasy and frenzy are but a hair's breadth apart!

A lot has been written recently concerning left-handed people. The left side of our bodies is controlled from the right side of our brain and vice versa, so it might seem logical to suppose that those who are left-handed work more closely with the right, or intuitive hemisphere of their brain. Studies of left-handed people have tended to show a high frequency of talent and intuition amongst them, but also a predisposition to certain illnesses. As some of the facts concerning these are still being debated, I shall refrain from including them, as science has a habit of reversing its conclusions in the light of further study, and until we have something in the way of a definite pronouncement, such information could prove misleading.

One final warning – parapsychologists working on research programmes that are designed to prove (or disprove?) the existence of paranormal phenomena have encountered what is termed the 'Experimenter Effect'. In simple language this means that whoever is conducting the experiment is in some way able to affect its outcome. Observers noticed that when a test was set up by an ardent disbeliever, the results achieved were abnormally low, whereas the accuracy of the performances of the subjects increased dramatically under the direction of a scientist or researcher who wanted to believe!

Exactly the same can apply where the psychologies are concerned. If your analyst is convinced that most of the world's major neuroses have sexual origins, he or she may well be able to convince you, the patient, that your libido is the cause of your problem. On the other hand, it could be your dreambody, your karma, your past lives, your emotions, your anima/animus, or your introvert/extrovert complex that is out of gear, depending on the personal leaning or inclination of the practitioner. I tend to believe that there is a right school of psychology (and a wrong one for that matter) for each of us, should the need arise. Finding our psychological niche is, to use a well-worn phrase, all part of the 'growth experience!'

Endnotes:

1. *The Alternative Health Guide*, B Inglis and R West, p. 163.
2. *Ibid.* p. 163.
3. *Ibid.* p. 337.

Chapter 12

HEALING IN THE PAST

As the history of healing would doubtless occupy many tomes, I can do little more than to effect a comparison between modern therapeutic methods and a few of those employed in some of the ancient civilisations of the past.

History is continually extending its frontiers even further back in time. Africa is now seen as the cradle of mankind rather than the Euphrates area so much favoured by the archaeologists of earlier times, but it is in Egypt that we make our first stop. According to Clement of Alexandria (AD 150) the healer priests or 'shrine bearers' learned their medical arts from six books which were among 42 works purportedly brought to Egypt by a different race of people before the Flood. Of the first 36 we need not concern ourselves, but those numbered 37 to 42 were titled as follows:

The Constitution of the Body
Diseases
Instruments
Drugs
Eyes
The Maladies of Women.[1]

Clement and other authorities of his time commented freely on Egyptian history and culture and made frequent mention of the fact that the names of the Gods of Healing – Thoth, Imhotep and, in Ptolemaic times, the Greek Asclepius, were assumed as titles by the medics of the time. Fragments from the writings of

other early scholars and historians also confirm the fact that the
Egyptian healer-priests believed their knowledge to have originated in some place other than their own country, having been
brought there just prior to the Deluge. It must be understood,
of course, that the ancient Egyptian civilisation spanned some
four thousand years, during which time medical practices no
doubt changed considerably. It is my own belief that much of
what has degenerated into so-called 'magic' is nothing more
than a folk memory of an advanced scientific knowledge that
became lost during one of those 'strange attractors' detailed
by the new Chaos Science, which now lend credence to the
'catastrophic change' that can alter the whole face of the
planet overnight. Perhaps we are are finally nearing the truth
regarding the Earth's early history which will, hopefully, help
us to rebalance both Gaia and ourselves. I shall be covering the
Chaos phenomenon as it relates to illness in Chapter 22.

It is possible to take any fragment or writing from the past and
interpret it to suit one's own pet theories, as may be evidenced in
the various versions of the Bible. It does strikes me as significant,
however, that the principal Egyptian God of Healing – Thoth, or
Tehuti to give him his correct name – was also associated with
time, karma and what are referred to in arcane writings as the
'Akashic Records'. These are said to refer to a point in timelessness (at which past, present and future converge) upon which is
imprinted every thought, action and experience undergone by
every single thing, at all levels throughout the infinite universe.
Other Egyptian healing deities include the Cat Goddess, Bast
who was patron of the mentally sick; in the light of what we
have already observed concerning the therapeutic attributes
of felines this is not hard to understand; Horus, son of Isis,
who according to the myth was born sickly but overcame his
disabilities, favoured the healing of young children and physical
wounds such as those inflicted in battle; Isis, Mistress of Magic,
was invoked for both her nurturing qualities and the healing
energies she bestowed during incubation therapy or narcosis,
while Anubis, Patron of Anaesthetics, was believed to watch
over the spirit (*ka* or *ba*) while it was away from its physical body
during surgery.

Archaeological discoveries from early Egyptian times have
yielded up plenty of evidence to suggest that the healers of
those early days knew what they were doing. Surgery was
practised with considerable skill and anaesthetics made from

the juices of plants were used to effect temporary oblivion and relieve pain.

Oriental medicine also goes back a very long way. Aside from acupuncture, which will be examined shortly, the Chinese have had a satisfactory system of medicine for centuries. In ancient China, however, one only paid one's physician when one was well. As soon as one became ill the payment ceased, this proving an incentive for the doctor in question to effect as speedy a recovery as he could! This practice, I am given to understand, survived until early this century. One wonders what might happen if people stopped paying their National Insurance contributions as soon as illness befell them! The Chinese shared the same concept of the 'subtle body' as the peoples of the Indian subcontinent. The two systems, along with the Aztec and Tibetan versions, are illustrated for comparison in Arnold Mindell's informative book *Dreambody*.

The Chinese goddess Kuan Yin was believed to be able to cure all illness. Usually portrayed seated on a lotus flower and holding a child, she is reminiscent of the Egyptian Isis with Horus, or Bast with her kittens. Every year long lines of pilgrims visit the Temple of Miao Feng Shan (the Mountain of the Wondrous Peak), situated about forty miles from Beijing (Peking). People with all kinds of sicknesses came to implore the goddess to heal them, the attendant rites and ceremonies being highly reminiscent of those at Lourdes. One cannot fail to note the similarity between these manifestations from the ancient world and Our Lady of Lourdes. Perhaps this particular archetype holds the key to the correction of many of our imbalances, and our own subconscious minds are trying to suggest that we redress the balance between anima and animus if we really want to alleviate the world's ills. Or maybe Bernadette's experience, and similar psychic manifestations, are nothing more or less than Gaia herself reminding us of her healing powers of which we were once instinctively aware, but which centuries of successful sacerdotal brainwashing have caused us to long since forget (see Chapter 20).

Records from ancient India, dating back thousands of years, mention plastic surgery, brain and caesarian section operations, herbal treatments for the rejuvenation of vitality, memory, teeth, eyesight, and many more. Should the lack of solid evidence cause the more sceptical among us to doubt some of these claims, it must be conceded that the memory came from somewhere in the misty past, which brings us back to our Chaos theory.

Ayurvedic medicine has dominated the Indian subcontinent for centuries and is still in popular demand today. Its healers often work side by side with doctors trained in Western medicine who frequently try to explain to them that some of its concoctions might even prove harmful! And yet these old remedies do appear to effect cures, probably in much the same way as placebos.

Some years ago I made the acquaintance of a Lithuanian doctor who had served with the Red Army during the war, and attended a talk he gave on the subject of placebos. During Russia's most difficult hours, he told his audience, just prior to the German retreat, there was a considerable shortage of drugs for the wounded and doctors were told to employ any method they could think of to alleviate the suffering of their patients. On one occasion an impressive looking vial was delivered which, the patients were told, contained a new 'miracle drug', guaranteed to cure all sorts of conditions. However, as there was very little of it available, the small supply in hand had been allocated to this particular hospital unit on account of the great bravery shown by the wounded comrades. It was duly administered by the doctor who related the story, and three other army surgeons, all of whom were fully aware that the contents were nothing more than sterilised water. Strange as it may seem, the recipients appeared to make miraculous recoveries!

The Indian knowledge of the body and mind, as exemplified in the disciplines of yoga and meditation, has proved invaluable to many people in both the East and the West. These practices are often recommended by doctors and specialists in Western hospital and clinics, their beneficial effects having been well noted and approved.

The Greek philosopher and physician Herophilos (*c* 300 BC) commented that 'Science and Art have equally nothing to show, that Strength is incapable of effort, Wealth useless, and Eloquence powerless if Health be wanting.'[2] A statement as valid tody as it was in his time. Unfortunately, the works of Herophilos are lost, the passage above being preserved for us by Sextus Empiricus, a third-century physician, in his attack on positive philosophy. Before Greek logic laid its disciplinary hand firmly on the shoulder of medicine, much of what was to be encountered in the Mesopotamian and surroundings areas was concerned with the theory that evil was the prior cause of all illness. Assyrian-Babylonian practices, for example, had much in common with primitive tribal healing. Having come the full circle, we are now beginning to realise that many witch-doctors, shamans and similar purveyors of paranormal skills were rather better at their jobs than we, or the Greeks for that matter, might give them credit for.

There is ample evidence that the Greeks, like the Egyptians and many other peoples of Mediterranean and Asiatic origin, inherited a whole system of medical or non-pharmaceutical medicine from a remote ancestry. Striking parallels can be drawn between these folk elements among the Greek and other medical systems, notably those of the early Romans, ancient Egyptians, Celts, Indian Vedas and Amerindians, all of which tend to lend credence to the 'single source' theory. The Greeks considered their approach eminently more practical, however, which ideal is to be found in the practice of medicine to this day.

The earliest Greek medical school is believed to have been that of Cnidus, a Lacedaemonian colony in ancient Doris. Scholars date it back to the seventh century BC. The physicians of Cos (or Kos), however, being their only contemporary critics whose writings have survived, considered that the Cnidian physicians paid far too much attention to the actual sensations of the patient and to the physical signs of the disease! The most important of the Cnidian doctrines were drawn up in a series of 'Sentences', called 'Aphorisms', which favoured treatment of the symptom or disease rather than the patient. There would seem to be little doubt that the Cnidian school drew upon Indian and Persian medicine.

The origin of the medical school at the neighbouring island of Cos was somewhat later than Cnidus, and probably dates from the sixth century BC. Fortunately, the Coan school has left us with a copious literary monument in the form of the *Corpus Hippocraticum*, which collection was probably effected in the early part of the third century BC by a commission of Alexandrian scholars at the order of Ptolemy-Soter (reigned 323–285 BC). The great Hippocratic work opens with the words:

It appears to me a most excellent thing for a physician to cultivate *pronoia*. Foreknowing and foretelling in the presence of the sick the past, and future [of their symptoms] and explaining all that the patients are neglecting, he would be believed to understand their condition so that men would have confidence to entrust themselves to his care.[3]

Galen made a point of explaining later that the word 'pronoia' should not be used in the philosophical sense, nor in the modern sense of prognosis, but rather to infer a knowing of things about the patient before he or she relates his or her symptoms. Observation based on training, one supposes.

Most famous of all the Greek physicians was undoubtedly Hippocrates, who was said to have been born in Cos in or before 460 BC. Learned in both medicine and philosophy, he travelled widely as a doctor and teacher and was consulted by King Perdiccas of Macedon and Artaxerxes of Persia. He is believed to have died at Larissa. Hippocrates rejected many of the superstitions with which the practice of medicine was riddled in his time in favour of inductive reasoning, the study of real medicine as subject to natural laws and individual treatment of people as patients by means of medicine and surgery. Of the roughly seventy works in the Hippocratic collection, many are not by Hippocrates, and there has even been doubt cast as to whether he actually authored the famous Oath. That he was the 'Father of Medicine', however, few – if any – will deny.

So while the more intuitive healing practices from ancient times could be said to equate with or refer to many modern fringe practices or alternative therapies, without doubt Hippocratic medicine, and that of other related Greek schools, has more in common with the orthodox medical profession of today.

Another significant contributor to early Greek medicine was undoubtedly Pythagoras of Samos (*c* 580–490 BC). For him the science of numbers was wholly important in all matters, medicine included. Unity, number 1, was the symbol of perfection and corresponded to the Creative Force, while the material universe was expressed by the number 2. The number 12 was also highly significant, being composed of 3 × 4 and representing the three worlds and four spheres. According to later Pythagoreans this gave rise to the four elements: air, fire, earth and water, a primary doctrine of the science of the time which was derived from ancient Egypt and survived for more than two millennia. The Pythagoreans also taught the existence of the *Anima Mundi*, or emanation of the soul of the universe which gave birth to the microcosm/macrocosm concept so beloved of the Platonic school, and later Neo-Platonic writers. The philosophy behind this school is, I believe, far more admirable and nearer to the spiritual ideal than that of Alcmaeon (c 500 BC) who initiated the medical practice of animal dissection (and, no doubt, vivisection!), in the aid of medical science. He is credited with the discovery of the optic nerves and Eustachian tubes, so one hopes, for the poor animal's sake, that he had a good supply of cadavers!

On the purely mystical side, the Greek divinities of healing were: Hermes, who represented practical or rational medicine; Apollo, master physician, and his fabled son Asclepius; Artemis, who favoured sick women and those in childbirth and who was also associated with mental illness; Athene, goddess of self-imposed discipline who was believed to teach the art of self-healing to those she favoured, heroes in particular; and Pan, who knew all about the healing properties of trees, flowers and shrubs. The Centaur Chiron was also a master healer, mythology informing us that he was actually instructed by Apollo himself in that art!

In stark contrast to Greek rationalism, let us now take a cursory glance at the healing methods employed by that branch of the Hebrew Essenes know as the Therapeuts, who, we are told, resided in Egypt. Legend has it that it was to the Master Physicians of this Order that the young Jeshua bar Josephus (Jesus) travelled for his healing tuition. The Order apparently earned its name, according to Philo Judaeus, philosopher and historian who died *circa* AD 50, because its healers:

> . . . profess an art of healing superior to that in use in cities (for that only heals bodies, whereas this, heals our souls as well) when laid hold of by difficult and scarce curable disease which pleasure and desire, grief and fear, selfishness and folly, and injustice, and the endless multitudes of passions and vices inflict upon them, or else because they have been schooled by nature and the sacred laws to serve.[4]

All this seems to have a rather modern ring about it!

Their studies comprised twelve stages in the hidden teachings and four in the community – novice, approacher, associate and elder. But only the higher grades were allowed to cast out evil spirits or handle those who were mentally ill. The Therapeuts employed mind-over-matter techniques rather than the rational medicine of the Greeks. They also had an extensive knowledge of herbs and understood the healing energies of the sun. Numerology and astrology were incorporated in their practices and Philo in his famous *De Vita Contemplativa* indicates that they possessed a comprehensive knowledge of the aura and etheric bodies, which they believed needed to be adjusted before a healing could be achieved at the physical level.

Once again we come across this strange claim that the knowledge they used had been handed down to them *since before the Flood!* They eschewed the eating of heavy meat, believing that it quickened the decaying process of the body. A light and healthy diet was therefore an essential prerequisite of good health. One interesting comment made by Philo caught my eye:

> Now they who betake themselves to the divine service do so not because of any custom, or on someone's advice or appeal, but carried away with heavenly love, like those initiated into the Bacchi or Corybantic Mysteries: they are set afire with God until they behold the object of their love.[5]

There is an interesting corollary here between the earlier mentioned close relationship between frenzy and ecstasy, the sublimatory inferences being unmistakable.

The Celtic Druids had their own particular healing skills which were mainly concerned with the therapeutic properties of trees and herbs, on which subject they were highly knowledgeable. The brews they concocted were believed to have a magical content, which fact was often commented upon by early historians. With the advent of Christianity many of their herbal skills in particular passed over to the monasteries, which frequently developed from what had originally been Druidic 'Cors' or Colleges of learning.

On the other side of the world the Polynesian Kahunas, those of the Huna faith who had attained to some degree of adeptship within that discipline, were credited with a full understanding of the natural laws of the universe. They believed that there existed in all things a life-force which could be contacted telepathically (shades of morphic resonance!), and conceived of man as consisting of a Higher, Middle and Lower Self. In truth, their philosophy and healing methods have much in common with certain branches of modern psychology and transpersonal psychology. Man, they believed, was a spiritual, intellectual and emotional being, and unless these three aspects of his nature were correctly balanced, he would become ill. Man's mind, they said, was largely responsible for any disorders from which he might suffer. Even accidents were simply the result of being in the wrong place at the wrong time (Psi-Mediated Instrumental Response?) and could only occur when the Higher Self was not in correct contact with its Middle and Lower aspects.

Huna is a profound and fascinating study and one which merits more mention than I am able to afford it in this chapter. I would rank it among the psychologies, rather than the instinctive or rational schools of healing. The ancient method the Kahunas employed for contacting the Higher Self, and thus effecting control of one's personal destiny, is known as the Ha Rite (see Chapter 22). For those who would like to try it for themselves, it is outlined in my book *The Psychology of Ritual*, while a more detailed explanation of the beliefs of the Kahunas of Hawaii is to be found in the writings of Max Freedom Long, Brad Steiger and Serge King.

Of course, there were many other forms of healing which were practised in those civilisations that rose and fell with such regularity throughout the pages of history. Some of the ancient methods, shamanic healing, for example, are still carried out in some countries to this day. Let us take the Eskimo shamanic healers. Called Angakoks, they work through a form of trance healing, with the guiding entity effecting the cure in much the same way that modern spiritualists hand over their consciousness to the persona of an American Indian medicine man, Chinese sage or Victorian surgeon. The only difference I can see lies in the fact that the Angakoks, being more aware of the other life-forms with which we share this planet, allow themselves to be entranced by the spirit of a bear, seal, dog, whale or *genius loci*. The results, however, are just the same!

Of the Dark Ages I have little to say although there were doubtless many good and sincere healers and medical practitioners who plied their trade in such times. The fire of truth which shrank to a lonely ember became rekindled by the controversial figure of Phillipus Aureolus Paracelsus. Born Theophrastus Bombast von Hohenheim (c 1493–1541), the famous Swiss physician improved pharmacy, encouraged a scientific approach and generally revolutionised European medicine. In spite of this apparent outburst of rationalism, Paracelsus was an intuitive mystic and a firm believer in astrology. His *Doctrine of Signatures* still stands well in the light of both modern science and fringe medicines such as homoeopathy and the Bach Flower Remedies.

Prince Charles devoted much of the content of his speech to the British Medical Association, on the occasion of its 150th anniversary in 1982, to the life and work of Paracelcus, including the statement:

> . . . we could do worse than to look again briefly at the principles he so desperately believed in, for they have a message for our time: a time in which science has tended to become estranged from nature, and that is the moment when we should remember Paracelsus.
>
> Above all he maintained that there were four pillars on which the whole art of healing rested. The first was philosophy; the second astronomy (or what we might call psychology); the third alchemy (or bio-chemistry) and the fourth virtue (in other words the professional skill of a doctor).[6]

After attending a series of lectures on the history of medicine and learning of the appalling suffering meted out to the sick through ignorance and superstition, I confess to feeling a sense of relief at being privileged to see what is perhaps the commencement of the courtship of reason and intuition. May they continue to grow in understanding of one another, for I sadly fear that if they do not, our planet and its denizens are in for a rocky future.

Endnotes:

1. *Thrice Greatest Hermes*, G R S Mead, p. 225.
2. *The Legacy of Greece*, C Singer, p. 201.
3. *Ibid.* p. 207.
4. *Fragments of a Faith Forgotten*, G R S Mead, pp. 66–67.
5. *Ibid.* p. 67.
6. *The Times*, 16 December 1982.

Part 2

ALTERNATIVE THERAPIES, COMPLEMENTARY MEDICINE, AND THE HEALING VOCATION

Chapter 13

THE MANIPULATIVE THERAPIES

OSTEOPATHY

Osteopathy was founded by Andrew Still (1828–1912), a practising doctor who worked on the Union side in the American Civil War, but eventually became disillusioned with the orthodox medical principles and methods of the time. Years of experience seemed to suggest to him that good health was dependent upon the integrity of the spinal column to the extent that vertebrae out of position could result in illness. Animals realise this instinctively, which is why, after a period of rest, they stretch themselves until the backbone is concave, while at the same time yawning and establishing that all the muscles are in working order. Children and many adults adopt a similar procedure instinctively, especially if postures assumed at work or play have necessitated their being hunched up or in some unnatural position.

In normal medical practice, doctors often advise their patients to take certain precautions against backache, such as keeping the spine erect or walking upright, while traction therapy is used for the relief of spinal discomforts in the physiotherapy departments of most hospitals. To that extent, the medical profession were prepared to go along with Still's views. But he also argued that the spinal cord regulates what is happening throughout the body via its link-up with the nervous system, and even claimed that the condition of the spine could affect the blood. Skin disorders, stomach aches, headaches and other such disturbances were, Still opined, due to spinal vertebrae being slightly out of position. The answer was therefore to be found in finding the errant spot in the vertebrae, effecting the correction, and then allowing the body's self-regulating system to put things right.

Needless to say, the orthodox medical profession found this a rather difficult pill to swallow and Still's osteopathic concept became relegated to the ranks of unorthodox and highly suspect practices. Although time has proved that many people can be helped by osteopathy, it is only in recent years that it has gained the respectability that Still would have wished for. One has to admit, however, to this day there are bastions of orthodoxy which see fit to frown upon it.

Central to osteopathy is the concept of 'lesions'. These lesions, which do not appear to coincide with the normal medical understanding of the word, are of two kinds. A pamphlet, *Osteopathy: An Explanation*, published by the British Society of Osteopaths, claims that it has 'contributed to medicine an understanding of an important – but not generally recognised type of lesion'. There are two kinds of lesions and when one occurs in the spine 'it represents an imbalance of normal tensions to the extent that the information reaching the spinal cord from the deep muscles of the spine become confused and contradictory',[1] perhaps because they have become unduly stretched, or are in spasm. This tension or 'irritability' can, we are told, affect the circulation to all those organs whose nerve supplies originate in the relative segments of the spinal cord. The term used is 'segmental dysfunctions', which encompasses the whole structure associated with joints: nerves, muscles, ligaments and, of course, the bones themselves.

The term 'lesion' does not necessarily imply an actual vertebral displacement, which has given rise to the medical establishment's condemnation of the whole concept as a myth. However, it is the idea that osteopathic manipulation can be used to treat a whole range of symptoms that constitutes the Establishment's real objection to the system.

In the United States, osteopaths have finally managed to establish themselves as doctors in their own right, and have even received recognition as such from the medical profession.

In Britain they are not yet formally recognised, although some qualified doctors have taken courses in osteopathy and practise it side by side with their normal duties. The qualification, DO (Doctor of Osteopathy) does not, however, imply full medical training and anyone who would like to receive osteopathic treatment, but would prefer to be in more orthodox hands, should look for an MB, or MD after the practitioner's name. This is in no way meant to imply that those who practise osteopathy exclusively are less adept at their work. In fact, the contrary could apply as skills are always improved with correct and constant use and for the majority of DOs it is the one and only service they offer. However, it is becoming increasingly popular for alternative practitioners to employ several methods of treatment. An osteopath I know well is also a fully qualified naturopath and homoeopath.

Modus Operandi

An osteopath does not rely on your version of the symptoms to draw his conclusions. He will watch the way you walk into the consulting room, how you hold your body, how you sit, and your general stance. How you express yourself will also be regarded as significant, as osteopaths, like many other holistic healers, readily admit the connection between the stress factor, the mind, and the unconscious outward expression of inner tensions.

An examination of the spine will obviously take place, by which time the practitioner will have decided on the course of treatment. If, for example, no more than a minor misplacement or 'ricking' is involved, this can be corrected by a simple twist. On the other hand, the problem may be a long-standing one which will need to be approached carefully and over an extended period. The high-velocity thrusts employed in osteopathy tend to frighten some people, and although they cause only the minimum of pain, if any, those of a nervous disposition might well be advised to combine the treatment with some psychological therapy. As pain has the tendency to 'habituate' itself to certain actions, a patient may expect to feel something if his or her bones are suddenly 'clicked', which is likely to precipitate a somatically unrelated, but nevertheless real, temporary discomfort.

Psychological Suitability Assessment

One must obviously assume that anyone visiting an osteopath is requiring help with the skeletal system in general, rather than the back exclusively, in which case osteopathy is ideal for the practical, but open-minded, person who likes to see something actually being done and is not of too nervous a disposition. I know of one older lady, for example, who wanted very much to visit an osteopath for many years, and would, in fact, have benefited considerably from the therapy, but was so frightened of the manipulative techniques that she backed out of three different appointments and finally gave up. Cases such as this are best treated by cranial osteopathy, which would better suit those very sensitive people for whom the high-velocity thrusts could prove too disorientating both physically and mentally. Which brings us to our next subject.

CRANIAL OSTEOPATHY

With cranial osteopathy, the 'osteopathic lesions' are traced through the skull and pelvic area. Few cranial osteopaths practise this method alone, as they have usually undergone the normal course of osteopathic training before undertaking the additional studies required for cranial specialisation. In the case of cranial osteopathy, the title can be misleading as it bears little resemblance to the type of manipulative therapy usually associated with osteopathic practice. Cranial osteopathy aims to treat not only the head, but the body as a whole by using the rhythmical pulse of the cerebro-spinal fluid as an aid to diagnosis and treatment.

Modus Operandi

I am indebted to Elaine Sturgess, DO, MRO, who specialises in cranial osteopathy, for the following description which says it all:

> Cranial Osteopathy involves the perception of the *Cranial Rhythmic Impulse* (CRI). This rhythm persists throughout life and involves the circulation of the *Cerebral Spinal Fluid* (CSF) within the brain *Central Nervous System* (CNS). The brain and the spinal cord are supported in a fluid filled sack called the dural

membranes or *meninges*. These membranes attach to the inside of the skull, to the vertebrae of the upper neck and then only again at the sacrum, situate in the middle of the pelvis. Hence the name *Cranio-Sacral Therapy* or, as we refer to it here, Cranial Osteopathy, for short.

A practitioner will usually begin a treatment by placing their hands lightly on the patient's head or under the sacrum, where the rhythm can be felt strongly, although with training it can be felt anywhere on the body. It is characterised by an expansion phase and a contraction phase in all the tissues of the body, as in respiration, but at a different rate – about twelve cycles per minute in a healthy individual. Contrary to popular belief, the skull is not solid, but consists of many bones hinged together which move subtly with these phases (called flexion and extension). This rhythm has a pumping effect on the CSF which contributes to its circulation within the brain and CNS. This movement is essential for healthy neuro-physiological functioning, as well as for the release and circulation of hormones from the body's master glands – the pituitary and hypothalamus – which govern directly and indirectly most physiological activities in the body. As you can imagine, Cranial Osteopathy can have a profound impact on one's health, effective in treating endocrine, autonomic, circulatory and metabolic disorder.

The practitioner first feels for the CRI, and often finds it to be low in amplitude or functioning eccentrically. There can be many reasons for this, starting from birth; for example, birth trauma, car accidents, blows to the head or falls onto the coccyx, and some dentistry. By locking some of the cranial bones which are functionally designed for movement, they can all have a brake-like effect on the cranial rhythm.

Aliments such as flu, glandular fever, meningitis and shock – both physical (such as whiplash) or psychological – can all have an effect on the natural elasticity or the dural membranes, the former making them sluggish and the latter, tightening them unduly.

Behavioural disturbances in children, such as autism, head-banging, hyperactivity, colic or epilepsy, are treatable conditions; as in later years are depression, anxiety, insomnia, headaches, eye, ear, nose and throat problems, tinnitus (sometimes) and asthma.

The cranial practitioner has a wealth of techniques to release restrictions, whether boney or membraneous, and to enhance the rhythm if it is low or slow. It is an excellent tool for stimulating general vitality and can be profoundly relaxing; patients sometimes fall asleep. The treatment itself is extremely subtle and the effect is not always immediate; patients sometimes find it hard to believe that anything has been done to them. I find it is like being treated from the inside out, unlike classical Osteopathy and Massage which treats from the outside in.

Cranial Osteopathy is an holistic science and art – knowledge of anatomy and physiology is given utmost importance during training. However, development of intuitive faculties is equally important, in order to sense areas of disturbance in the body–mind; releasing them is a way to enhance overall functioning.

Andrew Taylor Still, the founder of classical Osteopathy, before Cranial Osteopathy as known, wrote:

> The cerebral spinal fluid is the highest known element in the human body and unless the brain furnishes this fluid in abundance a disabled condition of the body will remain. He who is able to reason will see that this great river of life must be tapped and the withering fields irrigated at once or the harvest of health is forever lost.

The father of Cranial Osteopathy is William Garner Sutherland (1873–1954), who was a student of Still's. One day as a student

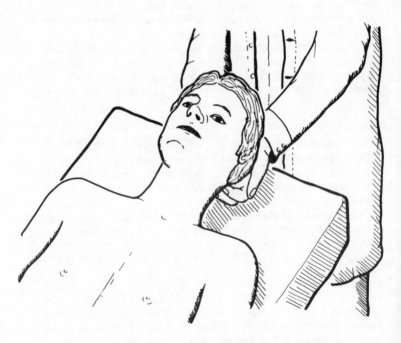

RELEASE OF CRANIAL BASE

he was comtemplating the bones of the skull when the thought struck him: 'Bevelled like the gills of a fish indicating a mechanism for respiration.' He spent the next thirty years of his life exploring and developing this concept. Like most geniuses, the value of his work was not appreciated or given credence until well after his death.

Psychological Suitability Assessment

This would seem to be an ideal therapy for those who do not wish to expose their inner feelings, but at the same time are in need of some adjustment that does not place too much strain on the autonomic nervous system. In fact, the lady I mentioned earlier who was apprehensive about the normal osteopathic treatment, eventually found a cranial osteopath and has been highly pleased with the results.

CHIROPRACTIC

Chiropractic has been defined by the British Chiropractor's Association as 'an independent branch of medicine which specializes in the diagnosis and treatment of mechanical disorders of the joints, particularly those of the spine, and their effects on the nervous system'. The term 'chiropractic', which is taken from the Greek and means 'manual practice' or 'treatment by manipulation', is believed to have originated with Hippocrates.

Founded by David Daniel Palmer (1845–1913) in 1895, chiropractic shares certain common ground with osteopathy. Both achieve the same end, but approach it from different ways. The chiropractor talks in terms of restoring normal alignment of the spine by adjusting the vertebrae. This he achieves by short, sharp blows. The osteopath talks of restoring normal motility (movement) to a joint. He does this by initially effecting repetitive movements to loosen the soft tissue around the fixed vertebrae and only later specifically manipulating the joint concerned. However, in the process the chiropractor also restores normal motility and the osteopath restores normal alignment.

Differences would appear to be mainly historical. The early osteopaths believed that their treatment became effective via the blood circulation, whereas chiropractors tended to emphasise the role of the nervous system. Chiropractors use X-rays far more frequently than osteopaths, however, and are more likely to subject their patients to orthopaedic tests and neurological or physical examinations. While osteopaths tend to use greater leverage in their treatment, chiropractors employ less leverage and more direct technique. In osteopathic leverage techniques, contact is frequently made some distance from the joint being manipulated. Chiropractic techniques, on the other hand, usually adjust a joint in a specific direction, the idea being to free it in that direction; osteopaths are less concerned with the direction of their manipulations.

Slight displacements of the spinal vertebrae were latterly called 'subfluxations' by Palmer's disciples. These might be reflected in many symptoms besides backache, ranging from indigestion to psoriasis. Unlike orthodox medicine, chiropractic does not aim to concentrate on the symptoms, but to identify the subfluxation and correct it manually, which would, in turn, result in a disappearance of the symptom. Although in theory chiropractors still owe allegiance to the original principle, many have, in fact, moved away from it. Chiropractic has therefore tended to branch off in several directions which vary according to the countries concerned. In the United States chiropractors have been taking over primary care in those parts of the country where general medical practitioners are scarce, which has resulted in their placing less reliance upon manipulation. In Britain, where there are fewer chiropractors in proportion to the population, and there is easier access to GPs, chiropractors have tended to remain in the area of specialisation. A survey showed, however, that many people who were reluctant to take drugs for the relief of pain resulting from skeletal problems had recourse to chiropractors or osteopaths without informing their doctors, as they no doubt anticipated their disapproval.

Modus Operandi

The diagnostic procedures in chiropractic involve taking a full case history, physical examination, X-rays, and in some cases blood and urine specimens, which are submitted for laboratory analysis before manipulatory treatment is effected. Some chiropractors advise patients to become active in relaxation classes or self-help systems, so that the work that they have begun can be carried on in some other way by the patients themselves.

Chiropractors frequently meet with the same criticism as osteopaths – that as as result of missing some simple diagnosis and proceeding with manipulation they may do harm rather than good, as in the case of a bone tumour. The use of X-rays by chiropractors lessens the likelihood of this happening, however, while a large number of GPs, in this country anyway, are happy to co-operate with specialists in the field of manipulative therapy and will make their records available to them. In fact if more people were honest and open with their GPs about consulting alternative practitioners many problems could be avoided.

Psychological Suitability Assessment

As with osteopathy, this is an ideal system for those who like to see and feel some evidence of the treatment they are receiving. The added support of X-rays and other tests is also reassuring, and tends to strengthen the patient's belief that he or she is receiving the best of both worlds. And if a GP has effected the recommendation, or is at least aware of the treatment, then so much the better.

THE ALEXANDER TECHNIQUE

Again we are dealing with a system which aims to treat and prevent a range of disorders by a system of postural changes. Australian F Matthias Alexander (1869–1955), who had enjoyed a successful career as an actor and reciter, started to lose his voice during performance for no apparent reason. Being of a practical mind, Alexander decided to find out exactly what was causing the problem, during which investigations he discovered the source and much, much more. The immediate cause of his vocal problems was the fact that he was pulling his head backwards and downwards during performance, and it was this, plus his other findings, which gave birth to the Alexander Technique.

Alexander agreed with Still and Palmer (the founders of

osteopathy and chiropractic respectively) regarding the importance of the integrity of the spinal column but with two fundamental differences. Vertebrae being out of alignment was caused by general misuse; bad habits during walking, sitting or talking, for example. When we adopt postures for which our bodies are not designed we subject them to unnatural strains. In fact, our postures result from rituals of habit in our daily lives. The other point which Alexander made was that where our bodies were concerned, 'our manner of use is a constant influence for good or ill upon our *general* functioning,'[2] and it would seem that he was not thinking exclusively in physiological terms. Mind and body were, to him, interrelated.

Alexander's basic message was to stop doing what comes naturally, as this is often the result of years of bad habits. Like negative thought patterns, destructive habits need to be deliberately broken and programmed out to make place for new, and more constructive attitudes, both physical and mental.

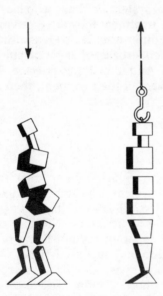

ALEXANDER POSTURE

Spinal energy should flow upwards – thus all movement comes from the head. The correct alignment of the spine is that of a gently curved vertical which is pulled into place by an imaginary hook.

Modus Operandi

There is no set method in the Alexander Technique, as necessities differ with each individual and it will be up to the therapist to ascertain these and render treatment accordingly. Therefore, there are no instruction manuals and no indication to patients as to what the treatment might consist of. This is one therapy which I have undergone personally. In fact, it was arranged for pupils at the Royal College of Music during my year's attendance there. I recall my therapist telling me how to adjust my neck, head and spine by a process of lifting and stretching, the practice of which also demanded a degree of mental visualisation in order to render it fully effective. The student was also encouraged to practise this alone, so that having once mastered the technique it could be applied in times ahead when a therapist might not be readily available for consultation.

Among many of Alexander's devotees, such names as Sir Stafford Cripps and Aldous Huxley make their appearance, while Noble Prize winner Nikolaas Tinbergen actually devoted his speech on the occasion of his award to a eulogy of the technique's many blessings and advantages, saying, among other things, that it 'made other forms of physiotherapy look crude in comparison'.[3]

Psychological Suitability Assessment

From my own experience I would suggest that this is a discipline best suited to the thinker or intellectual, rather than someone who is simply looking for a period of relaxation, enjoyment, and a chance for someone else to do the work for them. The Alexander Technique most certainly works, but it does require the participation of the patient to a greater extent, perhaps, than some of the other manipulative therapies, which suggest that there is a strong element of self-help involved.

REFLEXOLOGY

Not to be confused with metamorphic technique (which we will be examining in Chapter 19, and which also deals with feet) reflexology is sometimes referred to as 'zone therapy'. In the 1920s, Dr W Fitzgerald discovered that the body was divided into zones of energy which can be tapped to advantage via the feet for both the prevention and treatment of certain disorders. It is from the development and subsequent practice of this study that what we now call reflexology has arisen.

The reflexologist acknowledges ten channels which begin or end in the toes and extend to the tips of the fingers and top of the head. Each channel relates to a zone of the body and the organs in that zone; for example, the big toe relates to the head. By feeling a patient's feet in a certain way, reflexologists are able to detect which channels are blocked and, therefore, which organs or related parts of the anatomy might not be functioning correctly. By applying massage to the appropriate terminal, using a range of movements, they are able to restore the energy to its correct flow and thus adjust the related imbalance. Reflexologists and zone therapists claim that all the organs of the body are mirrored in the feet, and their method is a painless and drugless way of putting a lot of things right.

Reflexology is a very ancient therapeutic art. It was in use in ancient China as long as five thousand years ago, while one of the only pictures from the early Egyptian era depicts the practice of reflexology. This was found in the tomb of Ankhmahar at Saqqara – the Physician's Tomb – and dates as far back as the early sixth dynasty, around 2300 BC. An inscription above the figures reads: 'Don't hurt me, I shall act in a such a way as to obtain your favour.'[4] It was popularised in the United States in 1932 with the publication of a book entitled *Stories Feet Can Tell*, by Eunice D Ingham (the wife of Fred Stopfel), but it is only comparatively recently that it has become more generally known and accepted.

Modus Operandi

Although the reflexologist may commence with the customary case history, he or she may not need to know your problems in advance, as these will be ascertained during the treatment. Whether the patient is seated or required to lie down will be a matter of preference on the part of the practitioner.

The terminals of the energy channels in each foot will then be explored and analysed. This may consist of applying pressure at certain points, rotating the toes, moving the foot up and down,

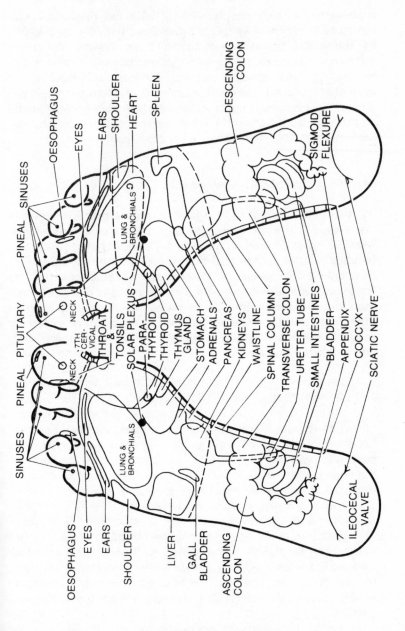

REFLEXOLOGY CHART

rubbing the skin or simply sensing with the fingertips. Any blocks of energy will be located and dealt with where possible by specialised massage techniques. These energy blocks are referred to in terms of crystalline deposits which need to be broken up or dissolved so that they are easily absorbed via the normal eliminatory channels. The type of massage employed will vary with the nature of the blockage; it may be very gentle and pleasurable, but on the other hand it can be, like shiatsu, quite painful, especially if one's feet are sensitive.

Psychology Suitability Assessment

As this would appear to be a fairly harmless practice, whether one chooses to avail oneself of the services of a reflexologist would seem to depend on how one feels about having one's feet handled. I have no personal experience of it myself, although I have talked with several people who claim that it does wonders for them. One rather suspects that the mind is more involved than the therapist might be prepared to concede as there is little doubt that for some people foot massage can be extremely relaxing. But then again if mind and body are so closely tied, why not reflexology?

APPLIED KINESIOLOGY – TOUCH FOR HEALTH

Our final therapies for consideration under the 'manipulative' heading are concerned with touch. Not those manipulative or postural practices which aim for specific physical effects, but the use of the hands for the transmission or arousing of the healing forces within. There are many treatments which one could classify as 'touch' therapies, of which Applied Kinesiology is probably one of the best-known. It is based on special muscle-testing techniques through which weaknesses are identified and treated, so that a corresponding rebalancing is effected in the body's energy systems. As such, it has points in common with chiropractic and massage, while it shares the energy-flow concept with acupuncture and shiatsu.

Touch for Health practitioners aim to teach the skills of the professional kinesiologist to those members of the lay public who are interested in preventive health care, which is a good thing in that it involves members of the community in the problems and sufferings of others.

All those healing methods which utilise the sense of touch – acupuncture, acupressure, the laying on of hands – could be classified as kinesiotherapies. Applied Kinesiology, however, really refers to those methods introduced by Dr George Goodheart, a chiropractor from Detroit, Michigan whom, we are told, 'stumbled across them by accident'. Goodheart, in turn, passed his findings to other chiropractors, one of whom taught Brian Butler who introduced Touch for Health into Britain.

It was generally believed that the main muscular troublemakers in backache and associated disorders were muscles which were either in spasm or too taut. Goodheart surmised, however, that it might be the weak muscles on the opposite side of the body which gave rise to tightness in the normal muscles. Effecting a combination of Eastern ideas of energy flows with his own chiropractic experience and some of the other ideas he had encountered among alternative therapies, Goodheart developed his new system: 'This involves using muscle testing to determine the need for and effectiveness of treatment, and applying various techniques of kinesiology – the science of muscle activation – to restore muscle balance which is essential to good posture.'[5]

Modus Operandi

The systems of Applied Kinesiology and Touch for Health are both concerned with the tactile search for muscle imbalance. Clues, which will be sought in the case history, often relate to muscle weakness, pains in the head and neck being prime examples. The overall aim is to restore balance to the body rather than concentrate on weaknesses in specific regions. Distortions need to be recognised before they can be reversed, so the kinesiologist's initial task will be to systematically set about locating the problem areas. As methods may vary considerably, patients should bear this in mind should they choose to compare notes. Muscle tests are normally carried out in the prone position, the therapist working first one side of the body and then the other to detect subtle differences. Imbalances are corrected as they are located, with the use of touch or pressure at the appropriate points.

Psychological Suitability Assessment

Kinesiologists claim that they do not rely on a clinical knowledge of symptoms, but prefer to glean the information they need from the body of the patient. Allergy cases appear to feature most prominently among their successes, food allergies in particular responding to this specific form of detection and correction. Introverted people, those who have difficulty expressing emotion, and older children might respond to their treatment. Self-help can also be obtained through these methods, but my advice would be to ensure that the teacher is either qualified himself, or is able to provide some evidence of his training under a professional.

Summary

The physically manipulative therapies all have one thing in common: their treatment is readily seen and felt by their patients, so there is never any question as to whether or not something has been done for them. Many people find this highly reassuring and tend to fight shy of those therapies which rely more on visualisation or creative imagination. There is also a type of person who always likes things to 'appear to be done' even if, in fact, little is actually being achieved. This does not really matter in the long run, as the treatment of their choice probably serves as a placebo which, in turn, generates the natural healing powers in their own psyche. Such persons will tend always to come out right, simply because they have programmed themselves into believing the infallibility of their own opinions or assessments. My advice to anyone who hears about an alternative therapy from a relative or friend who swears by its efficacy is to bear in mind what I have just said, as it may well be the will-power of that person, rather than the therapy, that has made it work for them. Read through the contents of this book, and any of several other, perhaps more comprehensive publications on the market at present, and make up your own mind.

A word on 'touch complexes', which must obviously be considered in relation to the therapies discussed above. These come in two main forms, the 'touch me not' neurosis, and those who suffer from a compulsion to touch anything and everything. While the former will naturally eschew any form of therapy which involves the tactile sense, the latter could possibly be helped by Applied Kinesiology and Touch for Health in particular, as the excessive use of the tactile sense surely represents a cry for help in that direction. People who have a dread of touch are usually wrestling with some deep-seated emotional problem which probably originated in a severe childhood trauma. There are several therapies which can help in such cases, and these will be dealt with in a later chapter.

Should you, the reader, be sufficiently open-minded to seek the good offices of an alternative therapist, but at the same time like to see something for your money, I am sure that among the excellent therapies I have just enumerated, you will find one that is just right for you.

Endnotes:

1. *The Alternative Health Guide*, B Inglis and R West, p. 81.
2. *Ibid*. p. 105.
3. *Ibid*. p. 108.
4. *Ibid*. p. 112.
5. *Ibid*. p. 116.

Chapter 14

NATURAL THERAPIES

NATUROPATHY

Naturopathy proposes three main principles. The first of these, which is fundamental to the naturopathic concept, is that all forms of diseases are due to the same cause: namely, the build-up in the system of waste materials and body refuse which has been steadily accumulating during years of wrong living habits. On this premise, naturopaths argue that the only way in which disease can be cured is by employing methods which enable the system to discharge this toxic stockpile which is daily adding to the clogging of our physical bodies.

The second suggests that as the body continually strives for the success of the individual, it follows that the symptoms of all acute disease are simply attempts on the part of the body to eject the accumulations of waste material, some of which are hereditary, that are preventing it from functioning to its full potential. In striving to suppress such symptoms, orthodox treatment is simply pushing them to one side which means that they will be likely to return another day when our resistance is low.

Principle three submits that the body has its own power to effect the return to the correctly balanced condition that we refer to as good health, provided the right methods are employed to enable it to do so.

These principles were originally defined by Harry Benjamin

in *Everybody's Guide to Nature Cure*, which was published in 1936. Since then, however, although these basic premises are still accepted, some naturopaths opine that the accumulation of waste material may itself by symptomatic of other, more complex disorders which could have psychological rather than physical origins. Opinions also differ as to the best methods for restoring the body's own recuperative powers. Benjamin proposed five of these: fasting, dieting, hydrotherapy, general body-building and hygienic measures and psychotherapy.

Questions which call for answers as far as these propositions are concerned include:

1. During a fast, is any food at all permitted?
2. What is the required length of a fast?
3. If nourishment is permitted, what would this constitute?

Individual naturopaths appear to have their own views regarding diet and subsidiary aids to health. Hydrotherapy, for example, is recommended by some and not by others, while there are a bewildering number of body-building and hygienic measures. As for psychotherapy, as this covers such a wide field, its application would naturally be decided by the practitioner's assessment of the patient's psychological needs.

Modus Operandi

The common term for naturopathy is 'nature cure'. One may consult a naturopath by appointment and receive a dietary prescription or some other recommended treatment, or one may spend some time at naturopathic clinic, more popularly known as a health farm.

As in the case of all therapeutic practices, the initial visit always commences with a consideration of the patient's case history, which is carried out in much the same way as it is in general medical practice. The naturopath pays more attention to the appearance, breathing, skin colour and other tell-tale signs which might indicate a clogging of the system, however.

Diet will be one of the first considerations in any naturopathic treatment. The requirement may simply consist of an adjustment in eating habits, but an actual period of fasting may prove necessary. Fasting is one of the oldest natural therapies known to man. An animal will always stop eating when it is unwell, during which period it will lie quietly, preferably alone, and just drink sufficient fluid to prevent dehydration. Primitive peoples, who were governed by instinct rather than reason, reacted to illness in exactly the same way. Complete starvation, which means no intake of any kind, may be recommended in some cases, but it is more usual that the bodily functions, although slowed down to enable them to rest, are kept slowly ticking over by the intake of a little fruit or vegetable juice.

Fasting can produce some rather unpleasant side-effects, however. Initial reactions include halitosis, diarrhoea, vomiting and headache, which are seen as the body's way of ejecting toxins. Although these may give concern to some people, they are, in fact, indicators that the treatment is working. Within a day or so they disappear, as do the pangs of hunger initially felt by those people who are accustomed to eating large meals. The appetite will then adjust to the natural needs of the body rather than to what it has been conditioned to accept as necessary to its daily needs. People who suffer from certain conditions, kidney trouble, for example, are advised not to undertake long or extensive periods of fasting, and one's GP should always be consulted if one is in the slightest doubt.

Naturopaths are quick to point out that the fast should not be seen only in terms of physical clean-out, as there should also be an accompanying mental reaction. Attitudes towards the unnecessary intake of alcohol, nicotine, coffee, and other substances harmful to the system, should also be reviewed and mental adjustments effected.

After the initial treatment is concluded it is very much up to the patient as to which regime of health is adopted. In other words, we become answerable for our own bodies and should accept that responsibility in a sensible and balanced way. Some naturopaths may recommend veganism, others lacto-vegetarianism, while there are those who see no harm in the consumption of a little meat and wine as long as these are taken in moderation. All advocate a balanced diet, however, and lots of fresh air and sensible exercise.

The Friends of the Healing Research Trust recommend a 60/20/20 diet – 60 per cent raw foods, 20 per cent carbohydrates and 20 per cent protein, to be taken by the individual in whichever way he or she finds the easiest.[1] Items to be avoided include refined carbohydrates (white sugar, white bread, cakes, sweets, etc.), tea, coffee, alcohol, milk in quantity, condiments, fatty and salted meats, and tinned and packaged foods containing preservatives. Alternatives consist of wholemeal flour, herb teas, yoghurt, lean meat, fish, chicken and so on. Diets as such will receive special attention later in this chapter.

It is interesting to note that certain herb teas have recently come under fire as containing substances which do not suit everyone. Further research is being undertaken, and until this has been completed there can be no specific recommendations either way.

Naturopaths are paying increasing attention to the psychological aspects of their therapies, although it is only fair to say that they have never really ignored these in the past. Mind and body interact so closely that if the body exhibits even the slightest symptoms of illness the fear engendered in the mind can cause those symptoms to become magnified to the extent that they assume a new reality. Although naturopathy may alleviate many of those distressing symptoms that cause us unnecessary concern, it also acknowledges that the contingencies of modern life are hardly conducive to a balanced state of health. Aside from the usual crop of anxieties that can be caused by such things as redundancy, financial or business pressures and emotional conflicts, there are also those socially imposed rules which require men in particular to eat or drink to excess in order to be accepted as one of the boys. Many women I know are confirmed vegetarians, whereas their husbands continue to eat meat. It is interesting to note that when questioned regarding this difference of diets within one family the answer is usually the same: 'I've eaten this way all my life and I can't stop now!' (Not strong-minded enough to break earlier programming.) Or, 'If I went vegetarian all the chaps would send me up and say I was a sissy!' (the safety of the 'collective').

Peer power always constitutes a danger for all age-groups, but the young in particular are usually more subject to it. The initiatory processes of student frolics, for example, which require the imbibing of abnormally large quantities of alcohol, can be harmless enough in most instances, but some have resulted in cases of permanent kidney damage and even death.

The health farm has become increasingly popular these days, often for slimming purposes, rather than from a concern for health. A lady journalist I know has a regular binge every Christmas which results in her putting on several pounds in

weight. In January she retires to a health farm and loses it all
– which somehow strikes me as being a socially accepted form
of bulimia nervosa!

People who visit health farms, ostensibly for health or slimming purposes, and then appear to gain some childish delight in
escaping after dark for a heavy meal and plenty to drink, strike
me as being either very rich or very stupid, as it is their bodies
that will suffer in the long run. Most of us, however, cannot
afford the luxury of a stay at a health farm, and it frequently
strikes me as sad that those very people who might genuinely
benefit from it, and who would be prepared to respect the discipline that goes with it, will never be able to avail themselves of
such naturopathic facilities.

There is something I have been meaning to say concerning
alternative therapies, and now seems as good a time as any to
say it. Many of the treatments I have enumerated could alleviate
much suffering and unhappiness, but the sad truth is that not
everyone can afford them. Some poor souls are hard-pressed
to pay for their National Health Service prescriptions, let alone
find £20 or more a session for the services of an alternative
therapist, no matter how effective that treatment is proven to
be. Perhaps the future might provide us with an answer and if
so, let us pray that it be a kindly one.

Psychological Suitability Assessment

A good 'clean out' never really goes amiss, provided the precautions given above are observed and one consults one's own
GP to make sure that there are no inherent dangers in either
rigorous dieting or fasting. Allergies should also be allowed for
as some people are allergic to certain fruits and vegetables,
while coeliacs cannot digest any food containing gluten. No
doubt these things are all taken into consideration during the initial consultation, although I did read of a case where a chronic
condition hitherto unrecognised medically came to light during
nature cure. Psychologically, however, it should be borne in
mind that many bodily ills stem from mental attitudes, so if the
beneficial effects of your nature cure treatment are short-lived,
and you have carefully observed the advice given, you may well
need to look to the psychologies for further help to uncover the
cause.

HYDROTHERAPY

Hydrotherapy can be obtained at health hydros, spas and those therapeutic establishments which provide thalassotherapy (sea-water therapy), sauna baths or Turkish baths.

'Taking the waters' had been recommended by physicians as a method of promoting good health for centuries. It was a recognised form of medical treatment in the times of Rome and classical Greece, when pure mountain water would be channelled into the towns via aqueducts for the purpose of drinking or bathing. Local springs and watering places were credited with health-giving properties, the *genius loci* being designated a god or godling of healing. Pliny insisted that the luxury of a steam bath helped rheumatics, whereas Horace opined that it was purely a luxurious indulgence. Hydrotherapy enjoys popularity in our present times, with hot tubs, jacuzzis, whirlpool baths and similar spin-offs from the technological age appearing side by side with the older forms of treatment.

Modus Operandi

Waters may be taken internally or externally, or the same water may be recommended for both purposes on account of its purity on the one hand, or health-giving minerals on the other. Certain spa waters are known to contain minerals such as sodium, calcium, zinc and many more which can help to compensate for body deficiencies. Inglis and West tell us:- 'Water can be used as a stimulant or as a relaxant, as a medium in which to exercise or one in which to rest. It can be drunk for pleasure or as a palatable medicine ('. . . the Bath waters', Charles Dickens' Sam Weller remarked, 'had a very strong flavour of warm flatirons').

Water has other therapeutic uses including hot and cold footbaths, compresses, fomentations, hip or sitz baths, steam inhalations, and many more. Sauna and Turkish baths afford both physical and mental relief to many people in that they encourage relaxation and ease muscular pain. Thalassotherapy, which derives from the Greek word *thalassa* – sea, has been revived of late in a much more sophisticated form than that used by our Victorian forefathers. Establishments specialising in its practice are to be found in many parts of Europe, and new applications include inhalations, massage and a variety of baths which often involve the use of mudpacks and seaweed compresses.

Psychological Suitability Assessment

Since the same criteria apply to this form of therapy as to naturopathy itself, there is little more to add other than to emphasise the fact that pleasant though many of these treatments may be, they may not be getting to the root of a specific problem. As long as this is kept in mind, however, much enjoyment and relaxation is doubtless to be derived from them.

DIETS

People adopt different diets for a variety of reasons. Although personal likes and dislikes may exert some influence on our choice of foods, and religious and moral attitudes also play a part in certain communities, what we eat is largely determined by convention or childhood programming.

Wild animals use their instinct to tell them which foods are good for them and which are not. In much the same way our primitive ancestors instituted dietary tribal taboos which were the origin of many later religious-orientated dietary formulae. There is nothing new in dieting. Hippocrates featured it in his writings in the fifth century BC, and it has played a role in both conventional and natural medicine ever since. Only the *raison d'être* has possibly changed, each successive cultural overlay displaying its preferences according to prevailing trends in medicine and fashion.

Modus Operandi

Today we are bombarded with a veritable array of dietary do's and don'ts. Foods which were previously thought to be nutritious and harmless are being seen in a new light, as science reveals all, and the list of things that are bad for us steadily grows. Saturated fats are known to be the culprits in many killer diseases, notably heart problems, strokes and cancer, while many substances such as tea, coffee and white sugar are also known to constitute health hazards. Since many of these and other potentially dangerous foodstuffs are part of the modern 'junk food' culture, there is a relationship between social background and those diseases which are primarily caused by nutritional imbalances.

There are religious diets, ethical diets, macrobiotic diets, megavitamin therapies, diets which are guaranteed to cleanse our systems of impurities, make us healthier and more physically and mentally alert, protect us from infection, or guarantee us against insidious illnesses in future years. There has seldom been a more health-conscious generation, but, on the other hand, what we also need to ask ourselves is – has there been (from a nutritional point of view) a more personally destructive one?

Aside from medical reasons, diets are also popularly employed for cosmetic purposes, mainly slimming. The shelves in most bookshops are packed with publications of all shapes and sizes which promise their readers *the* answer to their particular shape problem. Some of these are comparatively harmless while others, like the grape diet I mentioned in an earlier chapter, can constitute a health hazard if not medically supervised. The other factor which has to be taken into consideration is *why* we feel the need to be slimmer, fatter, or whatever. Is it what we really want, or has society once again imposed its standards upon us against our own better judgement? To what extent is our weight actually affecting our health and how much of it is simply a matter of 'keeping up with the Joneses'?

Psychological Suitability Assessment

The provision of a comprehensive analysis of food and diet is not my task in this book. What I am aiming to achieve, however, is a more balanced psychological attitude towards food consumption through a deprogramming of harmful conditioning, and a saner approach to the problem based on common sense and sound empirical facts. Old habits are hard to break, but when the question raised is one of life and death, then, surely, a more rational approach to diet is called for. In the light of new knowledge one can only assume that anyone who informs his physician (as did someone I know) that he would eat and drink whatever he pleased and to hell with the consequences, has a strong death wish and is taking the slow and respectable road to suicide.

All right, so it can be argued that our bodies are our own to do with as we wish, but this is not necessarily the case. Those who choose to pursue the easy downwards path to destruction also have a tendency to take their families, workmates and peers with them on the pretext that the more who do it the more right it must obviously be – 'Safety in numbers', as the saying goes.

Food can also be also responsible for certain mood changes, especially in children and young people. Studies carried out at the Massachusetts Institute of Technology, for example, have shown that when people eat carbohydrates their mood immediately becomes more relaxed and calm. In her recent book *Managing your Mind and Mood through Food*, Dr Judith Wurtman explains how carbohydrates apparently trigger a calming chemical in the brain which causes negative feeling to die down and anger to vanish.

Two books which are readily recommended for cancer patients in clinics and help groups throughout the country are *Cancer and its Nutritional Therapies*, by Dr Richard A Passwater, and *A Gentle Way With Cancer*, by Brenda Kidman. Both specify known food hazards which can contribute to the onset and exacerbate the development of different forms of this disease. As the mind and mental attitudes in general are so closely related to cancer, a drastic change in our thinking patterns is surely called for.

IONISATION THERAPY

This form of therapy involves the use of special machines which produce negatively charged air particles or ions. Air molecules generally are neither positively nor negatively charged. For example, 'pure' mountain air contains only one charged particle in every 500 million million molecules.[2] Those which do carry a charge are described as being 'ionised'. Ions, we are told, are essential to good health, but they should either be in balance or negatively charged. Positively charged ions can endanger health, and as most people tend to reside in areas where negative ions are in short supply (in towns and cities where dust, smoke and fumes tend to eliminate them, or where they are positively charged by central heating and air-conditioning systems) they need to be artificially created. It was not until 1970, however, that Professor A P Kreuger, of the University of California, established the possibility of utilising negative ions to kill bacteria. Since then the value of ionisation as an aid in the treatment of a wide range of disorders has been established by research teams in many countries.

Modus Operandi

Various models and sizes of ionisers are now available in many health centres and specialist shops. As they are usually no larger than a small transistor radio, ionisers can be easily installed in a car or a conference room where the 'fugs' are likely to cause drowsiness. They have also proved useful in the treatment of respiratory disorders and as they have so far shown no adverse side-effects, the US Food and Drug Administration has approved them as medical devices for the treatment of allergies, hay fever and other common respiratory disorders.

Psychological Suitability Assessment

I see no reason to disagree with the USFDA, as there would appear to be little chance of psychological problems arising from the use of these machines. Dependencies, however, can be built around the strangest things!

TISSUE SALT THERAPY

The need for the replacement or rebalancing of tissue salts was first expounded in the 1870s by Dr W H Schüssler, a German homoeopathic physician. It was later to form the basis of a new therapy which he called 'biochemistry'. This proved to be an unfortunate choice of appellation, however, as a scientific discipline of the same name, which covered a far wider range of studies, was also beginning to make its presence felt in the academic world.

Schüssler believed all disorders to be traceable to deficiencies in one or more of the elements which are essential to the balanced functioning of our system. He designated twelve basic tissue salts, each of which could be related to both a physical and psychological disorder. It is interesting to note that although for many years the medical profession tended to look askance at Schüssler's biochemic concept, orthodox biochemical research has since confirmed and enlarged upon many of his findings.

Modus Operandi

While tissue salts are frequently to be seen in the consulting rooms of many alternative therapists, on the occasion of receiving treatment for a shoulder injury I was recommended the use of one in particular by a hospital physiotherapist. So it seems that they are making the general rounds.

A deficiency of calcium, we are told, tends to produce disorders of nutrition and of the skeleton, while lack of sodium leads to digestive troubles, acidity, rheumatism and associated disorders. An appropriate dosage of the correct tissue salt will help put matters right. However, advocates of the system readily agree that a change in mental attitude or the correction of a mental imbalance is frequently followed by a quick return to normal in whichever part of the body is being affected. It is now generally accepted that the mind, particularly when it is distressed, can disrupt the body's chemical manufacturing system to create a deficiency. I view this, as I do many other physical imbalances, as a cry for help from the Psyche, which, if it is answered at the appropriate level, will naturally rebalance its physical counterpart.

Psychological Suitability Assessment

I have encountered many highly sensitive people who appear to respond well to tissue salts therapy. This I put down to the fact that they are more aware of both their bodies and psyches than many of us, and are therefore able to receive the call for help and deal with it at source. Whether it works so well for the less sensitive, however, I do not have the experience to comment on.

Endnotes:

1. *Alternative Health Guide*, Inglis and West, p. 20.
2. *Ibid*. p. 38.

Chapter 15

PLANT AND GAIA
THERAPIES

HERBAL MEDICINE

Although herbs are in everyday culinary use, and therefore readily available to everyone, to the trained herbalist they possess other properties which place them firmly in the therapeutic bracket. Herbal medicine, or herbalism as it is more popularly called, goes back a very long way. In days past, most villages in Britain and Europe had a wise woman whose knowledge of the healing properties of herbs had been passed down to her from earlier times. Such people were often members of what is now known as the 'old religion', or Wicca, which can be dated back to the matriarchal times referred to in classical texts as the 'Silver Age'.

The therapeutic use of herbs being so ancient, we may assume it to be part of that instinctive knowledge that is common amongst animals and primitive man. Most animals, even today, know when their diet lacks essential minerals and vitamins and will make every effort to correct the deficiency. As domestic animals are subjected to almost as much junk food as their human brethren, and many wild animals have been forced to adapt their eating habits on account of drastic changes to the environment effected by humans in the pursuit of economic wealth, it is sometimes impossible for them to pursue what they know instinctively to be correct. The same applies to many people, which is doubtless why herbalism and similarly related practices are on the ascendancy – perhaps our instinctive powers have not deserted us after all!

Herbal medicine has ever been tied in with magic and astrology, each plant resonating to a given planet or astrological sign and constituting part of an arcane knowledge, the basis of which has been long since forgotten. Gifted clairvoyants, members of the 'old religion' and pursuants of Druidic lore are believed to have an inner understanding of the healing quality of plants. In the west of Ireland the belief still lingers that the right herb to treat an illness can only be found if one allows the fairies to guide one to it. Since that particular coastline can count among its legends the arrival of the Tuatha de Danaans, or Fairy People, this is little wonder. It also tends to confirm my own belief that all legends which allude to the arrival of highly knowledgeable and advanced people from 'across the seas', be it in Egypt, South American the British Isles, Spain or Eire, are actually describing a race of high technological and scientific achievement, whose knowledge later degenerated into superstition and folklore.

The practice of clinical herbalism continued throughout the Middle Ages, becoming more and more sophisticated as time went on. Instead of single herbs, physicians would effect mixtures which they felt were appropriate to the disease, and animal substances were frequently added for supposed effect. In the seventeenth century, Nicholas Culpeper compiled his famous *Herbal*. Culpeper trained as an apothecary, which was the equivalent in those times of our modern GP. He believed in astrology and its importance in the lives of both plants and animals. In those days, such beliefs were not as contrary to science as they are today, Sir Isaac Newton himself being a firm believer in astrology. As medicine became a more exact science, however, the astrological aspect was cautiously dropped.

Simple herbal remedies slowly gave way to synthetic drugs, which were believed to be as effective as their herbal originals and more reliable. The advent of the twentieth century saw medicine and commerce marching hand in hand (or should one say 'hand in pocket?') with patent medicines slowly taking over from the old herbal remedies. Names like Thomas Beecham and Jesse Boot still adorn our bottles and shop fronts to this day. Although the herbalists were replaced by the chemists, the practice of herbalism continued and the Society of Herbalists has kept going to this day.

Following the exposure of the damaging side-effects of many drugs, herbalism is now enjoying a revival. According to *The Times Health Supplement*, 25 December 1981:

> Free courses in phytotherapy (healing through plants) are being offered to members of the French medical profession by the privately financed *Institut d'Enseignement de Phytothérapie (IEP)*.
>
> In the last three years, the demand in France for herbal cures has increased enormously. The Institute was only started last May, and its courses have attracted more than three hundred people a time, including dentists, pharmacists, biologists, veterinary surgeons and medical students.
>
> Dr Moatti, IEP president, hopes the Institute will soon be recognized officially. [1]

Modus Operandi

At the first consultation a medical herbalist will take a complete case history, consider diet and stress factors, and give a thorough physical examination. Most practitioners agree, however, that herbalism is more of holistic therapy than a symptom curer. Although there are obviously herbs which can alleviate such things as rashes, or pain, herbal therapists tend to search for the cause rather than the effect. Anyone wishing to make use of herbs for curative purposes is advised to seek the service of a qualified practitioner, as ignorance of certain properties can lead to unpleasant side-effects. Ginseng, for example, which is frequently recommended in advertisements as having life-giving properties, is now known to work via the endocrine system. Stimulation of the pituitary gland may be fine for some, giving them a lift and a sense of well-being, but for others the effects could cause discomfort, at the very least. I am personally allergic to it so I can speak from firsthand experience, but then I am also allergic to those medical drugs that are designed for pituitary stimulation.

Evening primrose oil is another such substance which is believed to help a variety of disorders from premenstrual syndrome to cardiovascular disease, although claims of this kind are hardly guaranteed to win the confidence of the medical profession. It would take more than a few pages to do justice to the pros and cons of herbalism, however, and those interested in pursuing the study are recommended to contact the Society of Herbalists, who will, no doubt, be pleased to recommend appropriate literature or approved practitioners.

Psychological Suitability Assessment

I would not recommend dabbling in herbs to anyone who is insufficiently stable or rational to accept professional advice. Use of the wrong herb is just as dangerous as using the wrong drug, and while many of us happily employ culinary herbs to titillate our taste buds, even these should be checked if we should feel unaccountably unwell after their use. Strange brews are definitely a no-no; there are herbs that can adversely affect the nervous system and the mind. So, it is well to remember that herbalism is as much a skill as is allopathic medicine, and we all know the dangers of using medicaments that have been prescribed for someone else! Cautionary words having been committed to paper, it is also fair to say that there are many herbs and herbal concoctions that are perfectly safe and proven beneficial such as garlic, comfrey and dandelion tea.

AROMATHERAPY

Aromatherapy probably originated in ophresiology – from the Greek *ophresis*, meaning smell – which was concerned with the study of the effects of different scents from flowers, herbs, woods, spices, etc. These days, however, aromatherapy infers treatment with essential oils or aromatic essences which are rubbed into the skin, inhaled, or added to one's bath water.

All the ancient civilisations had recourse to essential oils for one reason or another. Egypt, China, Mesopotamia – even the Bible contains references to the rubbing of oils and wine into wounds in order to effect a speedy healing. As time progressed, synthetic substances gradually took over from essential oils, although we are told that during World War I, when there was an acute shortage of antiseptics, essential oils were again employed with satisfactory results.

Modus Operandi

The usual way of applying essential oils is through massage, during which process the aroma is inhaled, while the healing qualities of the oil are said to penetrate through the skin. Different oils carry different healing properties and anyone wishing to apply these privately should ensure that they are using the right oil for the job; the mucous membranes of the digestive tract, in particular, being sensitive to them. Essential oils can also be dangerous if taken with other forms of medication, and one should not mix them with other therapies, alternative or otherwise. Only a day or so ago a Metamorphic consultant I know took on the case of a lady who had been having two different kinds of treatment at the same time. The aromatherapy, which is powerful enough in its own right, had appeared to help her considerably when she first started it. But on the advice of a friend she decided to try out something else, after which the problems came thick and fast. After all, we would not mix medicines, and the fact that people do flit from therapist to therapist (the butterfly syndrome) is in itself indicative of some deep psychological problem.

Psychological Suitability Assessment

Definitely not a treatment for the 'butterflies' of this world who are either constantly seeking new diversions, or are unable to make up their minds about anything. It is interesting to note, however, that experiments in Italy and Japan have shown essential oils sprayed from an aerosol to be effective in the treatment of anxiety and depression.

Care should also be taken not to confuse aromatherapy with herbalism. For example, the pot pourri and herbal pillows much beloved of our grandparents, which are at present enjoying a comeback, usually owe their scent to herbs rather than essential oils. Although these are comparatively harmless, it is worth watching out for the occasional case of allergy.

BACH FLOWER REMEDIES

Dr Edward Bach, who originated the now famous Bach Flower Remedies, trained as a pathologist and bacteriologist in London just prior to World War I. As in the case of many of the inventors of alternative systems, Dr Bach become disenchanted with orthodox medicine and turned his attentions to homoeopathy. It was during his work in this field that he became aware of the importance of the patient, as opposed to the patient's symptoms, which led him to conclude that there was a need for a type of remedy based on the patient's emotional condition.

Modus Operandi

Although during his medical career Bach had looked to empirical research for the answers to medical enigmas, with the advent of these newly formed ideas he started to concentrate more on his intuitive faculties, using these to communicate with individual flowering plants for the purpose of identification with and an understanding of their specific properties. Working this way, Bach selected thirty-eight wild flowers from which remedies could be prepared according to a special method he had evolved. This preparatory procedure, he insisted, was absolutely essential to their efficacy.

From a psychological viewpoint, it is interesting to observe how Bach's switch from left to right brain emphasis eventually ended on a highly transpersonal note. He would justify his treatment with mystical arguments which did little to enhance his work in the eyes of the medical establishment. He explained that his plant remedies worked, not because of their chemical properties, but because they had 'power to elevate our vibrations, and thus draw down spiritual power, which cleanses mind and body, and heals'.[2]

This deeply spiritual man, through allowing himself to work through his right brain hemisphere, obviously became aware of the intelligences which exist within the plant kingdoms and the effect these essences can have on our mental economy. In the course of my own work, I have continually noted how those people who do allow their intuition to guide them, providing they are reasonably balanced or psychologically integrated and

of benign intent, inevitably arrive at the same conclusions as
Edward Bach.

Psychological Suitability Assessment

The *Handbook of Bach Flower Remedies* assures us that the remedies
are 'absolutely benign in their action, they can never produce
an unpleasant reaction under any condition.' I can speak from
firsthand experience here, as I have often found the 'Rescue
Remedy', for example, to be invaluable in cases of extreme
distress and shock. I am also of the belief that these simple
plant essences do somehow convey a healing or balancing
energy which, in addition to being able to affect our states of
mind, also work at a subconscious level, touching our hidden
emotions and, perhaps, the psyche itself.

GAIA (EARTH) ENERGIES

The energies of Gaia herself can also be drawn for healing
purposes, and as we have already discussed in Chapter 9,
these may vary from place to place. Certain journalists have
recently criticised the new Gaia awareness on the grounds that,
in view of such occurrences as earthquakes and volcanoes
which devastate life and property, Gaia does not deserve to
be loved and cherished. There is an answer to this one, of
course which is: firstly, were we in touch with earth energies in the same way as animals, we would be instinctively
alerted to forthcoming natural disasters, which could be seen
as the Gaia equivalent to our own growth pains, illnesses and
periods of imbalance. Secondly, were our economic systems
better synchronised with the planet itself, communities would
be able to avoid living and erecting homes in known areas of
seismic and climatic instability.

Modus Operandi

How does one find the right geo-power source or location?
Dowsing is the simplest way. Using dowsing rods or a reliable
pendulum, concentrate your mind on your problem and then

dowse for a positive reaction. If you are not in a position to travel round searching for suitable sites to dowse, use a map. It works just as well. The ancient Celts believed streams and fast-flowing rivers to contain healing powers, so if you are inclined towards the ritual approach, and not too rational to acknowledge the forces of nature, I have outlined in *The Psychology of Ritual* a safe and simple healing rite of the type used in the days of our Celtic ancestors which can be carried out by three or more persons.

Psychological Suitability Assessment

Once again the principle of energy exchange must be emphasised. Always being 'on the take' does not make for good health or peace of mind in the long run. It has been the fashion among certain cults to gather at what they believe to be power centres in order to imbibe and revel in the energies. In my book of rules, this goes against cosmic law, and taking into account the present plight of our planet is it not time we did some *giving*, instead of always taking?

CRYSTAL HEALING

Crystal healing, which is very much in vogue in the United States, is fast gathering popularity in Britain. Crystal power is no new thing, however, although the healing energies of crystals appear to have only recently been rediscovered, thanks to the sterling efforts of Ra Bonewitz and other experts in that field.

From the literature I have perused on this subject, there would appear to be several schools of thought, not all of them in agreement. Some crystal healers concentrate more on their actual magnetic properties, and others on their psychic powers or the subtle energies they emit. Bonewitz refers to these in terms of '*mundane energies*, defined as those energies that can be measured by current scientific methods – energies such as electricity, light, heat and mechanical energy' and '*spiritual energies*, defined simply as energies that cannot be measured by current methods – such as the energies of thought, will, healing, and the energies that make up the higher spiritual bodies'. He continues: 'We make this division, artificial though it may be, for a very important reason: we can describe quite precisely the behaviour of mundane energies within crystals, and from these descriptions we see that there are certain parallels with the behaviour of spiritual energies within crystals.'[3]

Aside from Bonewitz's 'mundane energies', the properties of which can be studied in any good book on minerology or gemstones, crystals are believed to contain essences or intelligences unique to their own kind: the inhabitants of the mineral kingdoms. Crystal magic can be dated back to the earliest times and is believed to have originated in what I choose to term the 'Old Country' – Atlantis. There are numerous tales of how it was employed in those long-distant times, when laser power was both understood and utilised in ways that would astound even our present-day scientists. But as far as psychology is concerned, these pronouncements are purely conjectural, although many of us were born with this knowledge which, for obvious reasons, society has obliged us to suppress!

Modus Operandi

It is my policy wherever possible to experience something before I comment on it, otherwise I would surely qualify for Newton's remark to Halley concerning the subject of astrology: 'Sir, I have studied it, you have not!' Until writing this book, I had not worked with crystals, although I was given a fine cluster specimen consisting of three male crystals and one female by a friend in California, who is something of a crystal specialist. The gender of a quartz crystal is identified by its density, the clearer specimens being designated masculine and the more opaque or cloudy varieties feminine. Clusters frequently reveal a mixture of both. I affectionately christened the cluster I was given, 'the Carringtons', and they were put in a place of honour in my living room. However, I felt it only fair to consult with their essences before writing about them, and with amazing results.

In his book *Crystal Healing*, Edmund Harold, who specialises in psychic healing with quartz crystals, mentions that a good crystal could help one to recall one's dreams. Following his instructions, I established contact with the essences of my crystals, extended to them my love and acknowledgement, and asked if they could assist me in this way. That night I slept with the Carringtons under my pillow, with quite remarkable results.

My dreams were so clear that upon awakening I was temporarily unsure as to what was reality! Since then, I have worked with my little group in other healing ways, including helping one of my cats who was sick at the time.

A close link exists between crystal power, ley lines and the magnetic energies of the Earth, and it has also been noted that areas rich in quartz have a higher rate of hauntings! While stones (and bricks and mortar, for that matter) can capture and store incidents, like tape recorders, to be played back years later by anyone sensitive enough to receive them, this facility is amplified considerably in quartz crystals.

Crystals are very much the children of Gaia and, metaphysically speaking, as representatives of the element of earth they are naturally closely related to the gnomes. I have always believed that gemstones (and all minerals, in fact) house intelligences, albeit of a different frequency from our own, which could either help or hinder us according to the quality of their energy and its compatibility with our own PK. This has probably given rise to the many superstitions associated with priceless gems such as the Hope Diamond (not my branch of the family, unfortunately!) which obviously host elementals or devas whose energies are so powerful that they exert an unbalancing effect on the people who own them. In the Old Country, only those who, by a process of initiation and genuine soul-maturity, had earned the right to priestly ordination were allowed to wear or handle really powerful stones. When I was a child at a Catholic boarding school many years ago, we were told that only a cardinal was permitted to wear the blue corundum (sapphire – second in hardness and weight to a diamond) in his sacerdotal ring. Whether this is still the practice or not I cannot say, but it was doubtless a remnant of an ancient belief, the origin of which has been long since forgotten.

Electromagnetic crystal healing presents yet another way in which crystals can be used for therapeutic purposes. Harry Oldfield, who pioneered this particular practice, has successfully demonstrated his technique in Europe and America. Oldfield's appliances, which incorporate silicon chips and silica crystals and are powered by small batteries, are said to relieve pain and effect many other cures. His book *Dark Side of the Brain* has also served as a subject for interest and debate among healers and doctors alike.

Psychological Suitability Assessment

I would say, be careful! Some crystals are very powerful and could prove mind-blowing for the less balanced among us. Believing in a thing does not necessarily imply that one has the mental abilities to cope with it. Those who really feel drawn to crystal healing should start with a small crystal, preferably of the feminine gender, and heed the advice given by the experts as to which type of crystals are best designed for which purposes. But being utterly sceptical is no protection either. After all, how many of those rich owners who inherited the 'curses' supposedly associated with the gems which they or their families pillaged believed that those very stones housed living entities! I fully realise that I am on metaphysical rather than psychological ground here, but then many of the people who read this book will also be of metaphysical inclination, and those that that are not will take it all with the proverbial pinch of salt!

Endnotes:

1. *The Alternative Health Guide*, Inglis and West, p. 45
2. *Ibid*. p. 64.
3. *Cosmic Crystals*, Ra Bonewitz, p. 102.

Chapter 16

SYSTEMS OF MEDICINE AND ORIENTAL THERAPIES

HOMOEOPATHY

It is almost 200 years since Samuel Hahnemann (1755–1843), then a young doctor from Saxony, began his studies in biochemistry. During the course of his research into those drugs then in common use, he decided to experiment on himself to determine what effect they would have on him when he was *not* ill. One particular drug which interested him was quinine, which had been introduced in Europe by Jesuit missionaries who had observed its efficacy in the treatment of malaria by South American Indians. And so Hahnemann tried it, only to find that it made him feverish even though he had been quite well previously. In fact, it produced the exact symptoms of the very illness it was said to cure! This caused Hahnemann to assume that the usual indications of malaria were not so much symptomatic of the disease itself, as indicators of the body's fight to eject it from the system. He then proceeded to experiment with other drugs, each of which produced similar results, and from his research the homoeopathic concept 'like cures like' was born.

This was by no means a new idea, however. Tribal medicine men had used it since the earliest times, albeit in a different form from that employed in modern homoeopathy; the Hippocratic physicians were well aware of it, and it was featured by Paracelsus (1493–1541 – see Chapter 12) in his famous *Doctrine of Signatures*. Thomas Sydenham, acknowledged as the father of British medicine (seventeenth century), also regarded symptoms as indicators of the body's fight against illness. In spite of this, allopathic medicine continued to observe the belief laid down by Galen during the reign of the Emperor Marcus Aurelius in the second century.

In recent years, however, inoculation against disease – a homoeopathic practice – has become standard medical procedure, while homoeopathy is finally receiving the mantle of respectability. *YOU*, the magazine supplement of the *Mail On Sunday*, recently published a list of ten well-known people who use homoeopathic medicine: the Queen Mother, the Queen, Princess Margaret, Prince Charles, Sir Yehudi Menuhin, Linda Cierach, Twiggy, Renée Asherson, Katie Boyle and Wayne Sleep. I could add several more lists to that one, but healers, like doctors, also observe the rule of confidentiality.

Modus Operandi

Homoeopathy works on the principle that minute doses or 'potencies' work in much the same way as inoculations, in that they stimulate the body's immune system into rejecting a disease or adjusting an imbalance. A homoeopathic practitioner will commence his consultation in the usual manner, with a full medical history, which will not, as in the case of allopathic medicine, be limited to the physical symptoms, but will also take into account the patient's personality, constitution, temperament (both physiological and psychological) and general disposition. Any homoeopathic remedies prescribed will therefore be completely personal to the patient. These are prepared in a rather unusual way. If the selected remedy is a solid, '. . . it is pounded with a mortar along with some therapeutically inert substance; if it is a liquid, it is diluted in distilled water and "succussed" – rapidly shaken up on a machine until infusion is complete. Remedies are prepared to whatever degree of "potency" the homoeopath decides is required.'[1]

Homoeopathy recently hit the headlines as a result of some surprising findings from the French National Institute for

Scientific Research in Medicine, which suggests that homoeopathic remedies do work. An article by Judy Sadgrove in *The Guardian*, entitled 'Homoeopathy? A Drop in the Bucket' generously supplied us with details of the findings. Although many people in Britain, Europe and the United States have benefited considerably from the ministrations of homoeopaths over the past 200 years, many orthodox doctors are still scornful of the practice and believe that any cures which result from it are purely placebo effects. In 1986, the British Medical Association's report rejected homoeopathy out of hand considering the 'minimum dose' idea as irrational.

Professor Jacques Benveniste's paper on research into serial dilution of active substances was published in the June edition of *Nature*, alongside an editorial disclaimer calling on readers to suspend judgement as there was no physical basis for what Professor Benveniste and his team had found. What then were these findings?

> That it is possible to dilute an antibody in water virtually ad infinitum without the solution losing its biological activity. Benveniste had diluted a solution of antibodies until it reached one part of 10^{120}, way beyond the point at which a single molecule of antibody might possibly remain in the water. Nevertheless, white blood cells reacted to the liquid, by now expected to be pure water.[2]

This caused Benveniste to speculate that somehow the molecules of water retain a memory of the antibody molecule. Homoeopathy explains the esoteric workings of its remedies in the same way. Being a scientific journal, *Nature* was reluctant to publish Benveniste's paper. When he first submitted it in 1985, experts apparently insisted on the repetition of the experiments under more stringent scientific conditions. This was done, and the same results were obtained in France, Italy and Canada.

Dr David Reilly, a medically qualified homoeopath practising in Glasgow, compares the French study with one he carried out himself to test out a homoeopathic remedy for hay fever. This was published in *The Lancet* in 1986, and is one of the few tests of homoeopathy to be published in scientific literature. He draws attention to the work of Dr W E Boyd, whose research some fifty years ago produced the same results as those of Benveniste.

The Allopathy versus Homoeopathy conflict continues, however, and probably will for years to come unless science either broadens its concepts of what constitutes a valid research programme, or invents one itself that proves the matter to its own satisfaction.

Psychological Suitability Assessment

One could argue that if one does not believe in the efficacy of homoeopathy, but chooses to seek the services of a homoeopath, according to general medical opinion it will not work as the placebo effect would be nullified. This does not appear to be the case, however. I was once on the register of a GP in West London who was also a qualified homoeopath. He informed me that he had frequently prescribed homoeopathic remedies for National Health patients who treated them with some amusement – and no small degree of scepticism – only to find that they actually worked!

ACUPUNCTURE

The oriental therapies featured in this chapter all share common ground in that they are based on the conviction that the energy of the life-force courses through the body via a system of invisible channels called meridians, which correspond to different organs of the body. This life-force, which is called *chi* constantly interacts between two poles which represent the Yin – or negative, feminine or restraining element – and the Yang – the masculine, positive and outgoing element. Should either of these aspects become overemphasised, the harmony of the body is disturbed and illness can result.

The term acupuncture derives from the Latin *acus* (needle), and *punctura* (to prick). The dictionary describes the practice of acupuncture as involving the insertion of the tips of needles into the skin at specific points for the purpose of treating various disorders by stimulating nerve impulses – to which we may add: for the purpose of restoring that balance of *chi* energy which is essential to good health.

There are various speculations as to its origin. Some scholars are of the opinion that it derived from 'scarifying' the skin, while legend has it that the idea originated from an incident which

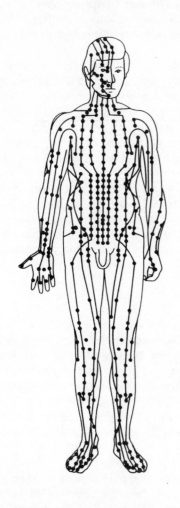

THE MERIDIAN LINES

involved a soldier who was injured by an arrow finding that his pain was relieved when he was struck by a second arrow. In China it can be traced back some five thousand years, and medical textbooks written in the sixth century BC which outline its practice are still in existence. Due to the fact that China was cut off from the rest of the world for so long, it was not until the seventeenth century that missionaries returned with information about its procedures. It was some years, however, before the traditional version of Chinese acupuncture became known and accepted in Western society, and since the 1960s it has become rapidly established as an ongoing area in natural medicine.

In spite of considerable opposition from the medical establishment it has fast gained popularity with the public, and many qualified physicians have made a point of studying and applying it in cases where orthodox treatment fails to produce results. Recent publicity in the media, notably an incident filmed in China of major surgery being undertaken while the patient was 'anaesthetised' by the insertion of needles at appropriate points, with no apparent discomfort or post-operational distress, have served to give the public a feeling of confidence in acupuncture. Acupuncture anaesthesia (or analgesia, to use the correct term, which implies insensitivity to pain without loss of consciousness) is an apparently recent development in Chinese medicine, however, and can be applied for the general relief of pain.

Modus Operandi

Acupuncturists proceed with new patients in much the same way as other practitioners, taking details of case histories and carefully observing any physical signs that might betray imbalances in the flow of *chi* energy. Those who work strictly according to Chinese tradition may ask for such details as the time and year of birth, which, according to ancient belief, influence our growth processes and incline us to either yin or yang imbalances.

When an acupuncturist checks the pulses, this procedure bears no relationship to that carried out in regular medicine. For example, there are twelve of these pulses, six to each wrist, one for each main meridian. From feeling these pulses, the practitioner is able to deduce any imbalances in the flow of *chi* which might be affecting the patient's health. Although each pulse corresponds to a vital organ, it is not exclusive to that organ, as the mind, body, emotions and physical reactions are acknowledged to be inextricably linked.

The needles which are employed to adjust the energy flows are very fine, and their insertion is frequently not felt at all.

Some acupuncturists, however, believe that a certain degree of awareness of the action, no matter how small, does indicate that the needle has hit the right spot or effected an accurate contact. Points at which needles are inserted may bear no relationship to the area for which treatment has been initially sought. This is because a symptom, such as a backache, may have arisen from an energy imbalance in another area of the body which has affected the kidneys.

There are various methods employed in the insertion of the needles, which may penetrate to whichever depth the acupuncturist deems fit. Sometimes the needles are rotated clockwise, or pumped, to stimulate the energies. The length of time they are left in position will depend on their effect, the practitioner continuing to check the pulses at intervals during the treatment.

Moxibustion may also be offered as part of the treatment. This consists of placing a cone of moxa (*artemesia vulgaris*) over the selected acupuncture point and lighting it. There is little, if any, sensation attached to this, as with the needles, but both treatments are designed to clear the channel in question and rebalance the energies throughout the body.

Psychological Suitability Assessment

Patients have been known to complain of side-effects following treatment by acupuncturists. These may take the form of a slight disorientation or the sensation of being somewhat light-headed, plus a certain drowsiness. But these soon pass. There can also be a temporary intensification of symptoms, but this may apply in most types of natural medicine and is purely suggestive of the adjustments taking place in the body. In cases where the energies have been out of balance for a considerable time, effecting their readjustment naturally requires a corresponding rectification in the system.

There are certain disorders which acupuncturists do not treat, and for very obvious reasons – sexually transmitted diseases, for example. And as it has now been established that other diseases can act as co-factors for AIDS, acupuncturists are ensuring that needles are never used for more than one patient, the additional cost involved in this precaution being shared equally between patient and practitioner.

From a psychological viewpoint, acupuncture falls into the category of the type of observable treatment which reassures patients that something is actually being done for them. I have had acupuncture in the past but cannot, I fear, be counted among its successes. Aside from a fear of the needles or moxas, side-effects would seem to be minimal, if any, and although the dependency angle should never be ignored in any treatment which can be readily purchased for a fee, this is more likely to apply to the psychological therapies than a practice which can involve a slight degree of discomfort on the part of the patient.

SHIATSU AND ACUPRESSURE

Acupressure works on the same principle as acupuncture, but with the fingers taking the place of the needles. In fact, shiatsu, which is a Japanese word, translates literally as 'finger pressure' and is the Japanese form of Chinese acupressure. These practices share much common ground with other forms of massage, although like acupuncture, shiatsu is based on the stimulation of *ki*, which is the Japanese for *chi*, through the use of pressure applied to the skin at points along the meridians which correspond with the vital organs.

Acupressure in its Western form is sometimes known as *g-jo*, which translates roughly as 'first aid' in Chinese, or *jin shin do*. Some practitioners insist on differentiating between acupressure and shiatsu, but in practice they bear too many similarities to effect distinctions which would be recognisable to the layman. Choice may, of course, be effected on ethnic grounds, some practitioners (or prospective patients) preferring the Chinese version to the Japanese, or vice versa as prompted by their karmic backgrounds.

Although the practice of shiatsu has been observed for several hundred years, it was only recognised as a therapy in its own right when it was officially codified by Tokujiro Namikoshi some fifty years ago. In modern Japan it serves as both a diagnostic technique and a preventive measure against disease, and forms part of the regular weekly routine of many Japanese citizens.

In China, acupressure originated as a form of first aid for

use in families who were cut off by distance from acupuncturists or other medical practitioners. These days it is used as both a self-help system and a regular form of treatment for many.

Modus Operandi

Practitioners of shiatsu and acupressure do not make use of any of the extras which sometimes accompany more orthodox forms of massage – special oils, equipment or machinery. This gives them the added advantage that they can be carried out anywhere and any time, which, as the Chinese so wisely observed, makes them ideal tools for use in first aid. A firm surface, in a room which is quiet, clean, well-ventilated but warm, provides a good place for home treatment, and if there is a soft carpet, blanket or rug for the patient to lie on, then so much the better. Many practitioners of shiatsu or acupressure prefer to visit their clients in their homes, although treatment is often available at therapy clinics and health centres. Tight-fitting, body-hugging clothing, or any kind of garment that could interfere with the practitioner's 'touch' should be avoided during treatment.

A comprehensive shiatsu or acupuncture session can last as long as an hour and a quarter. Unlike some of the more rigidly applied manipulative therapies, there are no fixed positions and the patient will be required to sit, stand or lie down at different intervals as the practitioner requests. The first session will commence with the customary case history, followed by the checking of the pulses as with acupuncture.

The treatment is a combination of massage and acupuncture, with the therapist applying pressure to the acupuncture meridians. This pressure may be administered in any of several ways, with the bulb of the thumb, the fingers, the palm or heel of the hand, a knee, an elbow, or even the soles of the feet! These techniques, which are very ancient, have been observed in classical texts, and can be traced back to the healing rites of early tribal communities. According to Namikoshi, the pressure should produce a sensation midway between pleasure and pain, which patients have frequently experienced and commented upon.

Psychological Suitability Assessment

Shiatsu and acupressure practitioners have met with much success in the treatment of cases of chronic headache, migraine and similarly related disorders which have been brought on by stress. The treatment can have either stimulative or sedative effects, depending on the location and emphasis of the pressure. Patients undergoing shiatsu or acupressure treatment are advised against the use of medicinal or social drugs such as alcohol, while the therapies are not recommended for pregnant women. If in any doubt, patients or prospective patients should always seek the advice of a trained therapist, or consult their own GP.

Neither of these practices would appear to carry suspect psychological connotations, as long as attention is given to the advice given. Any treatment which effects relaxation and helps to break down the patterns of tension formed by stress is recommended. And, as the practitioners of shiatsu and acupressure are able to work without the sort of impedimenta which tend to make make the more nervous types uncomfortable, these treatments would seem to have many advantages.

I also like the idea of the practitioner visiting one's home. Some people who need treatment suffer (as part of their condition) either from agoraphobia, or a fear of travelling around. Many such sufferers, who have relied on drugs like valium and librium (the adverse side-effects of which have now been proven) would surely be better served by a visit to their home from a trained shiatsu or acupressure practitioner. With home visits, however, the rapport between patient and practitioner is even more essential, as there is nothing worse than feeling uncomfortable in one's own habitat!

AYURVEDA AND CHINESE MEDICINE

Ayurveda derives from the Sanskrit *ayur* – life, and *veda* – knowledge. This ancient Hindu system of medicine combines naturopathy, homoeopathy and some aspects of modern medicine with astrology. As diagnosis and treatment are determined by the patients's horoscope, a detailed knowledge of medical astrology according to the ayurvedic system is required of the practitioner. Since Ayurveda is strictly a part of the Hindu faith and indigenous to the Indian subcontinent, it is seldom included in lists of alternative therapies and does not really qualify as a system of medicine or an oriental therapy, as such.

The same applies to Chinese medicine, which is concerned with herbalism, *chi*, the yin/yang principle, and Chinese astrology. Those interested in pursuing an in-depth study of these oriental medicines are advised to contact qualified people from the appropriate ethnic groups for although there are few books on the market which purport to cover the subjects, I am given to understand that the most reliable information is relayed orally.

Endnotes:

1. *The Alternative Health Guide*, Inglis and West, p. 71.
2. 'Homeopathy? A Drop in the Bucket', by J Sadgrove, the *Guardian*, 20 July 1988.

Chapter 17

EXERCISE, MOVEMENT AND SENSORY THERAPIES

Exercises which have been specially designed to benefit us physically, mentally and spiritually may not count as therapies in the strict sense of the word, but they do contribute to health in that they help us to effect that essential union between body, mind and spirit. The practices which follow fall into this category.

YOGA

The practice of yoga, which dates back some 6,000 years, is based on the concept of the union of body, mind and spirit which, yogic tradition tells us, cannot be separated. In fact, the word 'yoga' itself, which comes from the Sanskrit and is said to mean 'union', has the same root as the English word 'yoke'. Hindu philosophy, upon which yoga is based, subscribes to the belief that we are not only linked to our own higher selves, but also to all living creatures, and inanimate matter. It is interesting to review this belief in the light of modern science, as so-termed 'inanimate matter' is now known to be composed of individual particles which are capable of communicating one with another beyond the barriers of time and space.

As yoga was slowly adapted for Western use those disciplines which were essentially a part of the Hindu religion were dropped. The yoga one sees practised by Indian gurus may therefore not appear quite the same as that taught at the local school hall Keep Fit sessions.

Modus Operandi

Posture, breathing and meditation are the three main ingredients of yoga. The attitudes or bodily positions adopted are called *asanas*, and it is from these that the body derives the discipline which enables it to observe the required rigidity with the minimum of physical effort. When correctly executed, the *asanas* free the body from the minor discomforts, thus allowing the mind the tranquillity that is essential for deep meditation and union with the cosmos via the transpersonal self.

There are many different forms of yoga, each designed for a specific purpose. The most commonly used in the West is hatha yoga, which concentrates more on the control of the body. Other forms of yoga include:

Raja yoga	Connects or links the mind with the spirit, and the spirit with the Absolute.
J'nana yoga	The pursuit of wisdom.
Mantra yoga	Concerned with sound.
Bhakti yoga	The love of God and religious devotion.
Karma yoga	Concerned with action and service.
Laya yoga	Pertains to the chakric centres.

There are also other forms of yoga that are not so well known or easily recognisable to the Western novice.

Yoga, t'ai chi, akido and dance therapy all involve the visual sense to the extent that they are difficult to explain in print. There is an abundance of literature on the market which covers the subject of yoga, however, while the remaining three studies are well-represented in classes in most towns and cities in Britain.

Psychological Suitability Assessment

As an aid to good health, yoga is certainly to be recommended.
Nor is it purely the prerogative of middle-aged married ladies
with slimming in mind. I know several men engaged in high-
pressure executive business lives, who owe their serenity and
stamina to their weekly yoga sessions. The therapeutic effects
of meditative practices generally are now recommended by
alternative therapists and medical practitioners alike, so yoga,
if taken step by step under qualified instruction, can certainly
contribute to one's physical, mental and spiritual well-being.
One word of warning, however. Being adept at hatha yoga does
not necessarily guarantee strength of mind. I once handled the
case of an Indian gentlemen who could do anything with his
body, but on the occasion of a 'hex' being placed on his family
by someone he had inadvertently upset, he was quite powerless
to know what to do and was obliged to turn to a Western
occultist for assistance. On the other hand, there have been
holy men in the East whose paranormal adeptship has more
than equalled many a Western magician, so it all depends in
which areas one's expertise lies.

T'AI CHI

Closely allied to the ancient Eastern martial arts, t'ai chi has
been described as 'meditation in motion'. It also has points in
common with dance therapy although unlike that practice its
highly structured movements leave little room for individual
interpretation. Each exercise is symbolic, and representative
of some psychological or psychic factor in the human make-
up. The movements, which are always circular and essentially
flowing, aim at subtlety rather than strength, and in common
with yoga the emphasis is on the body–mind–spirit complex.

   The practice of t'ai chi contains elements of both Buddhism
and Taoism, although it is said to have originated in the latter,
where it was taught to children. According to another source,
however, it derived from the martial arts as a therapy for patients
convalescing after illness. In China it was regarded as an ancient
esoteric pursuit which did not find its way to the West until the
mid nineteenth century.

Modus Operandi

It is generally agreed that it is almost impossible to describe t'ai chi in print. Only by observing it can one really begin to understand what it is all about. But basically, it is concerned with finding the centre of physical balance which opens the door to mental and spiritual equilibrium. As with the martial arts, t'ai chi teaches the individual how to effect the build-up of physical energy, and direct and control its release through the discipline of movement. The aim, of course is to form a balanced link with the *chi*, or life-force.

Psychological Suitability Assessment

Some cardiologists have suggested that their patients take up t'ai chi as it is a form of exercise which imposes no strain on the heart. Many GPs have also been quick to observe its therapeutic effects on workaholics or those who drive themselves too hard. I would be inclined to place it in the Severity Code Rite category, i.e. those ritual practices which emphasise the control of body and mind, and as such it would prove particularly beneficial for anyone who tends to dispersion.[1] Oriental disciplines frequently fall into this category, and are therefore recommended as therapies for anyone lacking self-discipline. Unfortunately, however, and this applies to the martial arts in particular, they are frequently espoused by more aggressive types who are anxious to improve their personal power.

AKIDO

Modern akido was founded by Morihei Uyeshiba (1883–1969), who saw it as a form of combat which assumed dance-type movements of great beauty. While t'ai chi originated in China, akido is essentially a Japanese martial art which has developed into a form of therapeutic ritual dance. This dance involves what at first glance might appear to be a contest, but this is not actually the case. The objective is to exploit *ki* (the Japanese name for the *chi*) through the interplay of energies released through the rite, or what the British Akido Federation describe as 'self-realisation through discipline'.[2]

Modus Operandi

Akido is partly concerned with the art of self-defence in the form of non-resistance, a popular theme in the martial arts, especially those which are designed purely as protective exercises. There would appear to be Zen overtones in the practice of akido, as success among trainees is often acknowledged by punishment rather than reward, the lesson being that the ability to give and take is greater than the act of winning.

An akido master will take classes of up to thirty people in a special practice room which is called a *dojo*. Sessions are divided into classes for beginners, intermediate and advanced stages, and usually take place on a weekly basis. As in most Japanese rites, etiquette is very strict and students must observe the correct procedures when entering or leaving the class. Classes can last up to an hour, and are always preceded by a short meditation.

Psychology Suitability Assessment

As with t'ai chi, only more so, I do not feel this to be a suitable therapy for anyone who is of a nervous disposition. I can also think of several people, male and female, who would be reduced to tears very early in the proceedings. However, these comments would apply to all the martial arts. It takes a certain mentality and psychological type to adjust to disciplines of this kind. If one fits into this category, then there is obviously much to be gained from them.

DANCE THERAPY

Movement and dance have constituted a form of physical and emotional release since the beginning of time. The movements observed in tribal rituals throughout the world bear great similarities and have been described by anthropologists as representing an instinctive interpretation of the movements of the universe. Many ancient practices, such as the Tarantella Rite which was observed in Italy for centuries, involved dance movements some of which were highly explicit.

Raqs sharqi, which is the Egyptian name for belly-dancing, has been known for centuries in the Middle East to have health and fitness benefits. In addition to the usual toning of the body, it improves posture and circulation and cultivates pelvic mobility. The hip rotations, the experts tell us, massage the uterus and help to alleviate period pains.

Modern dance therapy aims to help withdrawn people, and those who experience difficulty in communication and touch, although it is generally felt that many people can benefit both physically and emotionally from movement to music.

Modus Operandi

Dance therapists tend to develop their own approach, with some favouring a more structured approach and others a freer style which simply moves with the music. Kinetic bonds are believed to be formed through the power of the music and the movements designed by the therapist, which both permeate the group and free the individual mind from anger, sorrow, frustration, fear, and other contingencies of everyday existence.

Psychological Suitability Assessment

Dance therapy classes may be attended for a variety of reasons, such as slimming, figure improvement, health, social contact, or simply to unwind. Mental patients suffering from 'institutional neurosis' resulting from hours of catatonic inactivity, have responded to music and movement after verbal psychotherapy has failed to reach them. Handicapped, retarded and autistic children in particular respond to music and find it an adequate form of expression in an otherwise isolated existence.

CHROMATHERAPY

Defined by the dictionary as a quality of light, colour is something which affects us all in our everyday lives. The ancient civilisations were well aware of the power and influence of colour. In ancient Egypt, where colour healing was regularly practised, its effect on the body, mind and spirit was well understood. Certain colours were avoided, especially those of a stimulatory nature – a tradition which some believe to have been brought over from Atlantis. Greens, blues and turquoise, in particular, were greatly favoured, whereas certain shades of red were believed to be associated with Set, god of evil and chaos, who was the traditional enemy of order and light. It therefore stands to reason that this colour was avoided in all healing practices, illness naturally resulting from some chaotic condition in the system.

Chromatherapist Mary Anderson tells us:

> Manuscripts from these early times show that in India, China and Egypt, the healer priests had a complete system of colour science, based on the law of correspondence between the sevenfold nature of man and the sevenfold division of the solar spectrum. Therefore the fundamental laws and principles governing the cosmic energy we know as colour have always been present in the Ancient Wisdom teachings for teachers and healers of all ages.[3]

Modern research into the subject has tended to confirm the effect of colour on the human psyche and other life-forms – plants, for example, which are highly sensitive to selected applications of light. Several respected medical authorities have added their weight to the idea that colour can have therapeutic effects on all organisms, notably Dr E D Babbitt and the Hindu scientist D P Ghadiali. In 1933, Ghadiali published *The Spectro Chromemetry Encyclopaedia* which has served as a working model for chromatherapists ever since.

Ghadiali taught that colours represent higher octaves of chemical potencies. Where healing is concerned there are those colours which stimulate the organs of the body, and those which inhibit their functioning. By understanding the essential correspondences a system of colour healing can easily be developed.

The vibrations emitted by colour may be evidenced in the work of Vicky D Wall, of Aurasoma fame, who is a member of the International Association of Colour Therapists. Vicky created her *Solar Colorcureum* after she had lost her sight. Like other healers she maintains that balance is the basis of well-being, and her crystal bottles contain dual combinations of striking colours, each embodying contrasting substances and emitting different vibrations. Composed of aroma essences, natural oils and herbs, the two-tone mixture can be easily applied to the body and is also visually therapeutic.

Esoteric science allocates us a sevenfold nature of subtle bodies which are believed to function on the following seven planes of existence:

1. Physical Etheric

2. Astral

3. Lower Mental

4. Higher Mental

5. Spiritual Causal

6. Intuitional

7. Divine or Absolute.

The question of planes of existence and subtle bodies, which received a degree of coverage in Chapter 6, is once again thrown into relief. To this we may now add the concept of the chakras or centres of energy, which interpenetrate with the physical body at certain anatomical points and are said to function via the endocrine system. Although there are believed to be more of these chakras than the number generally accepted, for the purpose of chromatherapy we will stay with the basic seven. Mary Anderson allocates the Seven Primary Rays and the centres which predominantly attract them as follows:

Colour	Chakra	Endocrine Gland	Area of the body
Red	Muladhara	Reproductory organs	Base of spine
Orange	Svadisthana	Pancreas/adrenals	Sacral or spleen
Yellow	Manipura	Adrenals/pancreas	Solar Plexus
Green	Anahata	Thymus	Breasts/heart
Blue	Visuddhu	Thyroid/parathyroid	Throat
Indigo	Ajna	Pineal	Between the eyes
Violet	Sahasrara	Pituitary	Top of the head

There is a variance of opinion regarding the chakras and their corresponding endocrines, the upper two and lower three being the most controversial. Some authorities allocate the Sahasrara chakra to the pineal gland and the Ajna to the pituitary –

beliefs also differ concerning the relationships between the reproductive organs and the Svadisthana/Muladhara complex (in radionics these occupy reverse positions from those I have outlined), while the Svadisthana centre is also referred to as the Splenic Centre.

Although the Manipura Chakra is frequently allotted to the adrenals due to the energising qualities of adrenalin, it is also associated with the insulin-producing pancreas. The adrenal cortex and medulla behave like two separate glands – the adrenal cortex, which is essential for life, producing hydrocortisone in addition to a certain type of sex hormone. Destruction of the adrenals can result in Addison's Disease, loss of salt, fall in blood-pressure, the inability to react to stress, and eventual death, which should serve as a clue as to which allocation is correct.

Modus Operandi

I have encountered many methods of applying colour therapy. Some psychologists are able to ascertain one's personality type from their choice of colour. A standard colour/personality test was devised by Dr Max Lüscher as a result of his research into people's colour preferences and psychological make-up. This is used by some psychologists to this day as a basis for job selection. In fact, a friend of mine (now deceased) was secretary to a managing director who hired a psychologist for this very purpose, who, being a good communicator, was only too happy to discuss his work with my friend. As a result, she asked him to effect an assessment for herself and her friend (yours truly!) – and uncomfortably accurate it was, too! In fact, I still have it to this day.

Research has shown that most of us find some colours stimulating and others relaxing. Nick Humphrey, Assistant Director of the Department of Animal Behaviour at the University of Cambridge, encountered some very strong reactions among his findings, which Inglis and West have recorded as follows:

> Large fields of red light induce physiological symptoms of emotional arousal – changes in heart rate, skin resistance and electrical activity of the brain. In patients suffering from certain pathological disorders, for instance, cerebellar palsy, these physiological effects become exaggerated. In cerebellar patients

red light may cause intolerable distress, exacerbating the disorders of posture and movement, lowering pain thresholds and
causing a general disruption of thought and skilled behaviour.[4]

Colour also affects the nervous system, and I was able to witness a case of this a few years ago when I was visiting Theo
Gimbel's Colour Therapy studios in Gloucestershire. I was in
the company of a young couple who had a small baby with
them. As we were about to enter the red room, Theo suggested
that the baby be left outside as the rays would most certainly
upset her. The parents, however, would have none of it: their
baby was very good, and she was fast asleep anyway, so there
was nothing to worry about. As we entered the room, which
was lit in various shades of red, the child started to stir and
within seconds she was awake and screaming for all she was
worth. Theo hastened us out of the room and into another that
was lit in shades of blue and green, whereupon the baby went
straight back to sleep without further ado.

Light is known to affect the pineal gland, a fact that did not
escape the ancients, being one of the influences behind the old
seasonal rites (see Chapter 6). Many people today suffer from
extreme depression during the autumn and winter months, and
treatment with light has been shown to afford them relief.

Psychological Suitability Assessment

My idea of how colour can best serve us is to incorporate it into
our daily lives in the most harmonious way. Unfortunately, we
are subjected to the whims of the fashion designers who earn
their huge fees by dictating to us what we should or should
not wear, and how we should furnish our homes. When winter
approaches the shops are filled with sombre browns, blacks and
greys – just the sort of shades we should *not* be wearing during
the dull months which lie ahead. In summer, when the sun is
brightly shining (well, hopefully, for us British!), the fashion
magazines and media bombard us with yellows, oranges, bright
greens, pastels and shimmering whites. No doubt there are
logical reasons for keeping the darker shades for the winter
months, but from the therapeutic viewpoint the whole thing is
back to front! People should be allowed a choice as to which
colours they wear. I have a dear friend who is never comfortable

unless she is dressed in shades of brown, fawn or tan, while I myself am happiest in blues, turquoises or greens. So we both wait patiently for 'our' year to come, when the mysterious 'they' allow us to be ourselves for a change!

ART THERAPY

The idea behind art therapy is to provide a way in which people can express themselves other than verbally, which process is believed to be therapeutic in itself. Art therapy is still comparatively new in Britain and it was not until December 1981 that the British Association of Art Therapists was finally granted the status of one of the Professions Supplementary to Medicine. I find this strange in view of the fact that occupational therapists have been working along these lines for many years, especially among the mentally ill.

Modus Operandi

Psychologists have long understood that art can reflect the subconscious mind, especially if it is expressed in some abstract form. As this is a comparatively youthful form of therapy there is little structure behind its application at present, and more research is needed in order to highlight those areas in which this therapy can prove of most use. General opinion, however, tends to favour the idea that the patient be allowed to use the brush or pencils in a semi-automatic way, without having recourse to the left brain hemisphere. In this way, the instinctive and intuitive awareness patterns are allowed free access from the right brain, via the hands. The results may be graphic or symbolic, and it will then be up to the art therapist or psychologist to make the necessary deductions.

Psychological Suitability Assessment

As an aid to the exteriorisation of the unconscious mind art therapy could prove an invaluable tool in the hands of the trained paramedical practitioner working closely with a psychologist or psychiatrist. It could also provide an outlet for those who are simply seeking to express their feelings in some way other than verbally, in which case it might, perhaps, find some future niche among the preventive therapies.

MUSIC THERAPY

There are several correspondences between music therapy and art therapy in that both are fairly new to the healing scene, and therefore to a degree unstructured. Healing through the power of music, however, is as old as mankind itself and history abounds with instances of cures effected through the agency of sound.

In primitive tribes, chanting formed a part of their most sacred rites, just as it constitutes an integral part of our present-day religious practices. Shamans would dance and chant themselves into those states of ecstasy they deemed necessary to effect their healing role in the community.

The Bible tells us that David played on his harp and healed Saul, and when Elisha was 'much troubled by importunate kings' he called for a minstrel, and when he played 'the hand of the Lord came upon him'. Ancient mythology abounds with references to the power of music. Apollo soothed Argus to sleep. Orpheus tamed wild beasts with his song and lyre and even gained entry into the regions of Hades himself through the sheer beauty of his music. Amphion built the walls of Thebes with the magical music of his lyre, and when Ulysses was wounded during the siege of Troy, Autolycus sang a magic melody to staunch the flow of blood. Asclepius antedated by two thousand years modern vibrational treatment for deafness, and Plato emphasised the influence of properly chosen music.

The Bards of Britain were skilled in the uses of harmony, and in the thirteenth century the Arabs used musical treatment for certain diseases. Even Galen recommended music for various ills. One could also add Pythagoras, Plutarch, Milton and many others to the list of believers in the efficacy of musical therapy.

Animals are certainly influenced by music. The snake charmer is a popular feature in the East, while in the West cows are said to yield more milk if certain types of music are played to them. Experiments have also shown that flowers are partial to harmonious melodies, while some varieties, notably primroses, have an aversion to pop music!

Some arcane schools maintain that we each have an individual keynote which can be ascertained by executing each interval of the scale on a violin. When the appropriate note is played a sensation will occur at the back of the neck! Those among us who have a reasonable ear for music will, no doubt, feel an affinity with a certain musical composition, the key signature of which will give a clue as to our personal keynote.

Compositions with no key changes are considered best for healing as typified by the Dorian music which David played to Saul. 'F' is believed to be the keynote of nature and to correspond to the colour green, while Pythagoras opined that 'A' and 'B-flat' possessed great potencies.

Music for healing, like Pythagorean medicine, is divided into four classes: tonic, stimulant, sedative and narcotic. Different notes also correspond to colours which in turn relate to the chakric system as follows:

Colour	*Note*	*Chakra*
Red	C	Muladhara
Orange	D	Svadisthana
Yellow	E	Manipura
Green	F	Anahata
Blue	G	Visuddhu
Indigo	A	Ajna
Violet	B	Sahasrara

Just as musical notes accord with colours, sound can paint graphic tonal pictures. The sombre cadences of browns, greys and dull reds contrast sharply with the light airy tones of the pastels, while the bright celebratory sounds of exultation loudly proclaim the primaries. Martial music blares the brighter shades of energising red, while peaceful blue-green tones are conducive to meditation, relaxation and tranquillity. As certain colours blend, so are some note combinations harmonious, or otherwise as the case may be.

The modern modes in European music consist of the major scale and the harmonic and melodic minors. It is interesting to note that the ancient Egyptians, who were adept at both colour and musical therapies, used a scale which went: C, D, E, F-sharp, G, A, B. On the colour chart I have just shown this would mean that their greens tended to partake of a turquoise hue, which in fact they did.

Modus Operandi

Since it is only comparatively recently that music has been accepted as a system of therapy, there is, as yet, no set form for its use in this connection. It has tended to become an accompaniment for certain forms of meditation, while a series of tapes labelled 'New Age Music' have appeared on the market ostensibly for the purpose of raising levels of conscious awareness and counteracting the stress of everyday living.

Music is, of course, closely allied to the science of sonics, and I have a theory (or perhaps it is a far memory?) that sonics will play an important part in the future of healing. But that is looking a long way ahead!

A line of demarcation needs to be drawn between music appreciation classes, active participation in the musical scene as with solo, chorus or group singing, and playing a musical instrument either in solo, or in a band or ensemble. The choice of approach will depend very much on the therapist, and will no doubt be governed to a degree by the age-group of the class, or individual, as the case may be.

Psychological Suitability Assessment

Music therapy must surely be governed to an extent by the musical taste of the participants. Playing a Brahms string quartet to a group of rebellious teenagers would hardly guarantee the best results, whereas group participation in folk music – which is a step in the right direction away from the jarring world of 'pop' – might fit the bill. I would personally like to attend exercise classes, but since they are inevitably performed to rock music I am unable to do so, as beat music of any kind can be guaranteed to give me a bad headache or an upset stomach. This goes to illustrate the pronounced effect rhythm and harmony have upon the automatic nervous system.

Music for therapy should therefore be chosen with care, and I would suggest that training courses for therapists include a comprehensive study of socio-psychology as well as a diploma in music. There are a variety of settings that could accommodate this particular therapy – hospital wards, mental institutions and community centres, in addition to groups or individuals in private psychotherapy sessions. Children can benefit greatly from music, especially those that are emotionally disturbed, mentally retarded or austistic.

Endnotes:

1. *The Psychology of Ritual*, M Hope, p. 9.
2. *The Alternative Health Guide*, B Inglis and R West, p. 147.
3. *Colour Healing*, M Anderson, p. 13.
4. *Op. cit.* Inglis and West, p. 155.

Chapter 18

THE PSYCHOLOGICAL THERAPIES AND BEHAVIOURISM

PSYCHOTHERAPY

Psychotherapy is basically the treatment of the mind or psyche by psychological rather than medicinal means, although the term now covers a wide range of practices which involve the use of mental techniques to sort out physical, mental and emotional problems.

The term 'psychotherapy' is used rather freely and sometimes to describe that which it is not – an extra-long chat with one's GP for example. What it really consists of is a form of verbal interchange between a therapist and patient, which may last up to an hour or even more, directed at locating the basic cause of the patient's problem speedily and efficiently. Should your GP refer you to a psychotherapist, this is the sort of treatment you will receive rather than a detailed psychoanalysis of the kind that may be spread over a period of weeks or months. Psycho-therapy may be administered by psychiatrists, psychologists, social workers or anyone who has been trained to do so.

We have Sigmund Freud to thank for the development and special character of psychotherapy. After using hypnosis on patients as a means of bringing to the surface the repressed traumas that gave rise to neurotic symptoms, he became dissatisfied with this method, feeling that it would be much better for the patient if he or she could be encouraged to recall and face up to these traumatic episodes for himself. He therefore developed the now-famous 'psychoanalysis' which is still used by Freudian psychologists, while C G Jung devised his own analytical methods following his break with Freud. Psychotherapy represents an abbreviated version which has proved more suitable in a society where time is at a premium and cost a stumbling block.

Very few psychotherapists have medical degrees or qualifications in Psychology – if they did they would be psychiatrists or psychologists. Nor is such a qualification essential as long as some training has been undertaken, backed up by supervised fieldwork. Many psychologists do not count themselves among the ranks of alternative therapists, in spite of the fact that some of the therapies they dispense have developed well beyond the territory of orthodox medicine. E L P MacPherson, principal clinical psychologist to the journal *World Medicine* wrote:

Psychologists are, and always have been, a profession independent of medicine. . . . Clinical psychologists have practised psychotherapy since psychotherapy first came into being. Rogerian psychotherapy was the brainchild of a psychologist – not a psychiatrist. Behavioural psychotherapy is . . . based entirely on psychological principles – not medical. Freud, the ultimate authority, argues cogently in *Essays On Psychoanalysis*, that a medical training is not only unnecessary for the practice of psychotherapy, but also that, in some ways, it could be a positive disadvantage in successful practice.[1]

Modus Operandi

When a course of psychotherapy is undertaken the patient and therapist should first of all agree on a goal. The purpose of the consultation will naturally vary with each individual, but whether it is for self-improvement, the resolution of a deep-seated problem, the improvement of relationships, or some emotional trauma, both sides should be aware of what is expected. Once the goal has been accepted the patient will probably arrange to see his or her therapist at agreed intervals: weekly, or perhaps twice a week to start with, depending on the seriousness of the condition or the availability of time or funds. Psychotherapy does not promise immediate results or instant insight, so many people may prefer to opt for physical therapies, such as primal therapy or bioenergetics which tend to produce somewhat faster – and sometimes more dramatic results.

Although some practitioners favour the traditional couch, the patient is more likely to face the psychotherapist across a table, or from a facing chair from which he will be encouraged to talk through problems, relate dreams, express pent-up frustrations, and even have a good cry on the therapist's shoulder. In fact, direct touch is recommended for achieving a better rapport with the patient, many people being unable to express themselves successfully through verbal interaction.

Psychological Suitability Assessment

This therapy is best-suited to those borderline patients who are the victims of emotional upsets, family stresses, abusive behaviour, bereavements or other socio-psychological problems. The therapist should be cautioned, however, to discourage the idea that the recipient of the therapy is in some way mentally ill. In fact, the term 'client' would be a kinder one to use, rather than 'patient'. Should the therapist be faced with a serious case of psychosis, the wisest course of action would be a referral to a psychiatrist. We each have our limitations, which should not be decided by our egos or our bank balances!

HYPNOTHERAPY

There is nothing new about hypnotherapy. It was, in fact, ably practised by the physicians of classical Greece in the healing Temples of Asclepius, and in later Graeco-Roman times in the Iseums (Temples of Isis). Even earlier, the ancient Egyptians designated their god Anubis as patron of all out-of-the-body experiences, which included those encountered during hypnosis or while under anaesthetics.

It was Franz Anton Mesmer (1734–1815) who revitalised the concept of hypnosis in the late eighteenth century, however, giving his name to the then popular practice of 'mesmerism'. Mesmer originally attributed his powers to the use of a steel magnet, but upon discovering that they worked just as well without it, he redefined the force as 'animal magnetism'. The kind of healing Mesmer practised was, in the opinion of many, more akin to shamanism than modern hypnotherapy, so while his original treatment consisted of inducing symptoms of severe disassociation, it was not long before he discovered the advantage of the trance state. Mesmer claimed that his methods guaranteed pain-free surgery, which statement was met with total disbelief by the medical profession. When he endeavoured to prove this before a panel of doctors, they accused him of paying the patients not to cry out and of practising what was nothing but superstitious nonsense.

In the 1840s a sceptical Scots surgeon, one James Braid, carried out an investigation of the hypnotic process and pronounced it genuine, but simply a condition of the nervous system which bore no relationship either to animal magnetism, the occult, or any such superstitious notion. Braid coined the term 'hypnosis' from the Greek word *hypnos* – sleep – although, in fact, a hypnotised person is not actually asleep but awake and alert, albeit in such a relaxed state that deeper parts of the mind become accessible.

Because hypnosis was accepted at a time when the medical profession was solely concerned with defining and treating organic disorders, it was judged to be a form of hysteria and therefore unworthy of inclusion in the new, and totally materialistic concept of medicine. Freud employed hypnosis for a period but abandoned it in favour of analysis, as he felt that it prevented patients from consciously facing the repressed material in their unconscious minds. His judgement in this matter is still observed by Freudian psychologists to this day.

Although hypnotherapy is becoming increasingly popular in our present age, it still carries a distinctly metaphysical flavour which the medical profession has endeavoured to eradicate. An article in *The Lancet* has urged new legislation on the use of hypnosis by the layman, claiming that it belonged within the confines of the medical profession and constituted a danger when administered by the untrained.

Modus Operandi

Hypnotherapy falls into two basic categories. Type One involves putting the patient into a state of trance and suggesting that their symptoms will disappear, while Type Two augments general psychological treatment by enabling the therapist to explore the patient's subconscious mind. In either case, the initial procedure is identical. A full case history is taken and if hypnotherapy is to follow, a description of the proceedings will then be given by the therapist. Some therapists will not introduce the hypnosis until the second session, although most practitioners known to me usually proceed with the induction of the trance state once they feel the patient is at ease and his or her confidence has been gained.

Hypnotherapists usually position themselves in front or beside the patient. Some like their patients to be seated upright while others favour the prone position. The popular concept of the hypnotic state induced by the swinging of a pendulum, watch, or other such object in front of the patient's eyes accompanied by the words 'You are feeling very tired . . . you are feeling oh so sleepy . . .' does not always follow. Many hypnotherapists make use of relaxing music during sessions, and simply talk very quietly to their patients. Sometimes a patient will enter a deep trance state (known as third-degree hypnosis) and after being brought round will remember nothing of what has transpired. But in most cases one is fully conscious during the whole proceeding.

Being in apparent control of one's faculties would not appear to diminish the efficacy of the autosuggestion used by the hypnotist. While I was living in Canada, a well-known hypnotherapist was being interviewed by a popular radio personality who upbraided him as a charlatan. The hypnotist threw down the gauntlet and the announcer accepted the challenge to be hypnotised, believing himself impervious to autosuggestion by virtue of his religious faith. The test was extremely short and the only suggestion made by the hypnotist was that prior to reading the six-o'clock news the gentleman in question should crow three times like a rooster! Although the listeners heard the hypnotist make the suggestion, the announcer appeared unaware of what had taken place and dismissed his interviewee with disdain.

Needless to say, an unusually large number of listeners tuned in to the six-o'clock news that evening. As the chimes were sounded, our sceptical announcer spoke. 'Ladies and gentleman, here is the six-o'clock news . . . cock-a-doodle-do . . .' (repeated thrice), followed by an embarrassed apology!

Which brings us to the inevitable question – while under hypnosis, can we be influenced to do something that is completely against our nature? The answer appears to be 'no', other than crowing at 6 p.m. of course! The subconscious mind seems to have a will of its own, in spite of 'post-hypnotic suggestion'. On the occasion of an experimenter making a suggestion that was totally out of character to the medical student who was playing unofficial 'guinea pig' for him, he was promptly told to 'get stuffed'. The young man in question had absolutely no recall later either of hearing the suggestion or rendering the retort!

There are some remarkable cases on record of conditions that have been cured through hypnosis. In their illuminating book *Explaining the Unexplained*, Eysenck and Sargent cite the case of a boy who was successfully treated by hypnosis of an intractable genetic illness which caused the boy's skin to assume a crocodile-like appearance. A well-known hypnotist, Dr A Mason, was called in. In order to convince sceptics in the medical profession that the cure was to be effected by hypnotism, he used the initial session to suggest to the boy that the hard skin would disappear from one arm only, which is exactly what happened. Dr Mason later went on to clear some 90 per cent of the affected areas of the boy's body in the same way. The case was fully reported later in the *British Medical Journal*.[2]

One of the fears often expressed by doctors is that the hypnotist who effects cures of this nature is simply suppressing the symptoms without removing the causes. Dare one suggest that those same physicians are doing just that in prescribing sedatives, tranquillisers, anti-inflammatory drugs, beta-blockers and similar symptom suppressors!

The hypnotic experience is believed to function at three different levels:

Stage 1 – light hypnosis, when the hypnotised person is often unaware that they have been hypnotised at all (as in the case of the crowing radio announcer);

Stage 2, in which one is relaxed, but perfectly aware of what is going on and cognisant of all that transpires, and

Stage 3, in which the patient has no later recall of the proceedings. Hypnotherapists frequently make a tape of each session in case they feel it necessary for the patient/client to refer to what he or she may have said while under the influence.

Stage 2 is usually related to alpha brain rhythms and Stage 3 to the theta frequency. When researching hypnosis in relation to regression, psychologist Dr Helen Wambach noted that the hypnotic state functions best at a brainwave amplitude of five cycles per second, a measure which she later employed in an experimental group biofeedback programme.

A hypnotist may see fit to regress a patient to the period prior to their birth and even further, if necessary, to seek the cause of a specific condition which cannot be traced to traumas in the earlier part of the patient's present life. This procedure may also be employed simply to satisfy a client's curiosity. Regression (like progression, which is sometimes employed to help alleviate anxieties which will obviously be resolved by the passage of time) is a practice that has its pros and cons, so let us consider these under our next heading.

Psychological Suitability Assessment

In earlier chapters I have cited several cases where hypnosis has proven to be a considerable help to the patient/client. I could add sufficiently more of these to fill half a volume, but then there is always the exception that proves the rule, and no doubt my medical friends would be able to produce a goodly number of those!

From my own observations and cases I have read about and discussed with several hypnotherapists, I have arrived at the following conclusions:

1. The subconscious mind does *not* know all the answers;
2. Subconscious delusions are as prevalent as conscious ones, and the same applies to ego-trips;
3. When 'progressed' (taken forward into the future), the

hypnotised person will 'relate' what he or she feels at the time rather than what is really likely to occur;

4. Conscious longings or wants are not always shared by the subconscious. We may proclaim how much we need to pursue a certain course of action, fulfil a stated desire, marry the man next door, and so forth, but when under hypnosis our subconscious mind may hasten to repudiate any such notions – even to the point of ridicule;

5. Details of 'past lives' rendered during exploratory regression probes are not always what they seem. While I subscribe to the idea that we do live more than once, I also believe that some people are able to tap into the collective unconscious (or Akashic Records) either during the sleep state or while under hypnosis and absorb the lives and personalities of others who have lived in different periods of time. This would account for the repetitious personae that emerge in some cases of hypnotic regression, and the numerous Queen Nefertiti's, Julius Caesar's and Jesus's who appear regularly during past life readings given by psychics.

My verdict? Where knowledge of the subconscious mind is concerned, we have not yet passed the infant stage. And as for hypnotherapic regression, refrain from trying to satisfy your curiosity unless you are strong-minded enough to be able to view your psyche in *gestalt*. Not all far-memory experiences are milk and honey. Some, especially death recalls, can be extremely traumatic and abreaction-producing. So think carefully before you step outside the safety of the 'now' – the first bogey you meet round the corner may well be your own shadow!

SILVA MIND CONTROL

This system derives its name from José Silva, a self-taught electronics engineer of Mexican-American origins who developed a particular interest in psychology and hypnotism. It was his work in electronics, however, that led him to the believe that the human brain might function best at certain wavelengths. While hypnosis and similar ecstatic or trance-like states enhanced receptivity and awareness, they did not allow sufficient access to left-hemisphere reasoning power to effect the rational translation essential for practical application of any knowledge gleaned from the experience. Silva therefore concentrated on the 'alpha' level, a wavelength of ten cycles a second – which is usually associated with what is popularly referred to as daydreaming or a 'brown study'.

In fact, 'mind control' implies what it is. The more transcendental practices tend to function at the deeper, or five cycles (theta) frequency which tends to leave the body functioning autonomically, whereas alpha waves assume voluntary physical control and allow the mind to be keenly tuned for analysis.

Modus Operandi

Silva Mind Control is based on a four-day course. Day one comprises an introductory lecture with exploratory exercises designed to enable the student to differentiate between the alpha and theta brain waves. Day two involves the student in the practice of mind control through dynamic meditation. Day three concerns the practice of disciplines appropriate to the development of intuition and time/space perception and negotiation. On the fourth and final day the student is instructed in either self-progression or the group experience according to preference. Overall, the course is designed to enable those who have successfully imbibed its message to function psychically at whichever level they may choose.

Psychological Suitability Assessment

I find myself in total agreement with those Philadelphia psychiatrists who, after investigating the system and analysing its effects on several people, arrived at the conclusion that it could present a mental hazard for a certain type of personality. A few of those who agreed to be under observation during the course benefited considerably from it, however, while the greater majority claimed some relief from tension and anxiety, and felt better able to use their own inner resources to sort out life's problems.

Unstable personalities who are unable to handle the space/time concept would be well advised to give this one a miss, although for the metaphysically advanced student it could prove to be just the right key for unlocking the door to externalisation.

AUTOGENIC TRAINING

Autogenic Training which, as the name implies, employs the practice of autosuggestion, made its first appearance in Britain in the 1970s when it was introduced here from Canada by Dr Malcolm Carruthers. One of its main aims is to teach the patient/client to control the autonomic nervous system by recognising the 'fight or flight' response and learning to modify and eventually cope with those symptoms which it inevitably produces. Increased heartbeat, rise in blood-pressure, loss of appetite – all are generated by the sympathetic nervous system, whereas these effects are counteracted by activity in the parasympathetic nervous system. The exercises in body awareness and physical relaxation which form part of the Autogenic Training regimen are designed to master stress and promote parasympathetic activity in the autonomic nervous system.

Modus Operandi

The term 'autogenic' (generated from within) works in two stages. Stage 1 involves a shifting from the state of nervous excitement to one of passive relaxation, and Stage 2, active participation by the individual in the health-promoting aspects of the system. The procedure has been likened to learning to drive a car. One commences by adjusting one's driving position, engaging the engine and moving systematically through the gears until one reaches top, which is represented by 'passive concentration'.

There is something of Couéism – a technique involving the repetition of beneficial autosuggestive phrases – in autogenics, in that specific commands may be given to the body in an autosuggestive way that are calculated to assist the participant in the pursuit of mind-over-matter. Visualisation is also used, and many patients have reported that their first efforts to gain control over what has hitherto functioned in a purely autonomous way may frequently cause some shock to the system. Abreaction is not an uncommon phenomenon in autogenic training, the link between somatic autonomy and the unconscious being emphasised by the procedure.

Psychological Suitability Assessment

Results appear to indicate that this particular treatment could help those who are suffering from psychosomatic disorders. Relief from asthma, skin problems, allergies, premenstrual tension and menopausal difficulties are listed among its successes, and it is also recommended as a viable self-help system. The basic exercises need to be practised two or three times a day in order to ensure its success, which might prove a stumbling block for the busy person who works long and arduously and returns home too tired to do anything other than sleep. Anyone who has (or can make) the time to study this therapy could doubtless benefit from it. As far as the abreaction and shock to the system aspects are concerned, however, I feel that these should only be experienced under the surveillance of a qualified teacher who can guide the patient through the stormy waters of confusion to the safe harbour of equilibrium.

MEDITATION

To me, the word 'meditation' conjures up a large umbrella under which many ASC practices conveniently shelter. Therefore, a deal of caution needs to be exercised in sorting the wheat from the chaff. Although in the eyes of many people it is viewed as an Eastern practice, meditation has, in fact, featured in every culture.

Shamans, medicine men, witch-doctors – all have meditated themselves and taught appropriate techniques to those who have sought their aid for healing or spiritual guidance. The meditative techniques of the East are perhaps better known, however, notably the Transcendental Meditation of the now legendary Maharishi Mahesh Yogi, whose mantras have found their way into all avenues of life. Since his rise to fame in the 1960s, TM and similar meditative procedures have become incorporated in both orthodox and alternative treatments, either in complementary form or as recognised adjuncts.

The goals of meditation are still hotly debated. New York psychologist Lawrence LeShan suggests four main meditative paths:

The Intellectual – the pursuit of knowledge and wisdom;
The Emotional – as in the Christian: 'God is Love' theme;
The Somatic   – the 'exercise principle'
               – Hatha Yoga or T'ai Chi;
The Active   – enlightenment through movement, as with
                 the martial arts such as Akido and
                 similarly related Severity Code rites.

Specific meditative practices have also been evolved for the purpose of combating disease, notably cancer, and these are now accepted in many cancer clinics as standard aids to the mental attitude towards the disease. Oncologists and physicians, however, are still inclined to dismiss meditation, psychic healing and similar practices as purely occupational therapies which may lift the patient's spirits but do not contribute in any way to the clinical cure.

While on the subject of cancer, it is interesting to note that Bernard Siegel, an assistant professor of surgery at Yale University Medical School, found that one in five cancer patients does not really *want* to live. About half would like to be cured, but want someone else to do it for them while the remainder will do anything to get well. Siegel encourages his patients to explore their intuitive and clairvoyant powers through their dreams. As he phrased it in an interview: 'We all have the ability to heal ourselves. Our brains know, but we've forgotten on an intellectual level. On the primitive level we still know . . . but on the intellectual level we don't know how to take charge and control the healing process.'[4]

Modus Operandi

As there are so many systems of meditation and ways in which these operate it would be impossible to do justice to them all in a brief précis. Some involve many hours a day, others only five to ten minutes at a time. Some procedures are designed to be experienced under the tutorage of a 'guru' or teacher, while others are of a more solitary nature. Over the years I have known people who have regularly attended meditation circles involving anything from three to thirty in all. Most of the big public psychic festivals hold meditation 'classes'. On one occasion I was asked to take just such a class myself, the interesting and significant results of which I have detailed in *The Psychology of Ritual*.[5]

Psychological Suitability Assessment

The therapeutic effects of certain meditative practices which serve mainly as stress solvents have been satisfactorily proven. Although the advocates of meditation may list its numerous other advantages both physical and transcendental, many of the former are still not accepted by the medical profession, while some of the latter are, to say the least, highly questionable. So, in the final analysis, it all depends on what you believe, the individual mind being the eventual judge as to the efficacy of any system. There are people who find their relaxation in meditation and allied practices, and those who are best able to work out their frustrations and anxieties in action. The Eastern sages were only too well aware of this fact, which is one of the reasons why we have a choice between the silent, inward-looking, contemplative approach, or the externalised procedures of the Chinese/Japanese exercise/movement therapies.

There are also many people who receive their inspiration in the ordinary, day-to-day process of living. There is more than one path to the transcendental, and the practice of certain set rites does not guarantee the user the mystical prerogative. The embrace of a child or much-loved animal, the scent of a flower, the caress of the wind, the divine cadences of Mozart, Brahms or Bach may also afford the kind of ecstasy usually associated with meditationally induced ASC's. During a recent tour of California I was able to snatch a few free hours in the company of a friend. These we spent by a stream in a small copse of redwood trees communicating with the friendly Dryads and exchanging energies with the Ondines – a pursuit every bit as effective as a couple of hours sitting cross-legged repeating a mantra. But then the world is made up of individuals, a fact which many purveyors of mystical package deals sometimes tend to forget.

BIOFEEDBACK

Biofeedback is not so much a therapy as an aid to self-healing, and as such its role in the therapeutic scene demands analysis and appraisal. There is also a significant difference between the process and the training. The biofeedback process involves feeding back to the patient vital information concerning such biological processes as heartbeat, brainwave activity, blood-pressure and muscle tension, so that these may be observed and noted, whereas Biofeedback training involves the use of this information to effect voluntary changes in the monitored responses.

Through biofeedback we can be made aware of those processes to which we have previously given little thought. By amplifying unconscious bodily signals one becomes conscious of them, after which control may be more easily effected. The key to the success of biofeedback in tension reduction is the alpha brainwave, which is the predominant rhythm in our brains when we are relaxed. Patients learns to generate alpha at will with the assistance of the machine – certain bleeping or flashing signals alerting them to the fact that they are not relaxing and therefore not generating the correct rhythm.

Modus Operandi

Biofeedback machines come in various forms, most of which are designed to gauge tension levels. The feedback may be illustrated by the rise and fall of a needle on a chart, or by changes of colour. More sophisticated gadgetry may throw up on a screen a picture of what is taking place in both hemispheres at the same time. The electroencephalogram (EEG) used for biofeedback displays brainwave frequencies measured in cycles per second, which illustrate different levels of consciousness – beta (normal consciousness); alpha (relaxed awareness); theta (drowsiness) and delta (deep sleep).

As far as biological control is concerned, biofeedback training has many other uses. Blood-flow, heart-rate, and other functions which are normally monitored by the body's own homoeostatic mechanism can be regulated at will, while experiments with rats have shown that is is also possible to exercise control over kidney and similar bodily functions. Interestingly enough, animals often fare better than humans when it comes to accepting the healing process, the reason being that we have become so left-hemisphere-orientated that the logic we prize so highly has tended to become our worst enemy!

Psychological Suitability Assessment

I have never had the opportunity to try a biofeedback machine but would very much like to do so, but then I have that kind of mind – there are those who do not. I see no harm in this method of biological self-analysis, however, as long as the machine does not become the prop.

DREAM THERAPY

> *The individual way is a peculiar serpentine way, and that is the way of the dream.*

> Carl Gustav Jung

Psychoanalysts have been using their patient's dreams to facilitate their analysis since the practice of psychiatry first began. And yet this form of therapy pre-dates Freud and his contemporaries by thousands of years. References to the study and practice of dream interpretation are to be found in the myths, legends and history or most races and cultures, and mankind's fascination with the torrent of subconscious images that accompany sleep has by no means diminished over the centuries.

Dream books are among today's best-sellers, and I have no intention of reiterating the information contained in such a concise and lucid little manual as Nerys Dee's *Your Dreams and What They Mean*, which takes into account the clinical, psychological and metaphysical inuendos of dreams. I would, however, like to mention a few scientific and historical facts which might serve to shed some light on the nightly outpourings of our brains.

Dr Jim Horne, who runs the Sleep Research Laboratory at Loughborough University and is the author of *Why We Sleep*, wrote an interesting article in *The Guardian* entitled 'Excitement

Under the Eiderdown'. It concerned an electrical event which takes place during REM (rapid eye movement) sleep that is unique to this sleep pattern, distinguishing it from both non-REM sleep and wakefulness. It is called PGO (ponto-geniculo-occipital) spiking, and comes in outbursts from the brainstem travelling up through the brain at the same time that the rapid eye movements make their appearance.

Drs Adrian Morrison and Robert Bowker, from the University of Pennsylvania, noticed that whilst brain recordings of sleeping animals in a normal quiet environment produced the classical PGO spikes confined to REM sleep, when some kind of external noise was introduced during non-REM sleep the PGO spikes reappeared. In fact, they could be initiated into the sleep pattern in both REM and non-REM sleep by the introduction of noise, or simply by touching the sleeping animal. This gave the investigators the idea that the PGO spikes are simply some sort of alerting response which is not unique to REM sleep and should also, therefore, be present during wakefulness.

Further research appeared to indicate that PGO spikes and eye movement potentials are simply part of generalised alerting responses which are produced during waking and REM sleep, each response being accompanied by a burst of eye movement. Morrison and Bowker have therefore assumed normal REM sleep to be a type of exaggerated awareness where the sleeper experiences a number of surprises which are generated from within the brainstem and not from the outside environment. These responses are accompanied by momentary physiological changes in the autonomic nervous system and could account for those times when we may wake up with a racing pulse, in a hot sweat, or icy cold.

There is far more to the subject than this, of course, and those whose interest extends beyond the vaguely curious are recommended to Dr Horne's book. However, it did strike me that these facts provide answers to those types of dreams which seem to defy psychological interpretation or reasoning.

Dr Montague Ullman, founder of the Dream Laboratory at the Maimonides Medical Center in New York, who pioneered the Dream Therapy referred to in our title, became cognisant of the limitations imposed by traditional psychiatric methods of dream interpretation. The term 'dream appreciation' struck him as being applicable to his ideas, so he proceeded to apply it in therapy.

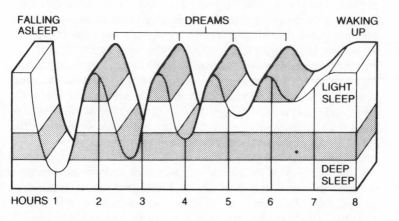

FALLING ASLEEP · DREAMS · WAKING UP · LIGHT SLEEP · DEEP SLEEP · HOURS 1 2 3 4 5 6 7 8

DREAM PATTERNS

Dreaming occurs during light sleep, and it is usual to pass through this level four times in one night.

After working several years in the Freudian school of dream analysis, Ullman came to appreciate that the symbolic language of the unconscious can work at many levels, so that while a snake might have phallic implications for one person, for another it could indicate wisdom (as it did in the ancient Egyptian magical tradition), while it might be viewed as a symbol of temptation by someone of the Christian or Judaic persuasion. A psychoanalyst may therefore be able to help us to understand our dream, but he or she cannot appreciate it for us, no matter how accurate the interpretation.

Modus Operandi

Dream therapy undertaken in groups usually involves each member relating their sleep experiences to the other members of the group who provide commentary and appreciation of the dream as they would relate it to themselves. This affords the dreamer a variety of interpretations, any one of which might seem to fit his or her particular case.

There are many other forms of sleep therapy in addition to Dr Ullman's dream discussion groups and the psychoanalyst's probings, however, Narcosis and Incubation Therapy being two examples. In Chapter 4, I mentioned the work of Dr Peter Nixon and his colleagues at Charing Cross Hospital who are using induced sleep for relaxation as one of their main weapons against threatened heart attack. Patients are put to sleep for long periods thus allowing the body time to recover its equilibrium and build up its resources. For some people sleep is the *only* answer to exhaustion and tension, as they are never able to relax fully when awake.

The Greeks of the classical era were, of course, pastmasters at this, the Temples of Sleep at Epidaurus being renowned throughout the then civilised world. Scholars still debate whether the Greek physicians induced their long healing sleeps narcotically or hypnotically, but either way we are given to understand that their success rate was high. In Greek mythology the winged Hypnos was the god of Sleep and his son Morpheus the giver of dreams. Incubation therapy was also practised in other religious settings, such as the Temples of Isis in later Graeco-Roman times, while in ancient Egypt the god Anubis was designated both patron of anaesthetists and those practitioners we would refer to today as psychiatrists and psychologists! Anubis's mother, Nephthys, was the ancient Egyptian goddess of Sleep.

Psychological Suitability Assessment

The subject of dreams interests most of us, if we care to admit it. Sometimes we would like to rid ourselves of certain repetitive patterns which can prove irritating or even disturbing, while there are other dreams from which we are almost reluctant to awake. Some people are fortunate enough to be able to practise lucid dreaming, meaning that they can control what is going on in their dreams. For example, if a dream involves the loss of a valued possession, the dreamer, being aware that it is only a dream, is able to 'imagine' its immediate return and lo and behold, there it will be! Another feat often practised by occultists and shamans is shape-shifting. Let us say that a particularly nasty dog is chasing us – the shape-shifter may assume the role of a full-grown male lion and send its assailant scampering off in retreat. I have tried it many times myself and it really does work!

The 'alternative experience' theory, favoured by some psychologists, sees the dream as a vehicle for the protection of consciousness, which can also serve as a kind of safety valve, or preparation for difficult times ahead. We may dream of an alternative existence which involves us in dramas of sickness, loss, suffering and even breakdown, none of which feature in our present lives. This is believed by some (myself included), to be the subconscious mind's way of relieving us of the necessity of undergoing such difficulties in the reality of material existence, while compensatory or complementary overtones can also be read into it.

I am inclined to the opinion that dream therapy of the normal, analytical type (as opposed to the deliberately induced Epidaurean variety) can be quite revealing and, as long as it does not develop into a compulsive routine, it can help us to understand what our subconscious mind is trying to tell us. Once we become aware of the nature of the message behind those recurring dreams that cause us concern, we can adjust our lives accordingly, whereupon the dreams will cease.

BEHAVIOURISM AND BEHAVIOUR THERAPY

Most people have heard of Ivan Pavlov (1849–1936) and his famous dogs which were conditioned to respond to a given stimulus. When this was changed, however, they displayed neurotic symptoms which were only rectified with reconditioning or 'overprogramming'.

The behaviourist school of psychology favours the view that neuroses, being conditioned reflexes, can be unlearned and replaced with more congenial thought patterns. In recent times the more influential behaviourists, notably Professor B F Skinner, while not ignoring the genetic or inner mental processes, hold that our thoughts, feelings and behaviour are effectively shaped by experience and the society in which we live.

Modus Operandi

Behavioural Therapy has, of course, existed since time immemorial in that we punish the naughty child and reward the good one, just as Pavlov rewarded his dogs when they complied with his conditioning. In modern times, however, it has many applications, the best-known of which is probably Aversion Therapy. People who are anxious to rid themselves of alcoholism, excessive smoking or drug-taking may be given a drug which will cause them to be sick should they resort to their former habit. There are less violent methods in which the emphasis is placed on 'reinforcement' – the human equivalent of the reward received by the laboratory rat if it rings the right bell. Fear of spiders, for example, has been effectively treated in this way.

Behaviourism is frequently attacked by philosophers and churchmen on the grounds that it presents such a circumscribed cause-and-effect view of human behaviour that its scope must also be limited. Many also object to the idea that human beings act and react in exactly the same way as rats, dogs or other animals. Where, they argue, do creativity, poetry, music, mathematics, and similar hominid achievements feature in the behavioural pattern? This kind of thinking automatically pitches us into a world of metaphysical suppositions that really form the subject matter of another book.

Psychological Suitability Assessment

I most certainly agree that people, like animals, *are* conditioned to thinking and acting in a certain way and, like Pavlov's dogs, they respond with a fear neurosis when confronted by anyone who does not comply with the thinking patterns of their particular collective. But unlike some behaviourists I also allow for the soul-age. Youthful psyches have ever felt safety in numbers and will continue to do so until they reach spiritual maturity. The process of individuation will then take them forward, out of the collective and into the realms of creativity, where they may express their inner knowledge through art, science, medicine, philosophy, music – yes – even psychology! As I have dealt with this individuation concept in several of my other books, I will refrain from further detail at this point.

Endnotes:

1. *The Alternative Health Guide*, B Inglis, and R West, p. 162.
2. *Explaining the Unexplained*, H Eysenck and C Sargent, pp. 111–112.
3. *Ibid.* p. 185.
4. *The Psychology of Ritual*, M Hope, p. 41.

Chapter 19

THE HUMANISTIC AND TRANSPERSONAL PSYCHOLOGIES

Humanistic psychology, which has been described as the 'third force', following after psychoanalysis and behaviourism is indebted to Abraham Maslow who saw in the science of psychology dimensions beyond the accepted escape from neurosis, psychosis and general mental malaise.

Its advantage over the more structured schools would appear to lie in its broad approach, being comprised of ideas and procedures from many different sources – Freud, Jung, Reich and Assagioli, for example. Its development went hand in hand with the Growth Movement which predominated the sixties. Human potential needed to be realised, and any method that might lead to this end was welcomed.

Inglis and West quote the British Institute for the Development of Human Potential as stating:

Although eclectic in nature, there are certain common themes –

First: Personal growth, responsibility and self-direction;
Second: Life-long education;
Third: Full emotional functioning;
Fourth: The need to learn, or perhaps to relearn, what play and joy are about; and

Fifth: Recognition of a person's spiritual dimensions: there is an acknowledgement of human capacity for altered states of consciousness.[1]

The humanistic psychologies are therefore often interchangeable, so although a practitioner may fall back on his original training, because of the need to accommodate the broad spectrum of human experience demanded by the growth movement, he may well employ whichever techniques are best suited to each patient.

ROGERIAN THERAPY

Carl Rogers, founder of Rogerian Therapy, was one of the pioneers of the school of therapies which seeks to ascertain the needs of the patient through the faculty of intuition. Rogers himself came up with the Growth Movement, which lifted psychoanalysis out of the private consulting rooms into the broader field of everyday life.

Rogers was one of many American psychoanalysts who became disillusioned with the normal procedures adopted by psychologists and other professional counsellors, which tended to keep consultant and patient well apart. The sense of touch appeared to him to constitute an important part of the analyst/patient relationship and therefore constituted an essential ingredient in the healing process.

Modus Operandi

Rogerian Therapy does not demand the use of set techniques. What it does insist upon, however, is that both client and counsellor have to 'meet' for growth to take place. The client must accept the counsellor and vice versa. Although Rogerian counselling does involve a one-to-one situation, a considerable amount of it is undertaken in encounter groups, which we will be dealing with next. Clients meet together on a regular basis, under the guidance of a counsellor, whose main job it is to listen and ensure that the group does not become out of hand when its members finally 'let go'

Rogers noted that clients appeared to pass through seven stages during their search for growth for what he termed 'self-actualisation'. The client would normally commence at Stage 1 with no concern for anything outside of his immediate life and worries, but having arrived at Stage 7, he or she would then begin to assume a trust in and responsibility for his own development and growth.

Psychological Suitability Assessment

This is a very popular form of counselling these days and one which is doubtless beneficial to many, with the proviso that the counsellor is competent. Sadly, however, this is not always the case. There is a tendency for some people to read a few books, attend a few weekend seminars, and then pronounce themselves expert counsellors. I would most certainly think twice about baring my soul to some of the counsellors I know personally, but this should in no way detract from the efficacy of the original practice as defined by Rogers. Problems may also occur if the counsellor does not see eye to eye with the clients ideas or persuasions, in which case it would be better for both if the arrangement was terminated as soon as possible.

ENCOUNTER

Encounter therapy developed from a combination of Rogerian Therapy and Group Therapy. As we have already discussed, Carl Rogers broke from orthodox psychoanalytic procedures in creating the one-to-one on equal terms system of counselling. He and other analysts then began to use the group situation which many people found more conducive to the release of emotive self-expression than being faced with a single counsellor.

In the 1960s, Encounter assumed a degree of mysticism due mainly to the fact that it became associated with the numerous guru cults which had mushroomed in California during those times. Since then, however, it has undergone many changes and modifications, although the basic idea behind it remains the same. Participants were advised to stay with their bodies, pay attention to the here and now, express themselves physically rather than verbally, speak for themselves – always directing their remarks to the person with whom they are communicating, refraining from generalisations, and accepting individual responsibility.

Several books on the subject have made their appearance on the market, notably *You*, by William Schutz, and Sheila Ernst and Lucy Goodison's *In Your Own Hands*.

Modus Operandi

The idea behind Encounter is an interchange of emotional expression with others in the group. Although this may some-times involve people screaming and shouting abuse at each other, we are assured that this is not indicative of conflict, but rather of the expression of hatred and anger which needs to be released and left behind so that those in question can then move on into a more stable phase.

Encounter groups come in all sizes, depending on the thera-pist involved. Sometimes they follow Rogerian lines, in which case there is less likelihood of the violent outbursts that have come to be associated with the 'ordeal' type, in which a thera-pist may set two people one against another or engage in the simulated conflict themselves. In spite of the tensions that must obviously build up in these sessions, they frequently end with hugs and kisses all round.

Psychological Suitability Assessment

There are, no doubt, many people who are only able to let go when they are in a group with others on whom they can vent their spleen and pent-up wrath in a thoroughly legal manner. Personally, I see no difference between this and the case I mentioned in an earlier chapter of the lady who felt obliged to assume a 'possession pose' in order to hurl abuse at those around her. The angry child who is not getting its own way behaves similarly. Of course it feels better afterwards, but by then it has usually gained what it set out to achieve by the performance in the first place!

Maybe I am being unjust in this judgement, but experience has tended to show me that those who are able to gain some form of release through the overt expression of anger are likely to repeat the performance from time to time, and not always in the safety of an Encounter Group. But there again, as the Egyptian Priest Anebo (*circa AD.* 304) so wisely explained to the Greek sage Porphyry, the corporeal nature needs to be exorcised and exercised from time to time in order to keep the peace in a society which is composed of souls from many spiritual age-groups. And is it not therefore better that this is allowed under controlled conditions? Nothing changes – or so it would appear.

GESTALT

Friedrich (Fritz) Perls commenced his career as a psychoanalyst in Berlin, but as in the case of many other gurus of the alternative scene he soon became disenchanted with Freudian methods. He worked for a while with psychiatrist Wilhelm Reich, but later became interested in the *gestalt* ideas proffered by Max Wertheimer towards the end of the last century. Wertheimer's theory was that we may experience different feelings and ideas at different times which, if taken separately, could render an erroneous picture of what is really taking place in our mind, but if viewed as a 'whole' (in *gestalt*) a clearer picture emerges. Perls combined what he had learned from his experience as a psychoanalyst with a tincture of existentialism, advising his therapists to avoid at all costs the instant cure syndrome and concentrate on helping their clients to think existentially (here and now).

Although he had turned his back on Freud, he was also extremely concerned about the dangers inherent in the cult of 'instant cure, instant joy, instant sensory awareness', which although well-intentioned, was of little benefit to the patient in the long run. He saw it as 'a dangerous substitute activity, another phoney therapy that *prevents* growth'.[2]

Therapist Claudio Naranjo referred to Gestalt as *humanistic hedonism*. Perhaps the following lines by Fritz Perls from his book *Gestalt Therapy Verbatim* might supply the clue as to why:

The Gestalt Prayer
I do my thing, and you do your thing.
I am not in this world to live up to your expectations
And you are not in this world to live up to mine
You are you and I am I,
And if by chance we find each other, it's beautiful.
If not, it can't be helped.[3]

Modus Operandi

Due to Perls' own objection to any form of 'technique', providing an adequate description of what takes place in a Gestalt group is difficult if not impossible. Gestalt therapists employ many different methods, movement and art, bioenergetics, primal therapy and transactional analysis – anything goes as long as it leads to the aims of Gestalt which are:

Live now: Be concerned with the present rather than with the past or the future.

Live here: Deal with what is present rather than what is absent.

Stop imagining: Experience the real.

Stop unnecessary thinking: Rather, taste and see.

Express rather than manipulate, explain justify or judge.

Give in to unpleasantness and pain: just as to pleasure. Do not restrict your awareness.

Accept no should, or ought, other than your own. Adore no graven image.

Take full responsibility for your actions, feelings and thoughts.

Surrender to being as you are.[4]

Psychological Suitability Assessment

Here we have the exact opposite of the 'use the imagination' schools of thought (autosuggestion), while Gestalt also runs contrary to those sensory therapies which promise instant illumination and release from problems and stress. While I am completely in accord with Perls in that the phenomenon of instant growth is nothing more than a pipe-dream from which the patient must sooner or later awake, this existentialist doctrine seems to me to have a hint of the 'I'm alright, Jack' attitude about it.

Gestalt therapy may well appeal to those people who are looking for what they feel to be a sound psychological excuse for doing their own thing at the expense of others. And it has, no doubt, given many the courage to climb the ladder of success, regardless of the personal identities of the rungs! Although good medicine for the materialist, I do not see Gestalt as an aid to *real* growth – but now we are talking ethics and that is dangerous ground. So having said my piece I will retire gracefully.

TRANSACTIONAL ANALYSIS

Transactional Analysis, more commonly referred to as TA, was the invention of American psychoanalyst Eric Berne, who shot to fame with his book *Games People Play*. The idea behind TA is that people interact with each other on three levels, which Berne called the Child, the Parent and the Adult, each person carrying these three characters within the basic 'ego state'.

The Child in us feels, wants, demands, plays, adapts, fights – in other words the kind of behaviour that is normally associated with young children – desire for immediate gratification, resentment, moodiness and temper if it is not immediately satisfied, and refusal to accept any responsibility either for himself or for others.

The Parent, which believes, protects, controls directs and nurtures, manifests in that part of us that is entrenched in beliefs, attitudes and values conferred upon us by our own parents, which we have not seen fit to question or discard by virtue of our own thinking powers and logic.

The Adult thinks, computes and analyses, therefore it is that self-activating part of our personality that considers each action in the light of its own experience and the general trends in the world around us.

This trinity has been seen by some psychologists as another

extension of Freud's id, ego and superego, while I am inclined to equate it with the Instinctive (Child), Rational (Parent) and Intuitive (Adult), which was fully understood and acknowledged by many ancient civilisations, the triple goddess concept (maiden, nubile woman, and crone) being a prime example (see also Chapter 4). In other words, it is one of those timeless phenomena which regularly appear under different names as each successive generation of psychologists 'rediscover' it. They would save themselves a lot of time and energy if they looked to the past, but then perhaps they have and are just going about the business of earning a comfortable living!

Modus Operandi

TA has certain points in common with pychodrama, another alternative therapy, both being dedicated to exposing the real personality behind the dramatic role-mask. How each therapist goes about the unmasking process may depend on his estimation of the client's growth potential, although many therapists still adhere rigidly to the original Berne formula. This consisted of a series of 'transactions' which take the form of a dialogue between the three personas, forming a sort of game which is acted out until any imbalances are exposed and dealt with.

Psychological Suitability Assessment

TA is still used a lot in character assessment. I recently met a young psychologist who works for British Telecom, his task being to assess the executive suitability of people applying for senior positions. This is obviously an area in which TA comes into its own. After all, who wants a senior executive who cannot make decisions, think expansively, or communicate successfully when in a 'mood'. The adult is obviously best for the job, while the parent would prove a good assistant, accountant or second in command. As for the child – he or she should go back to the school of life and learn to grow up!

As an exposer of our weaknesses, TA could prove invaluable. After all, how many of us see ourselves as others see us, and while the child and parent obviously play their roles from time to time, the situation is bound to arise when we really need

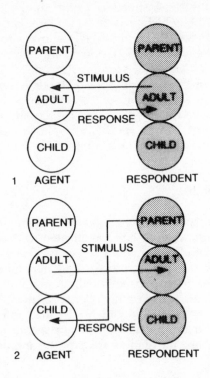

COMPLEMENTARY AND CROSSED TRANSACTIONS

the adult. Knowing how to call up the right role for the right occasion could prove an excellent mental discipline, as well as a useful tool in the workshop of life.

CO-COUNSELLING

In this system the professional is dispensed with. Two people simply sit down together to sort out their problems, which saves them the normal expense involved in psychotherapy and similar practices.

Co-counselling originated in Seattle, Washington USA, from

where it soon spread to many other countries. Regression, guided fantasy and the transpersonal quest were gradually added, although the original aim, which is concerned with personal growth and the recognition of such feelings as inadequacy, anger and loneliness, is still the prime object of the exercise.

Modus Operandi

Each prospective counsellor is required to take part in a forty-hour training course which also involves careful study of a manual of instructions. The idea is not to counsel in the accepted sense of the word, but rather to listen and only offer comment when it becomes absolutely necessary or is specifically requested. In other words, it is the client who has to do the work, but as both counsellors have worked through the same course, they know what is expected of them. At the end of the allotted time, client and counsellor exchange roles and the procedure is repeated. The advantages of this system for many people lies in the fact that they can make their own arrangements as regards getting together without the problems of a complicated appointment system. This makes it particularly viable for mothers at home all day with small children who can each take a turn of child-minding while the other confers with a neighbour or friend.

Psychological Suitability Assessment

A rather nice way of getting to know your neighbours or friends, no doubt, but it all depends on whether you are the sort of person who feels safer in the hands of a professional, who is at least bound by some form of confidentiality. And what if something should tumble out during a session with the lady across the street which might let a cat or two out of the proverbial bag? I suppose it all depends on whether or not you choose to exercise prudence when it comes to the baring of your soul!

A highly qualified friend of mine who works with several cancer help groups and has had a lot of experience with co-counsellors, alerted me to the pitfalls of the system as far as her patients are concerned. Experience has shown that the dominant personality inevitably ends up preaching his views to the less dominant partner, which does little to help the patient who is grasping at his own fragile life-threads. I am in no position to make judgements in these matters, but from advice I have received from this and other professional medical quarters it would appear that Co-counselling might not be the best therapy for the terminally ill, or anyone lacking in confidence or self-assertion.

POLARITY THERAPY

Polarity therapy has been described as holistic in that it embraces the whole person, thoughts, attitudes, emotional, physical and nutritional needs. In fact, it engages the services of several other therapies – manipulative, natural, psychological and paranormal in its efforts to fulfil the holistic ideal.

The Polarity concept originated with Randolph Stone, who was born in Austria, but later moved to the United States where he underwent training as an osteopath, chiropractor and naturopath, while also studying Eastern and Western medicine. The final ten years of his life were spent in India with his guru.

Stone based his new therapy on what he believed to be the five essential circuits of the body and their polarity relationships – positive, negative and neutral. These he ascribed to certain centres in the body and their related anatomical points in much the same way that the chakras are allied to the endocrine system. He chose five elements to represent these centres – ether, air, fire, water and earth and they were defined as follows:

1. *Etheric Centre* – governs the voice, hearing and the throat.
2. *Air Centre* – governs the respiration, circulation, lungs and heart.
3. *Fire Centre* – governing digestion, and bowels.
4. *Water Centre* – a generative and emotional force, governing the pelvic and glandular secretions.
5. *Earth Centre* – elimination of solids and liquids, governing the rectum and the bladder.

Polarity therapy requires that all these centres are perfectly balanced in order for energy to flow.[5]

Modus Operandi

Unlike some of the psychological therapies we have recently considered, polarity therapy follows more established procedures in that the initial session commences with the taking of a case history, followed by a check on the reflexes and pressure points to ascertain the quality and flow of the energy. Once this has been established, the therapist can then proceed with the manipulative techniques which are designed to ensure the balance and free-flow of the energy between the five centres. The pressures applied may be Neutral – a light, fingertip touch for soothing and balancing; Positive – movement created by direct manipulation; or Negative – a sometimes pain-inducing manipulation which goes deep into the tissues.

Stretching exercises are also employed in this technique, but the patient is advised to speak out if he or she is experiencing any discomfort during their practice. Patients are encouraged to express their feelings and to draw the therapist's attention to any physical, emotional or mental changes which might occur in the course of the treatment. Attention is also paid to diet and nutrition, and the treatment may commence with a short inner cleansing programme, the duration of which will be governed by the amount of toxins that need to be expelled from the body.

As with most oriental therapies, polarity treatment does not dwell so much on physical symptoms as on the need to keep the energy flow in balance. A vegetarian diet is recommended as being ideally suitable to the encouragement of a well-functioning system which allows the energy to flow freely through the five centres.

Psychological Suitability Assessment

There are similarities here between yoga (see Chapter 17) and chakric healing (see Chapter 20), although whereas one involves self-manipulation and the other psychic manipulation, polarity employs the manipulatory services of a therapist in much the same way as some of the earlier-mentioned manipulative therapies (see Chapter 14), but with the addition of an esoteric teaching. The combination of exercise, manipulation and diet is always helpful, being more in keeping with the holistic approach than some therapies. The benefits to be gained from this therapy could, to an extent, be governed by how one feels about the accompanying philosophy which appears to be central to its functioning. Although polarity therapy might strain the credulity of the more logically minded Westerner, I see no reason why it should not prove helpful to those with Eastern esoteric inclinations and good visualising abilities.

METAMORPHIC TECHNIQUE

Metamorphic technique, or 'prenatal therapy' as it was originally called, made its first appearance in the 1960s. Although it was originally based on reflexology, the two methods differ considerably. Metamorphic practitioners do not set out to treat a disorder, but rather to show the patient how he or she may heal him or herself.

It was Robert St John who first popularised the metamorphic practice, but in recent years Gaston St Pierre and Debbie Boater have assumed the roles of its gurus. The metamorphic idea is based on the conjecture that our physical, mental, emotional

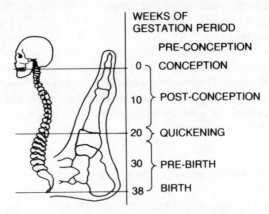

CHART OF THE PRENATAL PATTERN

The weeks of the prenatal or gestation period are correlated with the corresponding areas of the foot, which in turn reflect the spinal vertebrae. The dotted line running down the foot shows the position of the spine reflexes. (Devised by Robert St John)

and spiritual structures are established during the nine months of our gestation. By working on spinal reflex points in the feet, hands and head, which are believed to correspond with different stages of the nine-month development cycle, a formative period can be returned to focus which in turn releases energies that have been effectively blocked prenatally.

Modus Operandi

Anyone, we are told, can learn metamorphic technique, all that is required being the right attitude. There are no strict procedures, although the usual practice is to massage each foot for about thirty minutes. The rule is, however, no more than an hour's massage per foot, per week, although the period can be extended in the case of children if it is well spaced out. Massage may also be extended to the hands and head, the belief being that these represent points of contact connected with a person's receptivity to change.

Psychological Suitability Assessment

Not only do drugs (both of the legal medical variety and the abusive kind), junk foods, smoking, alcohol and similar intakes affect the future health of the unborn child, but also the mother's state of mind. There are numerous case histories which confirm this theory, such as the one quoted by Inglis and West from *Psychology Today* of a healthy 17-year-old who gave birth to an apparently healthy baby which died within twenty-four hours. The post-mortem revealed that the child had three peptic ulcers! A full case history of the stress placed upon the mother during pregnancy served to supply the answer.[6]

I have come across several similar cases myself, one of which I mentioned in an earlier chapter. Phobias can also be transmitted from the mother to the unborn child. I have firsthand knowledge of one case where the firstborn was savaged in her pram by a jealous Alsatian during the time that the mother was carrying her second child, as a result of which the new baby grew up with a fear of dogs which has never really left her to this day.

Metamorphic technique was originally designed to help

children handicapped from birth, but later extended to anyone anxious to effect a change for the better. I have a very dear friend who practises this form of therapy, with much success. She recently cited the case of an elderly monk, who had plaster casts of his feet taken prior to the commencement of the treatment and then again several months later. The feet had apparently changed during that time! She also tells me that the metamorphic practitioner can tell from the state of the feet whether the person in question has 'lived' – implying a degree of suffering and hard times – or whether they have enjoyed a fairly easy run to date.

I think I would like some of what she has to offer – I only wish we lived nearer to each other as I have known her for many, many years and trust her implicitly. There is one caution she is careful to emphasise, however: metamorphic treatment should not be mixed with other therapies. In other words, if you are having aromatherapy on Monday, osteopathy on Tuesday, psychotherapy on Wednesday, and metamorphic technique on Thursday – think again! You will only be harming yourself in the long run. My friend recently had a lady for treatment who was also having recourse to several other therapies at the same time, some of which were stimulating, others relaxing; the contradiction of aims resulted in a severe case of neurosis. It is little wonder that the medical profession are sceptical of many alternative therapies – the casualties frequently land on their doorsteps!

PRIMAL THERAPY/REBIRTHING

A single scream emitted by a patient during a session with Los Angeles psychiatrist Arthur Janov led to the formation of a dramatic new theory and treatment which Janov claimed to be a universal panacea for all neurosis. Janov explained that the scream had been caused by 'primal pain' arising from the critical episode in an infant's life when it is first denied its basic needs. Primal therapy is, therefore, involved with helping the patient to relive primal scenes: '. . . until the "primal pool" has been systematically emptied out', thus dismantling the patient's defences and exposing the true self.[7]

Rebirthing is an extension of primal therapy developed by American researcher Leonard Orr. But whereas primal therapy involves reliving not only one's birth pangs but all subsequent trauma-producing pains, rebirthing concentrates on dramatically recreating the actual birth process itself in the pursuit of mental equilibrium and so-called 'bliss'.

Reliving birth traumas, however, predates even Janov's primal therapy. In the 1920s, Otto Rank, a Viennese psychoanalyst, encouraged his patients to adopt the foetal position and re-experience their births, but later abandoned the practice, with good reason, no doubt!

Modus Operandi

Four basic techniques are employed in the primal or rebirthing experience:

1. Hypnotic regression;
2. Psycholitic methods – using psychedelics;
3. Simulation of the birth experience. The rebirther enters a tub of water heated to the temperature of amniotic fluid in the womb, and lies (or is held) face down in the water, using a snorkel or nose clips. The experienced rebirther then tells him how to breathe appropriately so that the birth memories are encouraged to come flooding back!;
4. Breathing. Similar to No. 3, but minus tub and water.

Method 2, which originally involved the use of LSD, has now been discarded for legal reasons. Primal therapy on its own is seldom used these days, the rebirthing version, which is felt to be more psychologically comprehensive, being preferred by most therapists and their clients.

Psychological Suitability Assessment

The first time I studied these twin therapies some years ago certain facts struck me forcibly. I think it best if I enumerate these as follows:

1. The 'dismantling' process is surely nothing other than a form of brainwashing.
2. The kind of primal scream experienced by Janov is too

close for coincidence to the bloodcurdling shriek emitted by a person during exorcism – which could hint at some form of childhood possession, parental or otherwise.

3. Religious rebirthing is as old as Methuselah, the idea being that the mind is 'cleansed' (brainwashed) of all previous programming and conveniently channelled into the faith in question.

4. Symbolic rebirthing rites were exercised in most primitive tribes, for the purpose of easing the psyche out of the child mode into the adult state, wherein it could assume its role as a useful unit in the community. Maturation rites involved the renaming of the young person, in much the same way as a baby is given a Christian name at baptism.

There is much more that could be said about this practice in the anthropological context, but to do the subject full justice would be too space-consuming.

Primal/rebirthing sessions can spark off a whole display of emotional fireworks bordering on the bizarre! Patients may whimper like babies, drool, crawl about the floor kicking and screaming, and temporarily lose control of their eliminatory functions, depending on their psychological make-up. Janov and Orr believe that any form of imbalance from neurosis to homosexuality, is the result of being left alone to cry for as little as three minutes, or being denied that much-wanted childhood treat. This type of thinking leaves me speechless! However, some comment has to be made.

I personally believe that our reason for being here on earth is to master the process of spiritual maturation – or individuation, if you prefer the psychological approach. Either way, however, implies us getting on with the business of coping with ourselves and seeking out the environment best-suited to the fulfilment of our karma (metaphysical), or the balanced integration of our personalities (psychological). If our harassed parents discarded us at the moment we demanded a bar of chocolate in order, no doubt, to prepare our lunch or launder our clothing, this should not constitute a cause for neurosis in later life. If, however, while undergoing primal therapy or rebirthing it seems that it does, then the remedy should be looked for elsewhere, probably through TA, Silva mind control, biofeedback or some therapy which helps us to assume the adult role more easily and effectively.

As I see it, a lot of nonsense is talked by psychologists who should know better, which rather causes one to suspect their motives. During a TV interview, because I have been labelled a 'natural psychic', the psychiatrist with whom I shared the programme asked me if I thought my psychic gifts (which he felt to be some form of mental aberration) could have resulted from my not being breast-fed up to the age of 2 years! Over the forty years I have spent investigating and working with psychics I have met many who did meet our psychiatrist friend's breast-feeding requirement period, and many who did not. Either way, it seemed to make no difference whatsoever to their psychic abilities on the one hand, or their integration and practicality on the other.

Coming back to the therapies in question, one wonders how the parents of these poor, deprived infants who were left without service for *three whole minutes* were expected to cope! Perhaps they were not, which was the idea behind it all (lots of lovely new clients!). But then I am being cynical, for which I apologise to those therapists who sincerely believe in the efficacy of their Rebirthing work.

One final comment: I have ascertained the opinions of several psychiatrists, social workers, and therapists from other disciplines, all of which have confirmed the high mental casualty rate resulting from Primal Therapy and Rebirthing. But as their practices demand confidentiality, they have naturally been unable to supply details that might serve to substantiate their experiences. Many people, however, do claim to have been greatly helped by these therapies so in the final analysis I must leave the reader to effect his or her own judgement.

TRANSPERSONAL PSYCHOLOGY

Contrary to what the majority may think, adjustment to the material world and a sense of feeling safe and comfortable within the 'norm' is not everyone's goal. There are many who seek something less mundane and more transcendental. Jung was more than aware of this and frequently commented upon it in his writings and lectures. Abraham Maslow, one of the prime movers behind the Transpersonal Psychology movement referred to such people as 'metaneeds', and it would appear that their numbers are growing fast.

Transpersonal Psychology has been called the 'fourth force', the first three forces being those we have already discussed: psychoanalysis, behaviourism and humanistic psychology. While the humanistic approach concentrates on people's need to strip off their conditioning, experience real feelings and contact their higher, creative selves, Maslow discovered that a number of people, when freed in this way, were able to transcend ordinary reality and experience mystical states.

Transpersonal Psychology draws from many disciplines which are not therapies in the strictest sense of the word. Some of these would be more accurately classified as philosophies, faiths, or even cults: Sufism, Buddhism, Zen Buddhism, the teachings of Gurdjieff – any accepted school of mysticism, in fact. Dreams, meditation, extrasensory perception, altered states of consciousness, cosmic awareness and the pervading life-energy of the creative force – all are embraced by the transpersonal concept.

Of course, there is always the danger that the ideal or cause may overstep the line of sanity, and instances where this has occurred have naturally provided some first-class material for the sensationalist press! But these are the exceptions rather than the rule, and most students of transpersonal psychology, or any of those faiths or philosophies which conveniently take shelter within its safe harbour, contribute much to the development and understanding of the human spiritual quest.

Transpersonal psychology is rooted in the ideas of Roberto Assagioli, a contemporary of Freud whose special interest was the higher consciousness, and in the work of Jung, who accented the collective unconscious.

PSYCHOSYNTHESIS

In 1910, Roberto Assagioli left Italy for Vienna to study the theory of psychoanalysis under Sigmund Freud, and later under Eugen Bleuler in Zurich. Although he imbibed Freud's teaching and returned to his native country to practise as a psychiatrist, it was not long before he broke with Freudian tradition and developed his own approach to the study of the mind which he called 'Psychosynthesis'. Although he set up an Institute in Rome to promote his findings, his work failed to meet with the approval of the authorities under Mussolini during World War

II, and it was not until much later that he was able to proceed with his calling and establish additional institutes in the United States, Greece and England.

Assagioli's theories differed from those of Freud in many respects. While Freud concentrated on probing the murky depths of the personality, Assagioli's interest veered more towards the higher unconscious or transpersonal self, the term 'transpersonal' relating to personal experiences that transcend what is normally accepted as ordinary reality. In this sense it hints at mysticism, although mysticism as such is not considered to be a part of psychosynthesis.

Assagioli disagreed with Freud's theory that we are a mass of unconscious motivations, preferring the idea that our individual wills somehow feature in our personal lives. Anyone who can acknowledge this can therefore command his own destiny, effect choices, and even change his personality. Assagioli felt that will was not so much the vital force, but the directing agent behind the personality which should function in conjunction with, and not in opposition to, the imagination. Ambivalence, therefore, results not from a split will, but from a confusion of

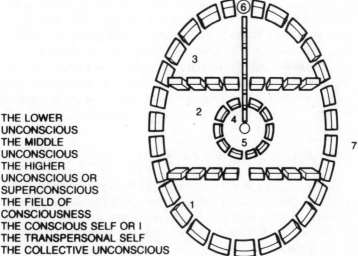

1 THE LOWER
  UNCONSCIOUS
2 THE MIDDLE
  UNCONSCIOUS
3 THE HIGHER
  UNCONSCIOUS OR
  SUPERCONSCIOUS
4 THE FIELD OF
  CONSCIOUSNESS
5 THE CONSCIOUS SELF OR I
6 THE TRANSPERSONAL SELF
7 THE COLLECTIVE UNCONSCIOUS

PSYCHOSYNTHESIS: THE PSYCHIC STRUCTURE

drives and desires. As life is constantly presenting us with a series of options, neurosis is the inevitable result of our endeavours to combine with the incompatible instead of effecting choices.

Modus Operandi

Psychosynthesis incorporates many techniques that are not exclusive to its practice. Painting, imagery, self-imagery, movement, music, visualisation and meditation. Clients are also advised to keep diaries, answer questionnaires and undergo a series of tests in an effort to uncover elements of both the conscious and unconscious mind.

Psychosynthesis courses proceed through four distinct phases of inner work and development as set out by Assagioli:

Thorough knowledge of one's personality.

Control of its various elements.

Realization of one's true self – the discovery or creation of a unifying centre . . .

Psychosynthesis: the formation or reconstruction of the personality around the new centre.[8]

Three main activities are involved in this four-part process: 'the improvement of the will by stretching the imagination; the development of creativity by the transformation of what are termed "biopsychic energies" (for example, sexual and aggressive energies); and bringing into consciousness, awareness of the superconscious and harnessing its energies.'[9]

Psychological Suitability Assessment

This would appear to be an excellent therapy for those who have reached that certain threshold where they stand poised between the world with which they are fully cognisant and the need to probe beyond the limits of knowledge defined by the disciplines of materialism.

It is interesting to observe how many of the psychologies, and spiritual disciplines for that matter, concentrate on the finding of the 'true self', the assumption being that once one has located one's real identity this serves as some kind of personal key to the rest of the universe. I would like to suggest that there are many who find themselves not through introspection, but rather through looking outwards and realising their unique role as a contributory unit in the workings of a Divine Plan.

Endnotes:

1. *The Alternative Health Guide,* B Inglis and R West p. 199.
2. Ibid. p. 204.
3. Ibid.
4. Ibid.
5. Ibid. p. 212.
6. Ibid. p. 216.
7. Ibid. p. 218.
8. Ibid. p. 222.
9. Ibid.

Chapter 20

PARANORMAL THERAPIES

The following therapies all assume the existence of psychic or supernatural forces, in other words energies that defy the normal laws of science or appear to run contrary to natural laws. It should be borne in mind, however, that the boundaries of science are widening at an ever-accelerating rate, so that last year's paranormal may be next year's normality, just as much of yesterday's science fiction has now become today's science fact.

The psychological suitability assessment will be omitted in dealing with the following therapies on the grounds that the same rules apply to all psychic, practices, these being:

1. Avoid over-indulgence in wishful thinking;
2. Guard against an over-active imagination;
3. Do not expect the paranormal to function in the same way as the material world of everyday life;
4. Watch out for those who are purely 'on the make';
5. Do not be taken in by the so-called 'spiritual' approach – there are plenty of wolves about in sheep's clothing, and being 'holier than thou' is no guarantee of true spirituality;
6. Always keep well-earthed when dealing with any form of psychism, and refrain from involving yourself too deeply unless you intend to make a serious study of the subject under experienced guidance.*

---

* Those wishing to make a more detailed study of psychism should refer to *Practical Techniques of Psychic Self-Defence* and *The Psychology of Ritual*.

Although the term 'faith healing' is so often applied to any form of therapy that might have paranormal connotations, it is something of a misnomer, as healing has been known to work without the involvement of faith of any kind. Psychic healing is therefore not the prerogative of any system, established religion, or ideology, but rather the manipulation of certain universal (cosmic) energies, the frequencies of which are conducive to the balancing (or rebalancing) of the life-force in all living creatures. It could equally be argued, of course, that cosmic energy is basically an impersonal force which is only transformed into an appropriate therapeutic quality by the mind of the healer. A third theory, proffered by many parapsychologists, concerns psychokinesis (PK) which can manifest in many forms, so that our psychokinetic energies may well carry a healing frequency.

Healers may employ a variety of titles to advertise their particular calling: spiritual healer, psychic healer, magnetic healer, shamanic healer, an so forth. The belief which they all have in common is their ability to channel healing energies to their patients. As I have already mentioned in Chapter 6, they may execute this in the name of Jesus, God, Aradia, Apollo, Kuan-Yin, the Holy Ghost, or whoever. If the results are effective it makes no difference in the long run, and one does not need to share the faith of the healer in order to benefit. Bearing all this in mind, let us now proceed to our first paranormal healing phenomenon.

HEALING SHRINES

Members of the Roman Catholic faith who display any form of psychic gift are watched very closely by the Vatican. Should those gifts involve miracles of any kind, those so blessed are subjected to rigid disciplines and frequently isolated in a convent or monastery for the remainder of their earthly lives. Some psychologists are of the opinion that miracle workers are viewed with suspicion by the Church authorities because they could constitute a threat to the overall authority of the Vatican if they were allowed too much licence to practise and display their paranormal gifts (shades of Pharasaical thinking in the days Jesus!). When such persons finally depart this earth, however, they are usually beatified (referred to as 'the Blessed') and finally canonised (proclaimed a saint), after which the more miracles the merrier!

Although a new shrine does occasionally make its appearance, there are a few which have been centres for healing pilgrimages for several generations. The best-known of these is undoubtedly Lourdes in southern France where, in 1858, a young peasant girl named Bernadette Soubirous claimed to have seen a vision of the Virgin Mary. The Vatican rallied with its usual anti-hysteria propaganda, but word quickly spread of the miraculous powers of the waters of a hidden spring which Bernadette had discovered in a cave. It is interesting to note that Bernadette herself received no relief from these healing powers and remained in chronic ill health until her early death at the age of 35.

Pilgrims arrived at Lourdes in ever-increasing numbers as stories of miraculous cures spread across the world. Although some of these remissions have been medically substantiated, the tendency has been to attribute them to the attitude of mind or will-power of the patient rather than to the emission of some miraculous healing energy from the Lourdes shrine.

To make the pilgrimage to Lourdes in all good faith and return unhealed must sorely test the faith of many Catholics; although there is always the usual 'Will of God' let-out which, let us face it, is used just as much by psychics, although accompanied by such statements as: 'Well, if it is your karma to go, then no one can help you,' or 'The spirits are calling you over to their side, you must go in happiness and they will be there to meet you.'

Of course, healing shrines are not exclusive to the Christian religion; the pagans had them, too. There were sacred rocks, groves of trees, ancestral burial grounds, ancient initiation caves – many of which were believed to carry healing energies, while the miracles attributed to the healing shrine of Kuan-Yin in China (see Chapter 12) bear many similarities to those of Lourdes. One is tempted to think that the 'Lady' whom Bernadette saw in her time-slip was Isis, Demeter, Aradia or any of the many manifestations of the Great Mother which had become imprinted on the stonework of the grotto to be viewed by anyone who might slip into the appropriate (ecstatic or paraphronesic) ASC.

Germane to this subject is a short report I read recently in the September/October issue of a magazine called *The Atlantean*, which is the organ of the Society of the same name:

Religious fervour temporarily gripped Guatemala City recently when, after a rainstorm, the face of Jesus Christ (or what he is believed to have looked like) appeared on the wall of a church; prayers were offered and miraculous cures were reported. More rain made the face clearer until it was recognised to be that of Willie Nelson, a country and western singer whose picture had been stuck to the wall and the painters who redecorated the church wall had painted over it. Not good paint, obviously!

Yet one more piece of evidence in favour of the power of the mind!

PROTESTANT HEALING

The Protestant churches tend to fight shy of what they see as the medieval hocus-pocus which used to be associated with healing in the days prior to the Reformation – supposed health-giving relics, healing shrines and similar paranormal manifestations. In fact, the rejection of any form of miraculous healing reached almost paranoid proportions in the mid eighteenth century when the historian W E H Lecky reported that 'nearly all educated men receive an account of a miracle taking place in their own day with an absolute and even derisive incredulity that dispenses with all examination of the evidence.'[1] Even the healing power of the Holy Spirit was denied, as though this might contain some hidden diabolical reference.

The Anglican Church has, however, revised its views on this subject of late and spiritual healing along New Testament lines is undergoing a revival. Protestant churches, of course, come in all shapes and sizes – which is not meant to allude to the structures of their meeting places! Although the Anglican or High Church may walk the tightrope between the Holy Spirit and the medical establishment, many less ritualistic Protestant churches have some form of healing rite or prayers for the sick, while their clergy are usually on call in cases of emergency.

Christian Science and the Pentecostal-type churches approach healing in very different ways, yet each and all of these acknowledge Jesus Christ as their founder and call upon the divine healing forces in His name, which is ironic when viewed in the light of the Anglican Church's irritation at the way in which Christ's healing powers were supposedly being exploited by Mary Baker Eddy, the founder of Christian Science, and her followers!

History has witnessed the occasional emergence of Protestant sects whose leaders have been intent upon restoring the phenomenal healing element. There were the Shakers and Quakers, for example, so named because of the tremors and convulsions they exhibited while being possessed by the Holy Spirit (paraphronesis). John Wesley himself compiled a book of herbal and other remedies for Methodists, in addition to subscribing to the efficacy of healing prayer.

The form of healing currently favoured in Protestantism today assumes the existence of a divine healing force which is dispensed by the Holy Spirit. This may be invoked at a special healing service or performed by selected individuals as sanctioned by the Church, in which case it will probably involve the laying on of hands, a central theme in the healing practices of the early Christian church.

CHARISMATIC HEALING

> And suddenly there came a sound from heaven, as of a rushing wind, and it filled all the house where they were sitting. And there appeared unto them cloven tongues as of fire, and it sat upon each of them. And they were all filled with the holy ghost and began to speak in other tongues, as the Spirit gave them utterance.
>
> Acts 2: 2–4

This statement from the book of the Acts of the Apostles, together with the many miracles performed by the disciples after the Crucifixion, have formed the basis of modern charismatic healing now being performed in the churches of several Christian denominations. St Paul made it clear in his Epistle to the Corinthians that he fervently believed in the need for the Holy Spirit to repeat its Pentecostal visit by descending on Christian congregations from time to time, and while the glossolalia might come as an unexpected bonus, this spirit possession (the Holy Spirit, naturally) was inevitably the deciding factor in Christian divination and healing.

As an outsider, I cannot help viewing with a degree of

suspicion the fact that spirit possession which takes place in a church is automatically born on the right side of the heavenly blanket, while anyone claiming spirit guidance outside of that sacerdotal canopy is either mentally ill, possessed of the devil, or fails to qualify as a son or daughter of the Celestial Father.

In the psychological context (or somatic, for that matter), there is little difference, if any, between the alleluias of the Christian evangelical fundamentalists and the ecstatic dances of the dervishes, while the utterance of the entranced shaman could be equated with glossolalia. The Christian mystic's vision of Christ and the yogi's samadhi are both fashioned in the same ecstatic mould. The autonomic nervous system does not distinguish between Christian or pagan, Muslim or yogi, shaman or saint when registering the somatic reactions of ecstasy.

It can be argued that those who indulge in the gift of tongues, either under the auspices of certain branches of Christianity, or in the psychic trance state, are grasping at collective unconscious race memories of earlier cultures. The psychologist would, no doubt, prefer Jung's diagnosis of cryptemnesia as the more logical explanation, as his research revealed that among the gibberish which normally passes as glossolalia there was the odd word from another language which was probably registered subconsciously at some earlier point in life.

Xenolalia, or paranormal speaking in real languages, has apparently yet to be proven, as not a single case has been recorded since the advent of tape recorders or computers. In 1926, Teresa Neumann, a famous Christian sensitive, allegedly cried out in Aramaic as she re-enacted Christ's passion, and in the 1930s, an English medium known only as Rosemary was reputed to have spoken in ancient Egyptian during seances, but as no living scholar would appear to know how the ancient Egyptian language was pronounced, the performance of the latter is obviously questionable.[2]

If you choose to attend a healing service and are touched by the hands of a member of the clergy or lay healer who feels him or herself to be possessed of the Holy Spirit, then you may well feel better afterwards. But in my book of rules, whether a healing is genuinely effected or not will depend on two factors – the power of your own mind, or the particular quality of PK emmited by the healer.

SPIRITUALIST HEALING

The history and development of spiritualism is a subject in itself and too lengthy for inclusion. Let us, therefore, join it at the point where the emphasis switched from private table-turning seances to communication with the spirits of the departed, when it was officially accepted as a religious cult dedicated to proving life-after-death. Several well-known mediums found themselves guided by the spirits of deceased doctors, American Indian medicine men or Chinese sages, whose knowledge of medicine and the nature of disease appeared to considerably outweigh the experience and erudition of their channels.

As with Protestantism there are several branches of Spiritualism, the best-known of which are the Spiritualist National Union, the Greater World Association, the Spiritualist Association of Great Britain, and the College of Psychic Science. The Church's Fellowship for Psychical Research is also favourably disposed towards the movement. Views within these organisations differ regarding the spiritual status of Jesus Christ, some members accepting his divinity, others viewing him as a manifestation of the Cosmic Christ or one of many Enlightened Ones who have come to this planet from time to time to help humanity. Others simply accept Jesus as a wise and sagacious teacher. So, while certain healers who function under the Spiritualist banner may believe themselves to be guided by Jesus, the Holy Spirit, or other exclusively Christian identities, the majority work with a guide or control who provides them with the information necessary to advise the patient on such things as diet or even orthodox medical help.

Those healers who are able to prove their gift by producing evidence of healing from four independent sources are awarded a certificate of recognition which entitles them to work as attested healers within one or other of the Spiritualist movements.

In emphasising the basic difference between Protestant healing in which God is requested to intervene, and the Spiritualist approach, the late Harry Edwards (1893–1976), one of the best-known of all spiritualist healers pointed out: 'Healings do not take place as a result of God's personal intervention on behalf of a favoured individual, over-riding His established laws.'[3] A rather good point, I believe, which reminds me of a similar statement I once read in a book by Vera Stanley Alder to the effect that God would not reverse the law of gravity to save one suicide jumping off a cliff, the logic of which is obvious if one considers what would happen to the rest of us if He/She did!

Many Spiritualists believe they are carrying on a tradition established by the disciples of Jesus in going forth and doing what the master did – healing, casting out evil spirits, comforting the sick, and so forth. A number of Spiritualist healers work through the trance state or, to use the currently popular term, effect a 'channelling'.

Some years ago a friend took me to a Spiritualist healer at their headquarters in London. My problem was a chronic kidney condition which was particularly troublesome in my youth. The medium concerned – a sweet, elderly soul – was guided by the spirit of an American Indian medicine man specialising in renal disorders who went by the appropriate name of Running Water! I cannot truthfully claim to have been healed by the good offices of this shamanic spirit, although the advice given regarding diet, herbs, etc. was both helpful and medically accurate. In hindsight, I view the experience as contributory to my understanding of psychism generally and my overall growth, and extend my thanks to the lady in question and her alter-ego (or American Indian fragment, as the case may be).

The National Federation of Spiritualist Healers which functions interdependently of the Spiritualist Movement, is one of the largest healing bodies in the UK, and a member of the recently formed Confederation of Healing Organisations. Other healing organisations included in CHO, membership are:

The Atlanteans (non-denominational);

British Alliance of Healing Associations
(non-denominational);

The Guild of Spiritualist Healers (non-denominational);

Maitreya School of Healing (non-denominational);

Healers of the Spiritualist Association of Great Britain (Spiritualist);

Healers of the Spiritualists' National Union (Spiritualist Church);

The Healers of the British Branch of the World Federation of Healing (non-denominational).

Affiliates:

Association of Therapeutic Healers (non-denominational);

Centre for Health and Healing, St James's Church, Piccadilly (Christian and non-denominational);

College of Healing (non-denominational);

College of Psychic Studies (non-denominational);

Fellowship of Erasmus (spiritual);

The Radionic Association (non-denominational distant lay-healing);

Sufi Healer Order of Great Britain

The White Eagle Lodge (non-denominational Christians).

The CHO describes itself as a confederation of sixteen independent and self-administering associations representing some 7,500 healers in the UK, and is a registered charity. CHO seeks to co-operate with fourteen other organisations including the Research Council for Complementary and Alternative Medicine, New Approaches to Cancer, the National Health Network and the Church's Council for Health and Healing. Its objective is to establish healing as a standard therapy for the NHS as well as private medicine. It is offered strictly as a complement – not an alternative – to orthodox medicine operating within the rules of the GMC. The doctor remains in charge of the patient and is responsible for medical diagnosis and prescription. Healing can also complement other therapies which establish themselves as 'alternative' to orthodox medicine. It complements and does not in any way interfere with the work of Chaplains or Social Workers.

The Confederation's organiser and chairman, Dennis

Haviland, is at present working to set up analyses of responses to treating post-surgical and critical cases in cooperation with the medical profession. Many hospitals are now allowing healers to work within their hallowed precincts, and although the doctors may be sceptical when it comes to the efficacy of their treatment, many are willing to admit that as therapeutic agents their effect on the mental health and outlook of the patient does serve as a stimulant to recovery.

PAGAN HEALING

There are many practising pagans and members of the Old Religion (and other beliefs from antiquity), both in the UK and other countries, who contribute substantially to the healing scene. Many Wiccan covens regularly send healing to animals, trees, plants and Gaia herself, as well as people, using the energies generated by their rites, and those who may deem fit to question the source of this and other pagan power are referred to the section on Exorcism later in this chapter.

Most pagans I know heal via their own PK or through invocation to the gods or godlings of healing, according to their traditional preference. Whether one actually believes in the existence of these divinities, or views them simply as aspects of the individual psyche appears to make little if any difference as far as the results are concerned. After all, the medical profession went about their business of professing allegiance to Apollo and Co. for centuries, so if there are (as some of us believe) archetypal identities which answer to some of the names man has seen fit to bestow upon them over the years, why should they not give answer to a sincere and selfless request – after all, who is the Holy Spirit, anyway?

HAND HEALING

The term 'hand healing' can be somewhat misleading in that ibzt conjures up a picture of a healer, hands extended either in the general region of the patient's body or in actual physical contact, whereas there are basic distinctions between hand healing and laying on of hands. These lie in the area of belief, hand healers being mainly secular rather than religious in outlook.

Hand healing can be dated back to antiquity. It was used by tribal shamans, medicine men and wise women centuries ago, and the Hippocratic school in Kos in the fifth century BC saw no reason to reject its efficacy. The onset of mechanistic medicine was responsible for it going underground for many years, its practitioners being accused of witchcraft and similar heresies as late as the seventeenth century when it emerged in the modes of 'stroking' and 'magnetised stroking'. In its latter form, healers use magnets as an additional aid to their treatment, and many hand healers to this day believe there is a bio-electromagnetic element in healing.

The PK element has, however, been confirmed in the work of international healer Matthew Manning, who experienced a considerable amount of PK activity while still in his youth. Realising he had access to a somewhat unusual energy source, he decided to employ this in healing rather than as a tool for display. Manning works very much through his hands, allowing them to guide his mind as it were (or vice versa, as some would see it). He receives his information mentally in a form of colour coding – 'red for pain, yellow for infection, black for malignancy'. As is the case with many healers, Manning finds that most of his patients seek his aid with disorders for which orthodox medicine has no effective treatment, although their initial diagnosis has been obtained from their doctor or consultant.

In his experience, Manning has found that a very high proportion of cases have been triggered off by some emotionally shattering event which occured from 6 to 18 months prior to the onset of the disease. Like most sensible healers, he makes no claims to providing miracle cures, the will to recover lying very much (metaphorically speaking) in the patient's own hands.

Research carried out by Dr Lawrence LeShan in the 1970s led him to conclude that there were basically two kinds of healers:

1. Those people who are able to lose themselves in the ecstatic state wherein time ceases and the ego is temporarily obliterated, so that the energies they channel are not under the direct control of their conscious minds. In such cases there is no need for the healer to 'do' anything, or even be present with the patient, as the psychic forces at work transcend both time and space; and,

2. Healers who consciously direct their energies, usually via the hands, so that both their actions and the intensity of their concentration are visible to the patient.

To these I would like to add a third classification, which comprises a combination of both (1) and (2). My own healing experiences, and those of the people I taught over a period of some twenty years or more, involved the employment of both right and left brain hemispheres. So while the healers could enter ASCs should the occasion arise, they were also required to understand what they were actually doing. In other words, work in 'outer-time' (timelessness) by all means, but keep to alpha rather than theta brain rhythms.

The type of healing effected by my group in those days also involved absent healing, using both visualisation and imaging which were executed during astral projection. During this procedure one definitely experienced a sense of timelessness, although our healers were not encouraged to enter the ecstatic state involuntarily, the accent always being on full mental control.

In the course of experiments carried out under scientific conditions to ascertain the validity of healing, healers have been required to undertake some rather amazing tests, one of which required working on a test tube of enzymes (catalysts formed by living cells which promote chemical changes). Laboratory animals have also been subjected to healing rays with highly satisfactory results. The truly beautiful thing about healing animals is that they do not offer resistance in the same way that humans often do, but then their overall psychology is much simpler than ours and they do not resist the sort of natural phenomena that many hominds tend to view with irrational suspicion.

THERAPEUTIC TOUCH

A variant on hand healing? Perhaps. But Dr Dolores Kreiger, Professor of Nursing at New York State University, who coined the phrase 'therapeutic touch', describes the technique as having '. . . recaptured this simple but elegant mode of healing, and mated it with the rigor and power of modern science'.[4]

Dr Kreiger became increasingly dissatisfied with the

impersonal lines along which nursing was developing, but was unsure as to how to improve matters until she heard of a series of healing experiments undertaken by Dr Bernard Grad at McGill University, in Montreal. These involved hand healing given to mice by the famous healer Colonel Estebany, a former Polish cavalry officer who had offered his services to several research projects on other occasions. Impressed by what she saw of his work, Dr Kreiger set up a trial herself to see if he could influence haemoglobin, the protein in the oxygen-carrying red blood cells. The results were sufficiently satisfying for her to arrange a training course for nurses in the secular version of the laying on of hands.

Dr Kreiger maintains that it does not require a trained practitioner to carry out therapeutic touch. Any two people can try it out on each other, one acting as 'sender' and the other as 'receiver', so that the sensations experienced and results achieved by one can be observed and evaluated by the other. The procedure starts with a form of stroking, the relaxing effects of which may be visibly observed in the slowing down of respiration and general relaxation.

Being psychic is not essential to this form of treatment which, according to Dr Kreiger, is basically psychological. It does, however, acknowledge the fact that the human body has an energy field (aura) which extends beyond its physical boundaries, and the stroking process is designed to encompass the limits of that field. Although this field can be detected by dowsing, science has yet to accept it, which places it firmly in the paranormal category – for the time being, anyway! More of this under the heading of Auric Therapy.

RADIONICS AND RADIESTHESIA

The use of aids for healing purposes is older than history. The shamans, witch doctors and medicine men of primitive times frequently employed a whole galaxy of paraphernalia during the process of effecting their healing. The magician's wand is believed by many anthropologists to have originated in the shamanic stick which was frequently used for conjuring up the spirits of ancestors, animals or elemental forces. Equally, the primitive prototype of the pendulum might have been a pebble suspended on a thread, to which questions would be addressed in the belief that some spirit resident in the stone might either know the answers itself, or have the appropriate psychic entity near at hand who could supply it with the necessary information.

Divining for water and other commodities has also been practised in many cultures over the centuries, the forked hazel twig being the tool most favoured for this purpose. In time the primitive stone gave way to the pendulum, although to this day some diviners will only work with the traditional hazel stick.

Radiesthesia is based on the concept that all substances emit radiations which may be tuned in to by dowsers or any other persons who appear to possess this ability. Although emphasis has been placed on the role played by the hands in this practice, it is now believed that our extremities only act upon impulses from the brain, which is therefore the true receiving station.

Radiesthesia has become closely linked with radionics, mainly because the use of a pendulum is a strong feature in the work of radionics practitioners. The history of radionics has been a somewhat chequered one, however. It was the American neurologist Albert Abrams who discovered that a diagnosis could be effected from a drop of a patient's blood or a lock of his or her hair without the need for the patient to be present, and the system has developed from there.

The idea that a piece of hair, clothing, or nail parings could act as an entré to that person's energy frequency has been known to magicians since the days of Atlantis and probably earlier, so what Abrams had discovered was nothing new to students of the arcane tradition. However, being a man of scientific leanings, he felt obliged to relate the phenomenon to the electromagnetic field and in due course he set about constructing a diagnostic instrument with which he could observe the effect of what he had come to call the 'biocurrent'. In time this became known as his 'box'. What Abrams failed to take into account, however, was that this bioenergy might be influenced by the operators of the box, in addition to the workings of the device itself!

Since Abrams died in 1924 a variety of diagnostic boxes have come and gone, the most famous of which is undoubtedly that constructed by an engineer named George de la Warr, who had decided to investigate radionics – the new name given to the use of gadgets to tune in to bioenergy for therapeutic purposes. Although de la Warr himself was perfectly satisfied with the result of his findings, the scientific community were anything but impressed and he eventually faced prosecution for selling one of his 'boxes' under false pretences. Although he was acquitted on the grounds that he genuinely believed his contraption to perform in the manner claimed, the episode did little to enhance the radionic cause.

Radionics, as it is practised today, is based on the belief that the universe is composed of a series of interlocking, all-pervading energy fields, of which mankind is a microscopic part. Because we are all linked by these subtle energy fields it is possible to tune into subtle energy signals which are normally filtered out by our five physical senses. In radionics this is achieved with the help of electronic equipment, so that the signals being picked up are converted into a recognisable form.

When asked to give healing, the radionics practitioner will concentrate his or her inner senses on the patient's subtle energy fields to locate the source of the problem which might well lie in the subtle bodies, using a pendulum as the detective device. There is no need for the patient to be present. All that is required is a lock of hair or a blood specimen via which the correcting healing is transmitted or 'broadcast'.

Modern radionic machines come in all shapes and sizes and often (to your author, anyway) resemble something out of Dr Who's tardis! Some practitioners avow that the impressive arrays of knobs and dials are purely show and not essential to the healing process, while others doubtlessly find security in equipment they feel to be substantially scientific (in appearance, anyway!) Although diagnosis was the fashion among radionics practitioners a few years ago, the approach has tended to become more holistic, so that the bioenergy is no longer projected at an isolated symptom, but rather at the patient's general condition.

Gadgets have never been my strong point, and if one can achieve the same results without them (and I believe this can be done) then constructing and tinkering about with them seems an awful waste of time and energy. I am bound to admit, however, that they do impress a certain type of 'psychic borderline' person, who still has one foot firmly planted in the nuts and bolts of technology, while the other is cautiously exploring the next step in conscious awareness!

PAST LIVES THERAPY

This form of therapy is based on the idea that some of the disorders from which we suffer in this life can be attributed to traumas carried over from former lives. A prerequisite for successful treatment by this form of healing would therefore be an acceptance of the reincarnation premise. One assumes, of course, that no one would embark on a course of Past Lives Therapy unless they had at least some leaning towards the general idea that their present life was not the first.

Reincarnation is a subject which fascinates some people and frightens others, usually on religious grounds. Interestingly enough, the doctrine of reincarnation was readily accepted by Christianity until its expurgation by the Second Council of Constantinople in AD 553, when it was declared heretical. This assembly was, in reality, only the final phase of a violent ten-year conflict inaugurated by the edict of the Roman Emperor Justinian in AD 543 against the teachings of the Church Father Origen. Justinian had assumed the leadership of the Church to the extent that Imperial edicts regulated public worship, directed ecclesiastical discipline, and even dictated theological doctrines. The Church was obliged to submit to a period of Caesaro-papism.

One teaching that did worry Justinian was that of reincarnation, the idea that an emperor could be anything less than exalted proving something of an anathema to him. Finding an ally in Iranaeus, Bishop of Gaul, he strove to bring about the change in doctrine that was ultimately effected by the Second Council of Constantinople. We are told, however, that this occasion was attended by very few bishops and was presided over by Eutychius, Patriarch of Constantinople, rather than Pope Vigilius himself. Apparently the Pontiff, although in that city at the time, refused to attend and add his *ex cathedra* touch to the proceedings. History is littered with similar instances which have resulted in the minds of future generations being programmed into erroneous concepts of our role in the universe.

In recent years more and more people are coming to believe that their present life is not the one and only. Questions are asked as to why some people are born with considerable knowledge while others never appear to have a chance in life due, perhaps, to handicaps of some kind or other, or just general ill health and the inability to adjust to life as we know it today. Reincarnation answers many of these questions, but even among believers there is a diversity of views as to how the system actually works.

Personally, I do not subscribe to the linear-life theory, the fragment concept appearing far more rational if we take into consideration the physics of the facts and acknowledge that there is much we still need to learn concerning the space-time continuum. As this subject has received extensive coverage in some of my other books (see *The Lion People*), I will say no more.

It is interesting to observe that a psychiatrist, Dr Arthur Guirdham, ranks highly among the modern reincarnation gurus. Years in psychiatric practice in a busy hospital led him to discover that people tended to reincarnate in groups, so that when those of a related group met up together they were able to share memories and experiences from the past. There have been numerous books written on the subject in addition to Dr Guirdham's *We Are One Another*, notably *Past Lives Therapy* by Los Angeles psychologist Morris Netherton, founder of the Institute for Past Lives Awareness, and his co-author Nancy Schiffrin, in which they describe the workings of their practice.

One particular case which supports the need to look beyond the present for the cause of an obsession concerned a man who, although successful in every material way, suffered from a knife phobia. In the privacy of his own home he was obviously able to control the situation and ensure that there were no knives around, but when attending business lunches, he was obliged to ask the waiter to remove the knives from his place setting, although he did not appear to be unduly distressed by those placed for his fellow diners. Being a rather macho type, he felt that this made him appear rather stupid in the eyes of his peers, so he decided to consult a hypnotherapist to see if he could get to the root of the problem. After the first treatment the hypnotherapist decided to regress him, during which he was able to describe in gory detail a horrendous death by cutting he had suffered as a Saxon villager at the hands of marauding Vikings. Needless to say, the memory was accompanied by a violent abreaction as he relived the death agonies, but although he was thoroughly exhausted after he was brought around, his fear of knives disappeared from that day onwards, never to return!

Past Life Therapy can either be administered via hypno-therapy or through the use of techniques similar to those employed in rebirthing or psychodrama. There should always be a qualified person present to supervise sessions of this kind, however, as they can be highly shock-inducing, and patients should never be allowed to leave the treatment room until the therapist is absolutely sure that they are completely grounded and in full possession of their faculties.

Personally (and I speak from experience here) I think that probing past lives (or the experiences of other fragments, as I prefer to see it) can be dangerous for some, especially the more sensitive person who would sustain severe shock in the 'now' upon discovering what they had been up to in the past. The secret lies in the old saying: 'Hope for the best, be prepared for the worst, and take what's coming,' for the odds are that you will be faced with a fair selection of all three of these categories.

AURIC THERAPY

Auric therapy is based on the belief that we each have an aura, or a kind of force field which surrounds our bodies, which serves as a protection against alien influences of any kind, from the more recognisable viruses, germs, etc., to the subtle influences of impinging minds, and ensures the containment of natural physical and mental energies. When the aura is weak-ened, as it is when one is ill or has sustained an accident, it needs to be built up again and strengthened, after which the body's own immune system can take over the work of disarming and vanquishing the invaders.

Auras come in several depths and colours depending on: (1) one's general state of health; (2) one's basic personality type; and (3) one's soul-age. Some healers claim to be able to diagnose from the aura by observing places where there might be breaks, dark patches, or irregularities in colour and line. In fact, auras are not difficult to see. A dear friend of mine, now deceased, used to claim that being very down to earth she could not possibly 'see' anything psychically. But one does not need to be psychic to see an aura, and after I had taught her the technique, no one was more surprised than she when she found herself able to see auras not only around people, but around *all* objects. Which raises another point. Of course everything has an aura, because everything has a force field, and as those force fields all form microcosmic parts of the macrocosmic whole, nothing is an island unto itself. No person, race or genus is exclusively exalted in status above any other, no matter how much certain religions may argue to the contrary.

Auric healers often diagnose from colours. Red in the head aura, for example, is not a good sign as it indicates hot-headedness, passions that are out of control, or mental confusion. A blue head aura, on the other hand, if not too deep in shade, represents self-control and clear thinking. Different parts of the body may display different auric colours. Thus, a person may have a clear shade of yellow in the region of the head, denoting mental activity and a medium soul-age, given more to intellect and logic than intuition, then shading to green from the shoulders downwards, indicating someone who is well-earthed and thoroughly practical in everyday matters. White head auras are frequently associated with mediums or mystics, and these may be observed to enlarge considerably when the person in question is in trance or a state of ecstasy. The auras around the hands of healers have been observed to spread and brighten while they are channelling healing energies to their patients, a phenomenon noted in Kirlian photography, which we shall be dealing with shortly.

How, then, can one learn to 'see' an aura? Quite simple. Never look directly at the object or person whose aura you are trying to locate, but focus the eyes slightly to one side. It is always useful if you can practise on a friend. Seat your subject against a suitable background, preferably a plain wall where there are no shadows, allow yourself to relax completely, and aim your glance between six and eight inches to the right or left of his/her head. Trying too hard never works, so avoid an over-concentrated focus. Once you catch your first glimpse of an aura, the natural reaction is usually to try to look directly at it, whereby it appears to vanish! Just try again, but this time resist the temptation to shift your focus.

Another way is to look for your own aura in a mirror. For this purpose you will need a fairly large looking glass which faces a plain background, subdued lighting (a candle often works wonders!), and nothing too fancy or bright in the way of clothing around your neck or shoulders. Sit fairly well back from the mirror and follow the procedures already given. Sooner or later you will be able to observe auras around flowers, animals – even articles of furniture!

Once you are able to see the aura (or sense it – that will do just as well) you will be able to heal it. Since the aura functions at the same frequency as thought, it can be manipulated by the mind. That is to say, you can think your aura open or closed at will, in the same way a healer can visualise a broken or discoloured aura being cleansed and fused together. In other words, it is all in the mind!

Interestingly enough, auric healing *does* work and a knowledge of auric manipulation is always a help, even if one is not a healer. For example, we may wake up in the morning slightly disorientated, which is a sure indication that our auras have not adjusted properly when our psyche has returned to the body after a night of exploration in some other dimension. Or perhaps we have been disturbed by a sudden noise or a myoclonic jerk. Being able to adjust the aura will soon put things right, as it will in cases of disorientation that sometimes follows meditation or other practices involving ASCs.

CHAKRIC HEALING

We have already dealt with the chakras in Chapter 17. These vortices of energy represent points at which the subtle bodies connect with their physical counterparts, so it stands to reason that should any one chakra become blocked or 'dammed' there will be an overspill of energy which will manifest through the related endocrine or area of the body. Let us take the *mulhadhara* chakra, for example.

At the advent of sexual maturity during early puberty, the sudden rush of energy into this chakra can result in all sorts of complaints that are usually associated with adolescence, not the least of which is some form of sexual imbalance. Unless corrected, either by the natural process of growth or the intervention of a doctor or healer, this may overspill (which is believed by some to be the cause of poltergeist and similar phenomena), or spiral inwards causing considerable sexual or emotional stress for the young person concerned. A skilled chakric healer can dispose of the blockage and channel the energy upwards towards the next chakra which will automatically take the teenager into his or her next stage of maturation. Many older people experience blockages in the *Manipura* (solar plexus) chakra or the heart or *Anahata* chakra, which are frequently caused by some deep-seated frustration or emotional experience with which they have never really been able to come to terms. Chakric healers believe these to be factors contributory to the onset of cancer and heart disease.

Good chakric healers are, however, few and far between. The reason for this is that chakric healing requires both accurate psychic diagnosis and the ability to judge the individual's soul-age. The latter is particularly important as younger souls often experience difficulty in handling the kundalini energy, and mental imbalances can result if one of their higher chakras is aroused before the time is right. In plain words, in order to make effective use of chakric healing the healer needs to know what he or she is doing, and that may call for many years of esoteric study, in addition to controlled sensitivity.

RADIANCE TECHNIQUE (REIKI)

It was originally suggested to me by a practitioner of *reiki* (pronounced ray-key) that it should be included among self-help/self-healing techniques. However, many of the paranormal therapies can also be used for those purposes, and the Radiance Technique does contain a metaphysical element which suggests to me that it would be better placed in this chapter.

Radiance Technique, which involves a knowledge of the life-force energy, had its origins in Tibet from where it spread to India and other countries where it became veiled in cryptic symbols and obscure language. In the mid nineteenth century it was rediscovered in ancient Sanskrit texts by Dr Mikao Usui, a Japanese scholar and minister. Dr Usui later called this particular method of activating and using natural energy *reiki*, a generic Japanese word derived from *rei* (universal) and *ki* – the vital life-energy that flows through all living things.

Full details of reiki and how it works are contained in a book entitled *The Reiki Factor* by Barbara Ray, PhD, an

American who received direct instruction in the principle from Mrs Hawayo Takata, an American-born woman of Japanese descent. Mrs Takata had returned to her native Japan in the mid 1930s in the belief that she was nearing death, but was restored to health by the ministrations of two reiki practitioners at the reiki natural healing clinic in Tokyo. In time she mastered the system's seven grades, and the late 1930s saw her moving to Hawaii to pursue her newly found life's work.

In the preface to her book Dr Ray tells us:

> Reiki is a powerful yet gentle, subtle yet precise art and science of restoring your depleted energy and of balancing natural energy within you to promote healing, positive wellness, wholeness, higher consciousness, and, ultimately, enlightenment.
>
> Reiki is not a religion, it is not a dogma, it is not a doctrine, and it is not a cult. Reiki is not a 'laying-on-of-hands' – a term that is used in a religious context and is a form of healing involving a strong degree of belief in a particular religion. Reiki is not a system nor is it a form of mind control, hypnosis or wishful thinking.
>
> What then is Reiki? It is a natural energy-activating method. It is a precise way of using 'light-energy' to restore and balance your own vital energy – physically, emotionally, and mentally – and to connect with your inner self – your spirit.[5]

Radiance Technique was brought to England by a former voice teacher, Ingrid St Clare, and centres have now been set up in London, Brighton and Hove, while introductory evenings and seminars are now being offered in many parts of the country.

This is not a system with which I am personally familiar, although from a perusal of Dr May's book it would appear to have much in common with Atlantean healing, a technique employed by the Atlanteans, a group belonging to the Confederation of Healing Organisations which functions under the Presidency of Dr H Beric Wright MB, BS (Lond), MRCS. Atlantean healers do not, however, work through a system of grades, their progress being judged more by experience and results.

SHAMANIC ECSTATIC HEALING

Shamans are sometimes referred to as the 'wounded' healers, as they have tended in the past to effect self-mutilations in order to attain the physical discipline they believed to be essential to entering the ecstatic state. Not all shamans work in this way, however, although their ministrations are usually accompanied by a series of rites involving the use of highly charged magical paraphernalia.

There would appear to be two main approaches to shamanic healings:

1. In which the shaman effects the healing by a series of magical spells which are believed to evict the evil spirits who have been the primary cause of the illness. This procedure usually involves ritual dances, chants and drumbeats and is often accompanied by paraphronesic display;

2. Where the shaman enters a state of trance in which his own psyche relinquishes control, and the healing process is undertaken by the spirit of an ancestor, animal, nature or elemental essence according to the tradition and totemism of the tribe.

Since it is a shamanic belief that all living things have a soul or spirit (animism), and therefore a consciousness, who and what is responsible for the healing will be governed by the beliefs of the tribe. For example, the Eskimo Angakoks (see Chapter 12), are frequently entranced by the spirits of animals – bears, seals, dolphins or whales being the most favoured. According to Eskimo tradition, the spirit of an animal is just as capable of effecting the healing process as that of a deceased relative or Angakok, especially if the shaman has diagnosed the illness to have its origin in the breaking of a tribal taboo in which an animal has been killed and its spirit not placated in the correct manner.

Those shamans who work via the magical rite place great stock in the power of their impedimenta, their wand or calling stick being the most important weapon in their magical armoury. It is with this that the shaman casts those spells that are calculated to remove the illness from the patient's body by dispensing with those disharmonious energies which he (or she) may see in the guise of evil entities.

Although we may look askance at such proceedings from

the comfort of our armchairs in front of our TV sets, there is little doubt that for many of the people concerned they do work. And when the shaman or witch doctor fails to achieve a healing the excuses given bear little difference from those rendered by practitioners of Western medicine. The patient has given his or her body over to the invading entity. (The cancer has progressed beyond the point of medical help.) The evil spirit has taken control of the patient's mind and is too powerful for the shaman to remove, and the sufferer must be confined to a hut on the outskirts of the village where the spirit will be unable to cause trouble to other members of the tribe. (There is little we can do for this patient who is severely mentally ill, other than confine him to an institution and keep him under sedation.) A rose by any other name!

EXORCISM

The traditional concept of exorcism rests on the premise that a body of discarnate spirits exist, some of benign and some of malign intent who sometimes trespass into places (and people) where they have no right to be and therefore need to be dislodged and despatched elsewhere. In the human context, however, a distinction should be made between possession and obsession, the latter being defined as:'(1) *a persistent idea or impulse, especially one associated with anxiety and mental illness; (2) a persistent preoccupation, idea, or feeling. (3) the act of obsessing or the state of being obsessed.*'[6]

Entities invading people or locations are traditionally classified under one of the following headings:

1. Souls of deceased people;
2. Entities from the 'lower astral' or those regions which are believed to accommodate the mischievous and less desirable denizens of the spirit world;
3. The minds of other people incarnate here on earth;
4. Demons in the service of some infernal master.

The psychologist is inclined to dismiss most of these categories as medieval nonsense, 2 and 4 in particular. Anyone who has exercised a profound influence on the mind of another can, of course, leave their programme imprinted on his or her subconscious mind to the extent that this will persist from beyond the grave. It is also possible for one person to manipulate another, even from a distance, especially if the recipient is easily influenced by more powerful personalities. As for the demons, most of these are, I fear, the product of our own ids, shadows or suppressed desire-fantasies, although I do not dismiss the existence of evil *per se*, but see it more in terms of misplaced energy.

The right to exorcise is believed by many to be exclusive to the priesthood, or those officially ordained in the service of the Christian Church. In Roman Catholicism 'exorcist' is the title given to one of the initiatory stages of preparation for the priesthood, while certain Orders within that Church, the Jesuits, for example, have come to specialise in the practice. Protestant vicars frequently fight shy of it, however, although there have been the occasional firebrands within the Protestant movement who have seen fit to exercise their calling in this direction.

The medieval grimoires abound with rituals designed to send possessing demons on their merry way. There is even a demoniacal hierarchy, complete with fallen angels and archangels which extends in rank and power up to Lucifer himself! It is interesting to note that in those days any form of displaced energy was automatically viewed as a distant relative of Old Nick, whereas in today's world it is fashionable to think in terms of the spirit of some person who has departed in sin, or an objectionable poltergeist! (One wonders how many of these poltergeists are related to the Gnomes of Zurich – they certainly appear to be blessed with the ability to make money via the obliging offices of the film industry!) Seriously, however, the exorcism concept does contain a certain reality, although not quite in the way that either the grimoires, or the movie moguls, might have us believe.

During my years working with a group which specialised in mental healing, I carried out many exorcisms. In fact, I could probably write a book about my firsthand experiences, although I must emphasise that these were purely part of the learning process which constituted the foundation of my later studies of psychology. I no longer work in the exorcism or healing fields, however, my role now being that of a teacher rather than a practitioner.

Among the many things I discovered the hard way was the fact that 90 per cent of mental disturbances attributed to possession were purely manifestations of mental illness or imbalance, and that instances which did entail an external impingement, involving either a person or a location, did not necessarily respond to religious commands. In other words, having a 'Reverend' before one's name does not guarantee one the necessary powers to be a good exorcist. It simply implies a spiritual vocation and the financial backing to see one through the appropriate seminary or university.

Good exorcists are born, not made, and their abilities have absolutely nothing to do with any religion, creed or cult-belief. There is a certain frequency of PK which neutralises errant energies, an anti-ray, if you like. Just as a computer will delete whole sequences from its memory banks if one presses the appropriate key, so is it possible to erase the memories of past incidences which have become recorded in stone, bricks and mortar, or even certain unbounded locations such as the corner of a field, a crossroads, or a section of a motorway, by the application of the appropriate mental discipline. I discussed this subject at length with an elderly Jesuit priest, himself an experienced exorcist, and he reluctantly admitted to me that after years of experience he had arrived at the same conclusion.

I recently established the Institute (for the Study and Development) of Transpersonal Sensitivity (ITS), at the suggestion of some Californian psychologists, who were either constantly faced with clients seeking the transpersonal experience or who needed answers to their psychic problems. I have designed a course which would serve as a bridge between the worlds of psychism and psychology, and also provide guidelines for those working in the orthodox field who are required to deal with the increase in psychic awareness which is fast becoming a phenomenon of our age. Under Session 4 of that course there comes the heading: 'Dealing with Unwelcome PSI and PK', subheaded: 'The Neutralisation of Errant PSI/PK and Similarly Related Energies', which I think rather sums up my conclusions on the subject.

In Chapter 5, I mentioned two cases which were referred to me for exorcism which turned out to be purely manifestations of suppressed unconscious desires or possible psychoses. A good percentage of the possession cases I came across fell into this category. But what of the others? Am I really implying that there are no spirits lurking around some astral plane (lower or otherwise), intent upon popping in where they are not wanted? Since parapsychology has presented us with evidence that mind can function outside of the confines of the physical body to the extent that it can influence the workings of complicated laboratory machinery, while the 'Experimenter Effect' proves that it is perfectly possible for one mind to influence another even from a distance, what then is to stop someone deliberately setting out to do this? Assuming, as many of us do, that death is not the end of our existence as a thinking Essence, is it not a logical assumption that somewhere along the line there might conceivably be a mind-minus-body which gains its entertainment from impinging on the minds of people, animals, and probably all living things for that matter. There have been cases of haunted objects such as jewels, articles of furniture and even cars! The New Testament abounds with tales of the casting out of evil spirits – the Gadarene Swine incident being one example in which animals are featured (Mark 1–14).

My own experiences incline me to place possession cases in the following categories:

1. Suppressed aspects of the subconscious which occasionally surface as a form of release;
2. Attention-gaining ploys;
3. Errant PK or psi energies that need to be neutralised;
4. Emotional manipulation (either consciously or unconsciously calculated);
5. Mental illness;
6. Genuine instances of impinging minds or intelligences, either incarnate or discarnate.

It has often perplexed me when Christian ministers look askance at anyone carrying out exorcism outside of their hallowed domains, such practitioners usually being accused of trafficking with the devil (whoever he might be!) One wonders why they do not heed the answer given by Christ when he was likewise accused:

Every Kingdom divided against itself is laid waste, and no city or house divided against itself will stand; and if Satan casts out Satan, he is divided against himself: how then will his kingdom stand? And if I cast out demons by Beelzebub, by whom do your sons cast them out? Therefore they shall be your judges. (Matthew 12:24–29)

In fact, this Gospel writer seemed to be somewhat fascinated by the exorcism theme, as he continues to quote Jesus in a later verse of the same chapter:

> When the unclean spirit has gone out of a man, he passes through waterless places seeking rest, but he finds none. Then he says, 'I will return to my house from which I came,' and when he comes he finds it empty, swept and put in order. Then he goes and brings with him seven other spirits more evil than himself and they enter and dwell there; and the last state of that man becomes worse than the first. (Matthew 12:43–45)

Any exorcist worth his or her salt knows that one of the most important rules in the neutralisation of errant energies is *never leave a vacuum*! If one does, as sure as eggs are eggs some other lost pocket of energy will sooner or later be attracted to it and prove even more of a nuisance than the first. But the mechanics of exorcism, as viewed by the occultist or parapsychologist, differ considerably from those adopted by the Churches. As my helpful and informative Jesuit explained to me: 'There are people outside of the Holy Church who are better able to accomplish these things than we, but such people have powerful minds, capable of strange feats, and are therefore best avoided by the likes of you and I.' Pure energy is, of course, totally impersonal and only receives its emphasis during the process of its transformation by the individual psyche. Could this account for the 'powerful mind' aspect, or are we back to our PK again?

So, what does happen in a genuine case of possession? If the exorcist knows his or her job, the intruding entity is removed and gently guided to its rightful level, after which the subject's aura is securely sealed (thus ensuring that nothing else enters – see Auric Healing), and a protective covering placed around him or her, according to the preferred persuasion. Christians usually like crosses, while pagans prefer the symbols of a god or goddess, or a protective rune. In the case of a house or location it is up to the exorcist to fill the vacated space with energies of light and love – again according to the favoured belief. And how is all this achieved?

If you are an exorcist who possesses the skill in the first place, you will know how to finish the job correctly. If not, then leave the matter to those who do know what they are doing. Referring to the biblical quote, a man I know who purports to be an occultist of some distinction once dislodged a haunting entity from a piece of land where it had been frightening passers-by during the late hours, by ordering it to move away! In the weeks that followed the poor lost soul was again seen two fields away, much to the distress of the animals with whom it was obliged to share its new pastures. Occultist or no, that was bad exorcistic practice – the entity, which was obviously out of its correct time-zone, should have been guided back to its rightful place in the cosmic scheme of things. But then, there are not all that many people about who possess the necessary know-how to effect these transitions.

In summary, a large percentage of what are believed to be possessions would be better served by a psychiatrist, while the occasional genuine case (and these are very few and far between) is best left to someone who has the right quality of neutralising PK, and the knowledge and mind-power to manipulate it.

Endnotes:

1. *The Alternative Health Guide*, Inglis and West, p. 233.
2. *Mysteries of the Church*, ed. Peter Brooke Smith, pp. 70–75.
3. *Ibid.* p. 240.
4. *Ibid.* p. 254.
5. *The Reiki Factor*, B Ray, p. xvii.
6. *The Collins Dictionary and Thesaurus*, 1987.

Chapter 21

PARANORMAL DIAGNOSIS

PSYCHIC DIAGNOSIS

During my days in a healing group it was customary to display a notice which made it quite clear to the public that as none of us were doctors we were not qualified to render a clinical diagnosis. Prospective patients who wished to know exactly what was wrong with them were therefore advised to seek a professional opinion. Some people would precipitate this, and I recall with amusement an instant of a family who presented us with a set of X-ray photographs '. . . just in case we arrived at the wrong conclusions'. As was more frequently the case, however, a patient would arrive complaining of a headache, but the healers would detect a digestive problem or some other apparently unrelated condition, of which their discomfort was purely a symptom. The patient would then be advised to see their doctor (if they had not already done so) and request an investigation in the appropriate area.

The term 'psychic diagnosis' refers to the use of paranormal powers to ascertain the nature of a discomfort which could be attributed to a disorder or possible illness. There are several forms of psychic diagnosis – intuitive sensing, etheric sight, X-ray sight, reading the aura, and via a spirit agency or channel (as in the case of the famous American medium, Edgar Cayce).

In the days before medicine assumed its mechanistic role all diagnosis was effected psychically, the shaman, medicine man or wise woman defining the nature and cause of illness in the old tribal communities. In pre-Hippocratic Greece those with health problems would seek guidance from the oracles, while their Egyptian counterparts invoked Thoth or Imhotep for help and advice. Not all doctors diagnose strictly by a process of logic based on what they learned at medical school. One elderly GP I knew, who had spent many years in India and was as familiar with Ayurveda as he was with Western medicine, told me in confidence that he found his intuition far more reliable than his training!

Etheric sight is a form of psychism which enables the healer to see the patient's etheric body, implying that the whole chakric system will also be brought into focus. Diagnosis obtained this way is more likely to get to the root of a problem than the next category, which is X-ray sight. Healers with this gift are able to see inside the body itself and note any abnormalities that might not be externally obvious. I have come across one or two healers in my time who were thus talented. The only problem lay in the fact that none of them had any medical knowledge, and they were therefore unable to explain what they saw in terms easily recognisable by a doctor. I recall one particular doctor, who was very favourably disposed towards psychic healing, complaining to me that he didn't understand what Mrs X meant by 'the bit that runs down from the lumpy thing round the side', as that could mean anything in his book! The answer would be, of course, for doctors to be trained in the faculty of X-ray sight (or similar psychic faculties that might facilitate diagnosis) at medical school. But this would probably not work, as modern medical training relies heavily on the left or logical hemisphere of the brain, while psychism is essentially a function of the right or intuitive hemisphere.

Auric readings we have already discussed in the previous chapter, so what about channelled communications in the Cayce mode? This is the form of psychic diagnosis practised by many spiritualist mediums and their predecessors, the shamans. The cynic may argue that much of what is served up as the words of some guiding entity is nothing more than:

1. the alter-ego, or a suppressed aspect of the psyche which has failed to find an outlet for its views in the normal channels of life; or

2. a fragmented section of the mind bordering on the schizoprehnic; or,

3. a convenient way of putting across that which the deliverer would dearly love to express but dare not for fear of ridicule.

The believer might add the higher or transpersonal self to this list, while there is always the disinct possibility that there might be another intelligence at work, as the mediums claim.

We have already discussed how radionics practitioners diagnose psychically or intuitively with the aid of a pendulum or some other gadgetry (see Chapter 20), but as many of us who have used these implements know, one is frequently aware of the outcome before one has picked them up or adjusted them. Jung was not averse to using a variety of methods in his diagnostic work including the *I Ching,* the Tarot and astrology, while I have also observed that both the Runes and Cartouche cards can help one to pin down a problem, especially a psychological one.

KIRLIAN PHOTOGRAPHY

Is it possible to photograph the aura? Many people believe that Semyon Kirlian, a Russian electrician from Krasnador in the Kuban, and his wife, Valentina, invented a machine that will do just this. Since their discovery was first brought to the attention of the West in 1970, Kirlian cameras have appeared at many of the major psychic festivals.

In his early experiments with leaves Kirlian noticed how the aura around them dimmed as they slowly died. When his work was examined by a representative of the Soviet research group it was found that the sickness in a contaminated leaf could also be detected by the instrument. Kirlian proceeded to photograph his own hand and was able to observe how the colours surrounding the outline became dim when he was feeling ill, but brightened up again after he became better.

The procedure employed when using the Kirlian camera for diagnostic purposes involves photographing the hands and interpreting the patient's condition from the patterns and colours displayed in the print. The therapist may then recommend treatment such as homoeopathy, dietary changes exercise, or psychotherapy, depending on the indications shown.

There would appear to be some problems in the diagnostic area, however – the degree of pressure used in placing the fingertips on the apparatus, for example, can influence the picture to a degree, as can temperature, humidity and certain electrical factors. It is my personal opinion that Comrade Kirlian's apparatus does not photograph the aura as such, but simply the electromagnetic and thermal fields surrounding the body. However, as these do tend to fluctuate during illness, some attention should be paid to them, and a check-up affected by someone who is legally qualified to dispense diagnoses.

PALMISTRY

I mentioned this subject in Chapter 4 when referring to the work of Dr Charlotte Wolff, who was able to diagnose both physical and mental illness from the formation and lines on the hand. Her work was purely clinical, however, and in no way connected with palmistry. Her best-selling book *The Human Hand* is available through the public library system for those who would like to pursue a more detailed study.

I was also privileged to know the late Beryl Hutchinson, whose invaluable work with the Society for the Study of Physiological Patterns is being continued by Mary Anderson, herself a skilled palmist, astrologer, hypnotherapist and psychic. The SSPP hold regular lectures and seminars, and for anyone with the necessary spare time, comparing the different physiological patterns

The Line of Life is related to vitality – it doesn't foretell the length of life. Breaks in it can either indicate a major change or an illness.

The Line of Head is seen in conjunction with the life line and is linked with intelligence and the mental qualities of the subject.

The Line of Heart governs the emotional and sexual life and should be looked at in conjunction with the head line.

The Line of Destiny indicates major events which may happen during one's life, though not what the reactions to them will be.

The Line of Health is not always present. If it is, extra care should be taken regarding health matters.

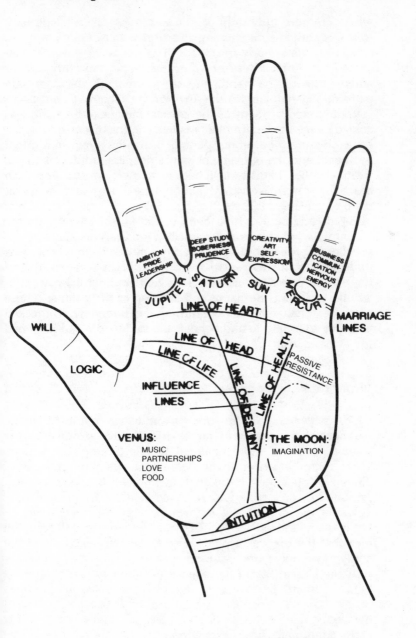

THE LINES OF THE HAND

which are sure indicators of our psychological (and spiritual) states, is both an enlightening and worthwhile enquiry.

Palmistry is a study in itself, but as far as diagnosis is concerned this is mainly taken from the shape, flexibility, colour and texture of the hand, and the dermatoglyphics, or skin patterns – particularly in the fingerprints. Cheiro (Count Louis Hamon), rated by many as the greatest palmist of them all, was able to gauge the length of a person's life, the diseases to which he or she might be prone, periods of mental strain that might lie ahead, and the outcome of future hospitalisation or surgical treatment. Beryl Hutchinson adopted a more somatic approach based on careful research, although she was also adept at reading the meanings of the lines. Were I to visit a palmist of repute and be told that there was an illness looming on the horizon, I would be inclined to seek a medical check-up.

Following the recording of a radio programme in which I was under fire from two psychiatrists and a brain surgeon, one of the men in question enquired in a very confidential manner if I could give him the name and address of the palmist whose accuracy I had emphasised during the interview. I checked with her later and, lo and behold, the said medic had hastened to pay her a visit!

IRIDOLOGY

I have never been quite sure why iridology is placed in the paranormal category, but far be it from me to question the wisdom of those more qualified to effect these distinctions. There is nothing new about looking into the eye for signs of illness. Hippocrates frequently mentioned the practice and orthodox medics have had recourse to it to the present day. Towards the end of the last century Ignatz von Peczely, a Hungarian, and Nils Lilequist, from Sweden, reinforced the idea that the iris was a precise significator of disease, and the study has slowly gained ground ever since.

In the United States the science of iridology was pioneered by Dr Bernard Jensen, who outlined his ideas and theories in his book *The Science and Practice of Iridology*. Dr Jensen developed detailed maps of both irises which show the points corresponding to the different organs.

Although a great deal may be read from simply looking into the

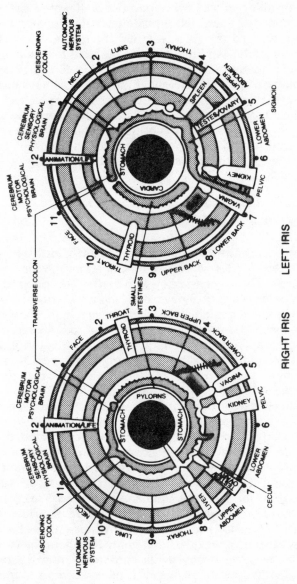

IRIS CHART

The left iris corresponds to the left side of the body, and the right iris to the right side. (Developed by Dr Bernard Jensen)

iris with a magnifying glass, specialists in iridology now equip their consulting rooms with purpose-built apparatus which photographs the eyes. Slides made from the photographs can then be projected onto a screen and the diagnosis effected in the practitioner's own time, without the need for the patient to be present. Many practitioners combine the diagnostic aspects of iridology with other alternative therapies, some clinics also providing naturopathy, homoeopathy, metamorphic technique and psychotherapy, for example. There would certainly appear to be some connection between the condition of our eyes and our general health, and should we obtain a diagnosis by this means, there is nothing to stop us checking it out through more orthodox channels.

BIORHYTHMS

The biorhythmic theory is that at the moment of birth we set off a series of three cycles which will continue through the duration of our lives. These are as follows: the physical cycle of 23 days; the emotional cycle of 28 days; and, the intellectual cycle of 33 days. Crossing the middle of each cycle from high to low or low to high constitutes a critical or unstable period, which receives triple emphasis should the critical periods of two or three cycles happen to occur on the same day. During these critical periods, we are more prone to accidents, illness and mental stress. In other words, we are not quite ourselves!

Dr Wilhelm Fliess, one of Freud's erstwhile friends, was one of the first to conceive of the biorhythm idea, which he developed from a study of the female menstrual cycle. Freud did not appear to think much of it, however, on the grounds that one could arrange statistics to prove anything one wanted. A former pupil of Freud, Professor Herman Swoboda, an Austrian psychologist, pursued the idea and produced some tangible evidence for the periodicity of certain disorders. This in time gave rise to the study of 'circadian' rhythms – those biological processes that occur regularly at twenty-four-hour intervals.

Computers have removed the hard work from the calculation of Biorhythms, and one can either send to a specialist firm for a biorhythm print-out, or purchase one's own mini-computer that will provide the information at the press of a button.

Knowing one's personal biorhythms in advance can prove a help when planning important events, although sometimes it has the opposite effect. There are always those situations in life over which we have no control – interviews for special jobs, auditions, holidays for which we have saved for a long time, and so forth. What could be more calculated to shake our confidence or spoil our fun than to discover that these fall right on critical periods! I suppose it all depends on how much control we have over the planning of important events, although there is always Murphy's Law to consider!

ASTROLOGY

Browse through any popular magazine, either of the male or female variety, over a period of time and sooner or later you will come across an astrological article which outlines the signs of the zodiac and their various significances. Among these will be included the different parts of the body associated with each sign. If, therefore, you were born under the sign of Virgo, the intimation is that you might at some point in your life suffer from digestive disorders, while the Aries person should watch out for head injuries or headaches. Oh, were it that simple!

Newspaper astrology is based on sun signs – the zodiacal position of the sun at the time of one's birth. In fact, we each have an individual horoscope or birth chart which takes into account not only the position of the sun, but also all the other planets within our solar system, and the fixed stars in some cases. When arranged into a chart based on the precise time and place of birth, these present us with a portrait of our *potential*; how we use this potential will depend very much on how we handle the challenges offered by the chart.

Research carried out by the French psychologist and statistician Michel Gauquelin and his wife have helped to raise astrology above the realms of pure superstition. Using the birth dates of 600 members of the French Academy of Medicine, Gauquelin found that a significant number of them had been born when Mars and Saturn occupied similar positions in the horoscopes. Taking care not to dismiss the chance element, Gauquelin applied the same test to a further 500 eminent doctors – the results were the same! He then proceeded to apply the test to athletes, politicians and military leaders. American

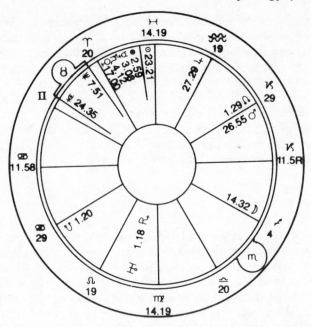

14 March 1879 11.36am LMT Donau, Germany   ALBERT EINSTEIN

sceptics decided to carry out their own tests to disprove Gauquelin's theories, but much to their embarrassment the Frenchman's findings were confirmed. Gauquelin's work has also been investigated by the eminent psychiatrist Professor Hans Eysenck, who pronounced it as perfectly valid.

Carl Jung was a great believer in astrology and frequently sought the answers to questions regarding his patient's problems by investigating their birthcharts. Being an astrologer myself I am naturally prejudiced in favour of the study, but I will be the first to admit that using the natus for diagnosis can be a hit and miss affair. One would need extra training and study in medical astrology – simply knowing the basics such as how to put up a chart, render a simple interpretation and calculate a few progressions is not enough. Even if we are able to see potential health problems in the positions of the planets at the time of our birth, the situation is rather akin to plotting our biorhythms – the best we can do is to take adequate precautions and try to avoid a life-style that might be conducive to the aggravation of certain areas of weakness. In the final analysis it will be our doctor we will have to turn to should our fears be realised.

Medical astrology is a subject unto itself and there have been several books written about it, notably the *Encyclopaedia of Medical Astrology*, by H L Cornell, MD.

A final word on the subject. Astrologers allocate each of the zodiacal signs to one of the four elements, air, fire, earth and water. A recent survey has shown that quite a few of the better-known healers have a preponderance of planets in fire signs (Aries, Leo and Sagittarius) in their natal charts, with air (Gemini, Libra and Aquarius) running a close second. In view of the transmutatory nature of fire and the communicatory nature of air, this is hardly surprising!

Chapter 22

SELF-HELP, SELF-HEALING AND THE PSYCHOLOGY OF FEAR

We have been looking at a series of therapies which involve a patient/client–therapist relationship. In other words, if we find ourselves in need of help, either physically, emotionally or psychologically, we may choose the therapy which obviously applies to our requirement – an osteopath or chiropractor for skeletal problems, for example – or we may effect an experimental choice and reserve judgement for the results. Several of these therapies are also designed for self-help and self-healing, meaning that once we have mastered their procedures we may practise them on ourselves in the security of our own homes.

There is a whole range of self-healing techniques outside of those already covered, however – visualisation and imaging being the best-known and most widely practised. But is it really possible to reject illness and achieve wholeness by the power of the mind, and if so, what forces are at work? Are these purely concerned with cerebral functioning, or is some other agency involved? And if so, what? I am inclined to the belief that the human brain was designed to accommodate far more talents and abilities than we make use of in our present state of development, and no doubt self-healing is among these.

But the mental stimulation necessary to activate the appropriate neurons differs in each one of us, some appearing to have far more control over these factors than others.

Dr Dudley Tee, Head of the Department of Immunology at King's College Hospital, London, stated in a recent interview with journalist Anthea Courtenay:

> We know there are connections between the brain and just about every other organ in the body, including those involved in the immune system. So theoretically there is no reason why either conscious or unconscious thought should not be expressed in a material way, and why feeling better should not influence significantly all sorts of body functions, including the immune system. However, it is another matter to actually prove what is going on.

Dr Tee seemed to doubt whether there was, in fact, a direct link between the mind and the immune system, although he conceded that there were other long-standing systems by which the brain is able to 'talk' to the body.

For example, experiments with hypnosis have evidenced that the mind can control the supply of blood, and the immunological cells it contains, to a particular site, while connections have been established between the brain and the endocrine system which functions under the baton of the pituitary gland. Messages from the brain can alter one of the hormones produced by this master gland which will, in turn, affect other hormones and organs in the body. As all organs have a nerve supply, it is possible to imagine a direct line between the central nervous system and any organ.

At a conference held by the American Association for the Advancement of Science in San Francisco, in January 1989, there were reports from eminent doctors and psychiatrists, notably Dr Janet Kiecolt-Glaser, of Ohio State University's Department of Psychiatry, Dr Lydia Temoshok, Assistant Professor of Psychiatry at the University of California in San Francisco, and Dr Carl Goodkin, of the University of Texas Medical Centre in Dallas. All reported in separate papers on the power of the mind to influence the body. It was generally agreed that positive thinking can delay the impact of AIDS, and so also can healthy food, a good night's sleep and a steady relationship. Dr Goodkin observed that stress affected blood hormone levels which, in turn, caused changes in the immune system and lowered resistance to certain diseases. Physicians, he asserted, had long been aware of the role of sleep, nutrition and calm in strengthening the immune system.

The scientists concerned also stated that the stress of caring for sufferers of AIDS or other demanding illnesses, such as Alzheimer's Disease, could depress the immune system, even of the uninfected. Men and women who were separated or divorced suffered greater depression and loneliness, and had a poorer immune function than their happily married counter- parts. So, while there might be a greater tendency for those who care for AIDS victims to fall ill, the sufferers were more likely to be able to help themselves by psychological motivation or self-help. In cases of early HIV detection, positive thinking, social support and stress reduction tended to delay the virus's development into its fatal mode.

Many other doctors throughout the world are supporting the 'mind over matter' idea. Two recent books – *All in the Mind – Think Yourself Better*, by Dr Brian Roet, and *Mind Power – How to Use Your Mind to Heal Your Body*, by Dr Vernon Coleman – explain how to change those attitudes that cause emotional and physical distress, both books being based on the personal experiences of the doctors in question and those of their patients.

The power of the mind to heal the body is hardly new; Hippocrates stressed it in his writings, and GPs have always been aware of the fact that prescriptions work best when the patient has faith in either or both the medicine and the prescriber.

One of the contributory factors in all forms of self-healing is undoubtedly inner stillness of the sort that comes with deep relaxation. Our modern world bombards us with sounds of the kind that are decidedly injurious to our health. As the old saying goes, 'Silence is golden.' Yet there are many people who have become totally dependent upon noise and find they are unable to live without it. As soon as they arise in the morning, on goes the radio, television or both, in some cases. A single moment of silence cannot be endured. I asked several such people why they felt the need for constant noise and the answer was always the same: 'It's company, the feeling that there is someone there and that one is not alone. Silence is spooky.' Which leads me into a subject which I see as totally relevant to the self-healing question and to why, in fact, many of us become ill in the first place – the Psychology of Fear.

Throughout this book we have examined the many reasons – physiological, psychological and metaphysical – why people suffer from this or that illness or disorder, but so far fear has eluded us. Or has it?

Let us return to the subject matter of Chapter 8, where we discussed the power of the social collective and the fear experienced by its members when confronted by a person or idea that does not form part of its accepted social codes or beliefs. This is the old tribal instinct emerging, and it is part of the same instinct which makes people fear darkness, silence, and anything which is suggestive of the 'unknown'. For a thing to be unknown implies that it is not controllable, and that which cannot be controlled constitutes a fear factor. Thus the person whose views do not coincide with our own is either a crank to be ignored, or someone sinister to be feared.

This primeval fear has formed the basis of every persecution and witch-hunt, political or otherwise. Fear is one of the great stimuli of this planet, a fact which the entertainment profession have been quick to seize upon. Horror films, the modern equivalent of the old tribal ghost story, have never been more popular. Fear of the kind that can be contained within the safety of the fireside has an almost erotic content in that it affords us a cheap thrill. But were we to be faced with those same situations in the reality of life, then that would be a vastly different matter. And yet the truth is that we are, only they do not necessarily assume the forms of ghoulies, ghosties and monsters from outer space.

The ancient Greeks, who were only too well aware of these facts, based their heroic cults on the psychology of fear. Thus, the hero (let us take the example of Hercules) was obliged to undertake a series of labours in order to expiate his guilt (karma). His crime, the slaying of his own children (whom he mistook for enemies during a period of madness which Hera had deliberately visited upon him), being suggestive of our own slaying of each other while under the cloak of delusory fear (the Hera or jealousy within us). The many monsters he encountered during his twelve expiatory Labours represent those everyday apprehensions to which our subconscious minds accord the imagined monstrous shapes of outer darkness and silence.

There inevitably comes an evolutionary point, however, at which collective fears refer back to the individual, from whom they stemmed in the first place. Enter self-help and self-healing. Like Hercules, until we conquer the dark shapes or shadows within our own minds we will not be able to control the manifestations of those terrors which take the form of malignant entities and other such invaders of our physical, mental and spiritual 'space'.

There is an old saying in psychology: 'A fear is an unrequited wish,' and it is interesting to observe that we frequently attract that which we fear the most. The reason for this is that we tend to visualise that fear. Nor are the results of this visualisation process limited to illness and similar disorders. The single man or woman, beset by fears of being left 'on the shelf', often experiences great difficulty in finding a partner, while if we have our doubts about whether we can cope with a certain job, the odds are that the difficulties we have visualised are bound to arise.

A certain degree of caution is, however, the natural heritage of all living creatures and constitutes part of the survival kit. The complete absence of fear, however, can sometimes hint at mental imbalance – courage and folly being ever blood brothers. It can also be argued that he who knows no fear has no awareness, and it takes little observation to note that the universe is not all sweetness and light. I once heard the transpersonal ascent likened to a trip in a plane or balloon: the higher one rises the wider the vista and the more one can see. But although this new perspective may shed light on many beautiful areas that were hitherto unexplored, it will also afford a clear view of the gas works, corporation rubbish dump and the seamier side of town. One cannot have one without the other.

If our mental processes can work against us, then surely they can be put into reverse so that they will work for us. Doctors tell us our aches and pains are psychosomatic – mentally induced, albeit at an unconscious level, or somatisations of tensions we are unable to release in other ways. What, then, is to prevent us mentally inducing a cure, but at a conscious level? Well, according to the experts the first thing we need to do is to seek that inner silence, which brings us round full circle via the nadir of fear.

Tranquillity, we are told, is a state of being more associated with the right brain hemisphere than the left, which has often prompted me to think that the parasympathetic aspect of the autonomic nervous system may well be influenced by that side of the brain. The sympathetic nervous system, on the other hand, would seem to be connected more with left hemisphere activity.

One of the common characteristics of self-healers is the refusal to be a passive victim. In other words, they decide to make every effort they can to combat their afflictions. But does it work for everyone? It seems not if one is judging the efficacy of that self-healing in terms of a final cure. Serious illness is often preceded by a negative self-image, and cases where energy has been seriously depleted by illness, drugs and depression often fail to respond to self-healing techniques. Sometimes we allow ourselves to become so run-down that we are too weary to even think of applying our minds to self-healing, although we may be consciously aware of its advantages.

The Polynesians supplied the answer to this in their 'Great Ha Kahuna Prayer Rite', one of the earliest self-healing techniques known which incorporates many of the ideas currently subscribed to by modern psychology. Hawaiian Huna (see also Chapter 12), which is part religion, part psychology, conceives of man as having three separate bodies, the Low Self, the Middle Self and the High Self. Each of these bodies generates its own vital force at a frequency appropriate to its level of operation. The Low Self operates with simple *mana*, the Middle Self uses *mana-mana*, which is of a faster and more powerful frequency while the High Self employs *mana-loa*, a form of supercharged energy which can effect miraculous changes. The Low Self *mana*, which is created from the intake of food, comes under the domain of will; *mana-mana* is the substance of thought with all that this implies; while *mana-loa* is the kind of energy that can effect immediate results such as instantaneous healing – the miracles of Jesus, if we are to believe the biblical tales!

According to Huna psychology, however, the Lower Self is unable to approach the Higher Self directly – this can only be achieved by way of the Middle Self (subconscious). The procedure involves the Lower Self building up its supply of *mana* which it then passes to the Middle Self, who conveys it to the Higher Self via the *aka* cord. Without that essential supply of *mana*, neither the Middle nor Higher Self can operate successfully. In other words, when our physical resources are severely depleted self-healing becomes more difficult, as any therapist or doctor will be only too happy to confirm. The idea is, therefore, to build up our supply of *mana* and start working on ourself before we reach those final stages. To put it another way, use self-healing as a preventive as well as a cure.

Although negative attitudes which adversely affect our health can be changed, a word of caution is called for at this juncture Some mental programming systems fail to take into account somatic limitations. A state of balance being the deciding factor, irrational overloading should be avoided, so do not push your body beyond the limits of what it can reasonably and naturally handle.

Doctors tell us that learning to love ourselves and enjoy life encourages the flow of of life-sustaining energies (*mana* to the Hunas!) Negative attitudes can be changed. As we have already discussed in Chapter 4, several medical studies have suggested that cancer is related to the type of personality that often tends to feel helpless and repress emotions. Professor Hans Eysenck and Yugoslavian Dr Ronald Grossarth undertook a study, the results of which suggest that by learning to change emotional responses with the help of cognitive behaviour, cancer patients can survive measurably longer. Simple enjoyments such as buying new clothes, changing one's hairstyle, having a good holiday and simply relaxing and forgetting about the urgency of work can all help. More attention needs to be paid to individual needs, the martyr being a prime subject for the cancer syndrome. So, a little bit of 'doing one's own thing' is not likely to go amiss.

Relaxation needs differ with individuals. One man I know cannot sit still for any length of time, but an evening's Morris Dancing does wonders for him. An afternoon on the golf course does more for my husband than a long meditation or sitting in silence. In my own case, the quieter the better! The antics of my four cats, and the love they give me, engender similar feelings of love and happiness which have sustained me over many a 'dark night of the soul'.

Self-help and self-healing centres are beginning to appear in many towns and cities in Britain. The first, and most famous of these is the Cancer Help Centre at Bristol, which was opened in 1980 to offer natural cancer control therapies to British patients. The methods are designed not just to treat the symptoms of cancer, but to restore the whole person to health. The Bristol approach to cancer management is designed to go hand in hand with orthodox treatments to give patients the best chance of long-term recovery.

The story of the founding of the BCHC concerns the illness of Penny Bron, and the efforts made by her friends, Canon Christopher Pilkington and his wife Pat, to help her and others similarly afflicted. The self-help programmes offered at the Centre were designed by Dr Alec Forbes, MA, DM (Oxon), FRCP (Lond), who spent twenty-eight years as Consultant Physician in Plymouth Hospital, during which time he became increasingly aware of the psychological and nutritional causes of disease as well as the old and new approaches to health care. In 1977 Dr Forbes became a healer – member of the National Federation of Spiritual Healers, and two years later the World Health Organisation appointed him adviser to its Traditional Medicine Programme. He left the National Health Service in 1980 to develop a working example of a new medical model for holistic health care.

Dr Forbes' BCHC programmes, which are based on methods which have been widely and effectively used by himself and other practitioners include diet, metabolic therapy, self-healing, psychotherapy and healing, and form part of a total therapy approach to cancer control which may be adapted by the therapists concerned. In her book *A Gentle Way With Cancer*, Brenda Kidman gives full details of the founding and work of the Bristol Cancer Help Centre, as featured in the BBC-TV series. She also outlines the work and research of the pioneers in this field, notably Dr Max Gerson and Dr Josef Issels, both of whom realised the importance of diet in the prevention and treatment of cancer.

The efficacy of guided imagery techniques has been proved in the field of research. Carl Simonton originally trained as a radiotherapist, but became disillusioned with that form of treatment and decided to make a special study of the effect of imaging on cancer cells that develop a strong resistance to elimination by the body's normal defence system. By teaching his patients how to achieve a state of deep physical relaxation, followed by a series of mental pictures of the cancer tumour being overcome by the radiation treatment, he was able not only to speed up recovery, but actually to effect complete cures! In one particular case, a 61-year-old-man who had been advised to practise the imaging exercise several times a day not only overcame the cancer, but ' . . . also rid himself of arthritis and impotence that had plagued him for more than twenty years!'[1]

More recent descriptions of the visual imagery used to help

cancer patients were discussed at the one-day Conference at Hammersmith Hospital which received coverage in Chapter 7. Some of the examples mentioned used were amusing, but also evocative of pathos. These involved such images as golden vacuum cleaners, which went round the body removing cancer cells, and a 'golden amoeba' which quietly effected the same job. One little boy, who had been visualising a host of small white mice making inroads into his cancer cells, when encouraged by the therapist to speed up the process, took great pride in telling her that his mice were now working much faster, because he had equipped them all with roller skates!

Cancer is simply a manifestation of chaos, as is all disease, come to that. Jung had a lot to say regarding the alchemy of chaos, highlighting the close and mysterious relationship that exists between the Mercurius, the planetary genius of Mercury, and Saturn, the Grim Reaper. Mercurius in his many names has always been associated with the healing process, but according to Jung his functions are closely related to those of Saturn. In Gnosticism, Saturn is the highest archon, the lion-headed Ildabaoth, meaning 'child of chaos', but in alchemy the child of chaos is Mercurius.

Jung comments:

> Mylius says that if Mercurius were to be purified, then Lucifer would fall from heaven. A contemporary marginal note in a seventeenth-century treatise in my possession explains the term sulphur, the masculine principle of Mercurius, as *diabolus*. If Mercury is not exactly the Evil One himself, he at least contains him – that is, he is morally neutral, good and evil, or as Khunrath says: 'Good with the good, evil with the evil'. His nature is more exactly defined, however, if one conceives him as a process that begins with evil and ends with good.[2]

Thus the symbol of Mercurius, which is the insignia of many branches of the healing profession to this day, features two serpents entwining the central, winged rod, one negative and chaotic, the other positive and orderly. Healing therefore involves the balancing of these two forces which, the symbol tells us, may be achieved by the mind or higher self, as represented by the surmounting orb and wings.

So, we are back to our notion of form being contained within chaos and vice versa, or the eternal dualistic conflict which has been understood by alchemists and metaphysical philosophers or centuries, but is only now re-emerging, cloaked in the new theories of self-help and self-healing.

Being the brilliant mind that he was, Jung was able to perceive the propensity for chaos or order within the human soul, and observe its manifestation in the physical vehicle – As above, so below.' Fear and chaos walk hand in hand. We are fearful of chaos, so we are fearful of disease and any other chaotic manifestations that life might threaten to impose upon us. Ignoring such contingencies is no answer, as Freud was quick to discover. Acknowledging their existence, studying them, coming to terms with them and placing them in perspective is, however. The element of chaos within us does exist, whether we like it or not. We may bury our heads in the sand and look heavenwards, but sooner or later its inevitable bell will toll and the form that has been our physical body will slowly give way to the chaos of death and disintegration. The mind of psyche, however, as symbolised by the Mercurial wings, will rise above the field of conflict, to return to it again in some other time-zone until the self-balancing principle has been mastered.

We all have our appointed time of departure, or do we? It could be argued that those who have defeated chaos through self-healing have also cheated Hades, or deprived the Grim Reaper of his prey. But there is another school of thought which postulates that if we are born with the potential for self-healing, then the employment of that ability has also been taken into account in the timeless Akasha, of which Thoth-Hermes-Mercurius (all gods of the mind or intellect) is the celestial librarian. In other words, it is up to us to discover our hidden potentials and use them, which practice, if perfected, will eventually enable us to control our lives to the extent that we can choose when and how we eventually exit, thus alleviating the necessity to negotiate a humiliating and painful demise.

Endnotes:

1. *A Gentle Way With Cancer*, B Kidman, p. 57.
2. *Alchemical Studies*, C G Jung, pp. 227–228.

Chapter 23

CHOOSING YOUR THERAPIST

After writing about so many healing methods, albeit briefly, I could not fail to be struck by the fact that the majority of alternative therapies were either conceived of, resurrected, or developed by qualified doctors or psychologists from the fields of orthodox medicine or science – a fact worth bearing in mind when assessing their original purpose and present potentialities.

We may not be so much out of tune with our GPs as in need of a change, a breath of fresh air as it were, or perhaps just someone with whom we can discuss our problems and discomforts. So we start to think in terms of an alternative therapy. Many therapists have noticed that people who feel they would like to switch from orthodox medicine to a more natural therapy often preface their request for an appointment with the words: 'I have back trouble (skin problems, stomach pains, etc.). Can you cope with that sort of thing?' To which the therapist will usually reply: 'Come along and see me, and then I will be able to judge whether I can help you!' While this may prove daunting to a few enquirers, most people are prepared at least to give it a try.

There is obviously the likelihood of encountering the occasional practitioner who is more interested in his or her bank balance than the patient's health, but then that applies equally to private medical practice. If you are receiving treatment, and it does not appear to be doing you any good, you are at liberty to stop it at that point and seek relief elsewhere. Sad to say, stories have come my way of therapists who have deliberately contrived to form dependencies with their patients for other than therapeutic reasons. One such case concerned a lady who had become inextricably involved with her therapist to the extent that when she did finally realise what was going on and sought to escape he threatened her with all sorts of dire results which made her quite ill. She was eventually rescued by her local GP and only managed to sort herself out completely after moving to a new area. This can, of course, happen with practitioners in any field from allopathic medicine to spiritual healing. One just has to be careful and watch for the tell-tale signs.

It may also be argued that no dependency is one-sided and a degree of complicity must have been offered by the patient at some point during the treatment. It would be up to a trained person to recognise this as a cry for help, however, and adjust his or her treatment accordingly.

Holistic treatment calls for more than a well-trained, highly intuitive and thoroughly dedicated therapist. It also requires the full cooperation of the patient at all levels. Past conditioning, entrenched attitudes and habits, incorrect diet – all these must undergo adjustment if the treatment is to be considered totally holistic; it is a two-way exercise. It is no use approaching your therapist with a stomach ache and complaining bitterly if he or she spends most of the consultation asking you about your relationships at work and in the home. The cause of your discomfort may well originate from tensions built up in either of those environments and not as a result of something you have eaten or a suspected growth.

The World Health Organisation has been pressing for a change of attitude to primary health care. Natural therapists, lay counsellors, paramedics and psycho-social workers, it suggests, could do more to help many cases than doctors. I think it all boils down to the question of finding the right therapist, which brings us to our next consideration – compatibilities.

How many of us have, after moving to a new town, sought out a local GP and duly signed on, only to be dismayed when circumstances oblige us to come face to face with the physician to whose care we have been assigned? I can most certainly be counted among that number, and so can many of my friends.

Now that I am older, and maybe a little wiser, I make a point of asking around before handing in my medical card. It does pay to do so. This is not meant to imply that the previous practitioners in question were not adept at their ministrations, but rather that there was a clash of personalities or an incompatibility which proved to be a stumbling block in the process of treatment and healing.

Each human psyche, like everything else in life, emits its own particular wavelength or vibration, and not all of these frequencies are consonant one with another. So when we meet someone to whom we take an instant dislike rationale goes flying out of the window, and upon occasion not without good cause. Our subconscious minds are simply telling us that our energies are not compatible with those of the person in question, and uncivilised as it may sound, trying to reason it out will get us nowhere. Therefore, when it comes to alternative therapies, as the choice is much wider than that offered by conventional medicine we should be careful to bear this in mind and take the compatibility factor into account, transpersonally, psychologically and physically.

Sometimes we may find ourselves in a position where we have signed on for a course of treatment only to discover after the first two sessions or so that we do not wish to continue with it. If the therapist is particularly nice it makes the break even harder, and besides, we might not be in a position to forfeit the fee! There are not, to my knowledge, any hard and fast rules regarding the return of fees paid for a full course of treatment that is not pursued, so one is very much in the hands of the therapist. Most of us are not financially overly-endowed, however, a fact which any intelligent therapist will be quick to note, in which case payment can be arranged per session.

The essential thing is not to allow oneself to be bullied into anything with which one is not fully comfortable. During the course of writing this book I have contacted several organisations to ensure that I am reporting them accurately. In most cases my enquiries have been met with courtesy, but there have been the occasional instances where the organisers have bombarded me with literature and insisted that I enlist (as soon as possible) in a series of their courses for some exorbitant fee, the implication being that unless I comply with this request I could not hope to render a true account of their great and marvellous work!

The reader would be well advised to watch out for this kind of practice and give it a wide berth unless, of course, he or she falls into the category of those people who are misled into believing that if a thing costs a lot, then it must be good. Where the products of the consumer society are concerned this is no doubt the case – you get what you pay for, as the saying goes. But surely the healing vocation is concerned with loftier principles, so while we may heed the biblical advice and 'render to Caesar the things that are Caesar's' (bearing in mind the exchange of energy principle and the fact that 'the labourer is worthy of his hire'), the therapist should, in turn, heed the final sentence of the first phrase and 'render to God the things that are God's'.

Chapter 24

THE VOCATION AND ROLE
OF THE HEALER

Are healers born or made? Can the faculty be developed? Do we all have some degree of healing power?

Training alone does not make a healer, any more than taking a child at an early age and putting it through the correct classical training programme will guarantee its talent as a ballet dancer. In using the term 'healer' I am taking into account all the healing arts, although some of my emphases may appear to apply more to the transpersonal or psychic faculties rather than the ability to pass the required Medical Boards. However, several doctors have hastened to point out to me that the gift of healing is just as prevalent among the clinically trained as among the psychic or alternative therapy contingents – and more so in come cases! And, although we may see healers as people who effect miracles, who can make us whole again, alleviate our discomforts and generally aid our well-being, what actually happens is that we heal ourselves; healers simply act as catalysts.

Many scientists and researchers are of the opinion that both healing and self-healing are effected by psychokinesis (PK). Eysenck and Sargent comment:

> From the point of view of a parapsychologist, any power of mind which claims to produce a direct effect in the physical world

– in this case on the human body – is a candidate for possible operation of PK.[1]

This idea is also endorsed by Professor Stephen Braude in his reference to the wide range of PK:

> Some have suggested that ordinary volition might be a case of PK, in which an intention directly produces a bodily change. Similarly, psychosomatic ailments and self-healing through hypnosis might be classified as types of PK.[2]

The case of Matthew Manning would certainly appear to support the PK theory, Manning himself admitting that the PK he manifested so strongly in his youth, which took the form of various psychic phenomena, could have been utilised in any of several ways. He chose to direct it into healing channels, a decision for which many grateful clients have no doubt never ceased to thank him.

Braude has made a particular study of the PK effect, however, and his research has led him to conclude that it has many variants or different qualities. I often joke with my husband about this, and if we meet or read about someone who has, say, amassed a fortune in a very small space of time we jokingly remark 'That man obviously has good money PK!'

In observing the workings of PK in everyday life, Braude writes:

> . . . one would not expect typical PK effects to be flagrantly obvious. But once we entertain the possibility that small or large-scale PK might insinuate itself into everyday affairs, we can see how an appeal to PK might explain phenomena or regularities that would otherwise be considered mysterious or fortuitous. Persuasive and refined PK (and ESP) could explain why some people are healthier than others, or remarkably luckier or unluckier than others. For example, it could explain why some soldiers escape serious injury, despite taking repeated heroic risks on the battlefield. It might explain why incompetent or reckless drivers continue to avoid the automotive catastrophes that befall others, and emerge unscathed from those which they initiate. It might even explain why some always seem to find parking spaces. And however distasteful the thought might be, consistent bad luck or misfortune could be an external PK analogue to psychosomatic illness.[3]

It would appear that we are born with a certain quotient of PK, the quality of which varies according to our life's purpose or, as the metaphysically inclined would say, our karma. If, as in the case of Matthew Manning, our PK has a 'universal donor' quality about it, meaning that it could be channelled into any of several avenues, that ultimate choice may form part of our karma for that life.

It has often been observed that gifted people seldom have one talent only. During my days in the classical music profession I met many multi-talented artists. People who were accomplished instrumentalists, could also paint, sculpt or write, in addition to displaying a proficiency in many of the more mundane avenues of everyday expression, such as cooking, DIY, interior design, and so forth. In fact, there was an occasion in my youth when a young lady with whom I was sharing a ride home from the theatre actually helped me with a healing case without ever having done such a thing before in her life – or even given it a thought for that matter. And yet after following my instructions, as she described later, she 'just *knew* how to do it'. She was also a multi-talented lady.

Really good healers may indeed be born and not made, but this does not mean that others should not train and try their hand at it. After all, every doctor cannot be a specialist (and probably would not want to be, anyway), and the ministrations of a nurse are as important in the therapeutic scheme of things as the operation performed by the senior surgeon. Your local reflexologist may not receive the same acclaim as Manning, but her service is just as meaningful to her particular clientele.

Simply being 'clever' – having the mental agility and retentive powers to imbibe pages of facts – does not necessarily endow a practitioner with true healing ability. However, such people may impress their patients with their knowledge to the extent that a placebo effect is generated which causes them to heal themselves. This was beautifully illustrated in one of the instances mentioned in Chapter 7.

Many doctors work subconsciously through their right brain hemispheres (intuitively rather than clinically), whereas there are 'psychic healers' I know who are not really psychic (sensitive) at all, in the strict sense of the word. Another mistake often made by psychic healers is the assumption that 'power', as such, is the universal panacea for all ills. Healing energy, like all universal energy is, as we have already discussed, coloured by the mind of the user. It can, therefore, be channelled in tonic, narcotic, stimulant or sedative modes. But no doubt my critics will be only too happy to inform me that all this is totally unnecessary as long as one 'thinks whole', says one's prayers, and hopes that some unseen divinity will take care of the work. If that is what you believe, then fair enough. No doubt those patients who are attracted to you will believe the same way, and so believing they will be healed. Or will they? A few words with disappointed travellers on their way home form Lourdes might present a different picture.

The PK inference should not, however, be taken as an indication that good psychic healing cannot be dispensed during an altered state of consciousness (ASC). There is a difference between a straight ASC and the ecstatic state (the latter often carrying paraphronesic overtones), wherein all conscious control is relinquished. During alpha ASCs one is fully aware of what one is doing, but there is a temporary cessation of the time factor when the intuitive faculty becomes acutely alert. While one is experiencing this particular state of consciousness any sudden noise, touch or interruption can have the same effect as those myoclonic jerks which seem to propel one back to consciousness with some discomfort during the early part of the sleep process, the severity of the jolt being determined by the level or frequency of the ASC. The same kind of thing is experienced by some mediums if they are brought out of the trance state too quickly.

Psychic healing demands a degree of spontaneity, and will often be accompanied by the kind of ASC that could easily be broken by someone chattering away in the background. The method I employed during my own healing days tended to produce a corresponding response in my patients, who often lapsed into alpha or theta brain patterns and needed to be 'brought round' (earthed) afterwards. It has been pointed out to me, however, that many healers are able to work successfully in noisy atmospheres such as psychic fairs or festivals where there is a lot of movement going on around them, so in the final analysis it would seem to be a very individual thing which defies objective classification.

There are series of contributory factors that determine which ASC or PK frequency a medium or healer is likely to function on at any given time. These include the general state of the healer's own health, the atmosphere prevailing in the venue at which the healing is taking place, and the compatibility (or lack of same) between the healer's personal 'keynote' and that of the patient, which can often manifest as either a subconscious empathy or antipathy.

When discussing healing my attention is often drawn to the alleged miracles of Jesus who, we are assured, drew his healing power direct from God. I seem to recall an instance in the New Testament where someone was healed simply by touching the hem of Jesus' garment – of which fact Jesus was fully *aware* – a clear demonstration of PK if ever there was. The tragedy is that if Jeshua bar Josephus was to reincarnate in this day and age and endeavour to put his 'followers' right on a few facts, he would probably be branded a crank, heretic or pagan – and decidedly anti-Christian!

Is accurate diagnosis essential for effective healing? There are many recorded cases of healers (and doctors for that matter) who have rendered their services without being at all sure as to what was wrong with the patient, or on the basis of an inaccurate diagnosis, and the treatment has worked – or appeared to, anyway. There are two explanations for this: (1) that the patient's faith in the practitioner has induced self-healing rather after the fashion of the placebo effect I mentioned earlier; or (2) that the practitioner has unconsciously channelled the quality of universal energy (or PK if you like) appropriate to the patient's real needs. In other words, a rebalancing can be effected without congnisance of the true cause, so the doctor does not need to consciously alert his intuitive faculties, nor the pyschic healer to have an advanced knowledge of anatomy.

It is currently fashionable in certain quarters for healers to 'counsel' either prior to or following a healing session, the idea being that this makes for a more holistic approach, while also helping the patient to unwind, and affording the healer a deeper insight into his problems. There are however, pros and cons in this system of working. Many psychic healers prefer to generate their PK, 'tune in', or allow their healing energies to build in tranquil surroundings before confronting their patients, whom they can then approach without prior knowledge of the condition for which their help has been sought. They feel that this way they are able to make an assessment which is based purely on their intuition, while the flow of their energies has not been disturbed by a lot of idle chatter.

I am given to understand that many doctors, and surgeons in particular, feel the same way. They need to work in a quiet and impersonal atmosphere in order to give of their best. This is not meant to imply that they do not care about the patient as a person, but rather their talents are best executed according to their temperament and calling. Having good healing PK (or surgical skill as the case may be) does not necessarily imply that one is a good counsellor, and healers who have been subjected to the healer/counsellor system have often complained to me that by the time they have listened to a catalogue of woes, which are usually calculated (albeit unconsciously) to convey the desired impression, the peak of their psychic energies has sadly dropped!

Counselling and healing appear to me to be two different callings, and this also applies where other forms of therapy are concerned. For example, one's skill as a chiropractor, metamorphic technique therapist or masseuse is not diminished by a lack of counselling ability. Some people pride themselves on being both good healers and good counsellors which may or may not be the case, however, the patient being the ultimate judge. In order to avoid the danger of projecting their own frustrations or problems onto the patient, or risking the possibility of triggering some unresolved trauma, counsellors are advised to take regular counselling themselves, although there are doubtless many who do not pursue this policy.

Counselling has recently come under fire from other quarters. Elizabeth Grice, writing in *The Sunday Times* (1 January 1989) had some rather harsh but nevertheless realistic words to say about it in connection with the tragedies that preceded the 1988 Christmas period:

> What we have now, often whether we want it or not, is door to door grief management. The professional response where the homespun might have been more appropriate. It takes little imagination to appreciate that some of it, like the court ordeal of a rape victim, might actually be worse than the original pain.

She quoted Peter Goold, senior chaplain at Basingstoke and District Hospital, as stating that counselling services should be targeted and *not automatically offered to all*. It was dangerous to assume that nobody could cope.

In the final analysis it is the needs of the patient or client that count. Should he or she feel the need for counselling, and the service be available, then all well and good. But if the request is for healing alone, then this should be respected.

I have tried to show a variety of different approaches to the healing vocation within the context of this chapter, many of which may appear contradictory, a fact of which I am quite aware. These are not designed as guidelines for the aspiring healer, but simply as illustrations of the profusion of opinions one is likely to encounter within the divers healing practices and communities. Nor do they necessarily represent my own views on the subject, which are irrelevant anyway.

I should like to end this chapter with Dr Arthur Guirdham's most apt description of the healing temperament:

> The most characteristic attribute of the natural healer is his passive attitude. This implies his total renunciation of the principle of power. This is what distinguishes the natural healer from the varieties of unorthodox practitioner. It also characterizes the best doctors in the faculty. The proportion of medical practitioners with this attitude is probably larger than we are given credit for. The number of really natural healers in the unorthodox groupings is probably exaggerated. A number of the latter tend to be more Roman than the Romans and are always conditioning their patients to something.
>
> The natural healer does not demand or even ask for faith from his patient. After all, it is quite common for the healer to be unaware of his powers for a considerable period. Faith in the healer may enhance the latter's powers but essentially he does not ask for it. The natural healer always says little, at any rate on the subject of healing. He does not propagandize or even exhort. Too many words, and above all too many devoted to the subject of disease tend, if anything, to diminish his powers.[4]

Dr Guirdham – I heartily concur!

Endnotes:

1. *Explaining the Unexplained*, H Eysenck and C Sargent, p. 111.
2. *The Limits of Influence*, S E Braude, p. 221.
3. *Ibid.* p. 279.
4. *The Nature of Healing*, A Guirdham, p. 63.

CONCLUSIONS: THE TRANSPERSONAL DILEMMA

Some of the facts I have uncovered during my research and analysis of the different methods of healing employed in today's world have given me cause for concern. For example, although there are signs that the chasm between orthodox medicine and alternative therapies is slowly closing, I feel there could be a danger of things swinging to the other extreme. Both orthodox medicine and alternative therapies have their place, and I have endeavoured to be impartial in assessing the merits and drawbacks of both camps, neither of which are all right or wrong, or have all the answers.

On the alternative therapy side, there would appear to be a lot of sorting out to be done. Many therapies are practised by unqualified or inexperienced people who have attended a few seminars, read a few books and set themselves up as 'experts', and while it has already been agreed that the ability to pass examinations set by the Medical Board does not necessarily make for a good doctor, nor a signed piece of paper a good healer, the situation does, however, call for some definite guide-lines and possible future legislation. Dabbling with people's physical or mental health is a dangerous pastime – and this applies to both the orthodox and alternative sides of the fence.

In some of the preceding chapters much emphasis has been placed on seeking within for the solutions to illness and the general inconsistencies of the life experience. Various therapists, doctors and psychologists have advised us to 'discover our real selves' in the belief that to do so will release our hidden potential to effect a control over not only our health, but also our general destiny. Now this all very well, as long as that control does not involve impingement on the space of others, which would result in an inevitable battle of minds. It may be argued that this has ever been the case, but were we each to gain sufficient mastery over our circumstances to enable us to manipulate our own lives, could this not result in a world in which the Chiefs far outnumber the Indians?

'Goodness no,' exclaims the metaphysician, 'for whichever plateau of mind control is eventually reached by the majority, there will always be those who are able to progress just that much further. Remember the Law of Equalities!'

The inference is that as we overcome one obstacle another rears its head, so we will have to content ourselves with the fact that complete equality is a luxury only to be enjoyed when we have finally reached the apex of our evolutionary journey, seen by some as God and by others as a union with the Infinite and all other Essences therein. But enough of the metaphysics. Let us return once more to the conditions of Earth.

One point I am trying to make is that not everyone finds themselves by looking within. In fact, many have found their reality in quite the opposite way – by looking without. Following a recent television series on the senses (extra and otherwise) possessed by other life-forms on our planet, several people have commented how far we are behind many animals when it comes to the understanding and use of our senses.

One young lady remarked to me: 'They know all these things, and we don't, and yet we're supposed to be the intelligent ones!' This is because we have become separated from the instinctive side of our nature, while many are totally unaware of the existence of the intuitive side. And even if we have received flashes of inspiration from time to time, we are too timid to voice them for fear of ridicule by the collective.

I once worked in an organisation in which I was only woman employee. One day, one of my male colleagues noticed that I was reading a metaphysical book and confided in me that he had always been drawn to such things, but he would rather I did not mention it to the other chaps. On another occasion a similar event took place involving a different man, the conversation being repeated almost word from word. After some weeks I discovered that all my male colleagues were either inclined towards or definitely interested in my subjects. So I decided on a confrontation, which was naturally greeted with much laughter, hints at my leg being pulled and claims of total disinterest in all that 'hocus-pocus'. But the tone of the conversation slowly changed, starting with the statement, 'Mind you, there were a few strange things occurred in our regiment during the war, come to think of it.'

Which met with the response: 'Such as . . .?'

This was, in turn, followed by: 'It's funny you should say that, a similar thing happened in my squadron.'

The subject was finally capped when the senior person in charge added the weight of his strange experiences which were legion, and the paranormal outpourings that ensued covered a period of several weeks: End result: we were all in total agreement!

Finding oneself and experiencing one's own revelations is not really much fun, however, if one cannot discuss these with others either as a result of one's inability to expresss oneself or through sheer fear. I am fortunate in that I tend to mix in circles where psychology, metaphysics and allied subjects are treated as adult conversation, but there have been situations in my life where this has not been the case. One is frequently greeted with remarks such as: 'What is all this metaphysical rubbish you write about, haven't you anything better to do?'

One sweet little lady was most apologetic about her attitude. 'I'm sorry I can't talk to you any more, dear,' she explained, 'but my vicar says people like you who write about all these strange things are in league with the devil.' No doubt many people of such persuasions still think their ills are caused by the local witches' coven.

Such people are so conditioned that they would fail to find their own intuitive (or reasoning, for that matter!) faculties if they were harnessed to them around a lamp-post! What does impress them, however, is the *appearance* of sanctity (or erudition, in some cases!), so let us hope that some of those who have received enlightenment from looking inwards will be prepared to turn their attention outwards in such a way that the psychologically or spiritually timid will not flee for safety at their first utterances.

Many who have managed to come to terms with their transpersonal selves will have gained an awareness of the oneness of all life, and possibly their own cosmic roots. But are the rest of us out of harmony with our higher selves, our native planet, and the cosmos itself to the extent that the rift adversely affects our physical and mental well-being? And does this malaise communicate itself to other life-forms with which we share this world – the animal, plant and mineral kingdoms, for example?

Judging by the dramatic ecological changes that are taking place it would appear to be so. If this is the case, by putting our own house in order we will also help to heal Gaia and all those other life-forms which she hosts. But before we can achieve this we must first come to terms with our own transpersonal selves which, in addition to constituting a healing process also captures the essence of our *raison d'être*.

Pipe-dreams? Hardly, since Martin Wollacott, Foreign Editor of *The Guardian*, chose to launch 1989 with the following lead-in to his article entitled 'Planet Politics':

> A new ideology is waiting in the wings to provide both a common system of thought and, in a sense, a common enemy. Call it environmentalism, greenism, planetism. It has been growing for years, but in the last few months it has begun to acquire the status of an official world religion.

Congratulations, Gaia, your children are at last coming of age!

BIBLIOGRAPHY

Anderson, M *Colour Healing*, Aquarian Press, Wellingborough, 1985.
Bonewicz, R *Cosmic Crystals*, Turnstone, Wellingborough, 1986.
Braude, S *The Limits of Influence*, Routledge & Kegan Paul, London, 1987.
Brookesmith, P (ed.) *Mysteries of the Church Orbis*, London, 1984.
Coleman, V *Mind Power: How to Use Your Mind to Heal Your Body*, Century Hutchinson, London, 19—.
Dally, P and Watkins, M J *Psychology and Psychiatry*, Hodder & Stoughton, Sevenoaks, 1986.
Dee, N *Your Dreams and What They Mean* Aquarian Press, Wellingborough, 1984.
Edgley, J *Jeni Edgley's Nutrition Book* Lansdowne, Dee Why West, NSW, 1985.
Equinox – A Guide to the 1988, ITN Channel 4 Television, London, 1988.
Eysenck, H and Sargent, C *Explaining the Unexplained* Weidenfeld & Nicholson, London, 1982.
Green, D *Incredible Cats*, Methuen, London, 1986.
Gribbin, J and Gribbin, M *The One Per Cent Advantage*, Blackwell, Oxford, 1988.
Guirdham, A *The Nature of Healing*, Allen & Unwin, London, 1964.
Harold, E *Crystal Healing*, Aquarian Press, Wellingborough, 1987.
Hippocrates *IV trans.* W H Jones, Heinemann, London, 1979.
Hope, M *Practical Techniques of Psychic Self-Defence*, Aquarian Press, Wellingborough 1983.
——*Practical Celtic Magic*, Aquarian Press, Wellingborough, 1987.

——*The Lion People*, Thoth, Bognor Regis, 1988.

——*The Psychology of Ritual*, Element, Shaftesbury, 1988.

Hopkins, S J *Principal Drugs*, Faber & Faber, London, 1988.

Horne, J *Why We Sleep*, Oxford University Press, Oxford, 1988.

Inglis, B and West, R *The Alternative Health Guide*, Michael Joseph, London, 1983.

Jung, C J *Archetypes and the Collective Unconscious, Vol.9. Part 1*, Routledge & Kegan Paul, London, 1959.

——*Alchemical Studies*, Routledge & Kegan Paul, London, 1983.

Kerenyi, C *The Gods of the Greeks*, Thames & Hudson, London, 1979.

Kidel, M (ed.) *The Meaning of Illness*, Routledge & Kegan Paul, London, 1988.

Kidel, M and Rowe-Leete, S *Illness*, Routledge & Kegan Paul, London, 1988.

King, S *Kahuna Healing*, Quest, London, 1983.

Kretschmer, E *A Textbook of Medical Psychology*, Hogarth, London, 1952.

Mead, G R S *Fragments of a Faith Forgotten*, Theosophical, London, 1906.

——*Thrice Greatest Hermes, Vols. I, II & III* Theosophical, London, 1906.

Mindell, A *Dreambody*, Routledge & Kegan Paul, London, 1984.

Morgan, C *Aspects of Healing*, Headquarters, London, 1985.

Oldfield, H *Dark Side of the Brain*, Element, Shaftesbury, 1988.

Ornstein, R and Sobel, D *The Healing Brain*, Macmillan, London, 1988.

Passwater, R *Cancer and Its Nutritional Therapies*, Keats, New Haven, CT USA, 1978.

Pelletier, K *Mind as Healer, Mind as Slayer*, Delacorte/Seymore Lawrence, New York, 1977.

Readers Digest Family Medical Adviser, Readers Digest Assoc., London, 1988.

Readers Digest Illustrated Dictionary, Readers Digest Assoc., London, 1983.

Roet, B *All in the Mind/Think Yourself Better*, MacDonald-Optima, London, 1987.

Rossbach, S *Feng Shui*, Rider, London, 1986.

Sagan, C *Cosmos*, Random House, New York, 1980.

Sheldon, W H, and Stevens, S S *The Varieties of Temperament*, Harper & Row, New York, 1942.

Sheldrake, R *A New Science of Life*, Granada, London, 1983.

Singer, C *The Legacy of Greece*, Oxford University Press, Oxford, 1947.

Steiger, B *Kahuna Magic*, Para Research, Gloucester, MA USA, 1981.

Wambach, H *Life Before Life*, Bantam, New York, NY USA, 1979.

Witt, R E Isis in the Graeco-Roman World, Thames & Hudson, London, 1978.

Wynn, D *The Whole Mind Book*, Fontana, London, 1980.

——*Experiences of Abortion*, Optima, London, 1988.

INDEX